PRENTICE HALL

BRIEF REVIEW FOR NEW YORK

Physics
The Physical Setting

2004 Edition

W9-BZU-651

Bernadine Hladik Cook
Johnstown High School
Johnstown, New York

ORDER INFORMATION

Send orders to:

PRENTICE HALL SCHOOL DIVISION
CUSTOMER SERVICE CENTER
P. O. Box 2500
Lebanon, Indiana 46052-3009

or

CALL TOLL-FREE: 1-800-848-9500
(8:00 A.M.–6:00 P.M. EST)

or

FAX TOLL-FREE: 1-877-260-2530
(24 hours a day, 7 days a week)

•Orders processed with your call.
•Your price includes all shipping and handling.

PEARSON
Prentice
Hall

Needham, Massachusetts
Upper Saddle River, New Jersey

STAFF CREDITS

The people who made up the Brief Review in Physics team—representing editorial, editorial services, and design—are listed below.

Ken Chang, Kathy Dempsey, Terence Hegarty, Caroline Power, Kim Schmidt, Jerry Thorne

Additional Credits

Matt Walker, Ann Bekebrede, Black Dot Group

ISBN 0-13-125580-0
1 2 3 4 5 6 7 8 9 10   08 07 06 05 04

Brief Review in

Physics: The Physical Setting

About This Book

This book is designed for students planning to take the Regents Examination Physical Setting/Physics. Most students using this book will be taking or will have taken an investigative-approach physics course. This book is useful for studying to pass the end-of-year Regents Examination in physics as well as studying for topic tests during the course. Some students taking this course will need to pass the Regents Examination to meet the requirements for high school graduation, whereas other students taking this course will have already passed the Regents Examination in science needed to meet the requirements for high school graduation.

The Regents Examination will be based on the content and understandings addressed in the core curriculum for The Physical Setting/Physics (as covered in your physics course), the *Reference Tables for Physical Setting/Physics,* and the laboratory skills learned during the course. This book is organized to enhance your review of the concepts, skills, and application of the core curriculum that may be tested on the Regents Examination for physics. Since the core curriculum does not specify a preferred order for the teaching of physics concepts, this book is organized according to a syllabus prepared by the author. For students used to a different order of topics in the classroom, note that each topic (chapter) of this book is independent of the order of presentation in this text except for the listing of vocabulary words (see below). The use of the table of contents and the index will enable you to find any topic that you need to review.

- *Review of Content:* This review book focuses on the basic content that will be tested on the Regents Examination. It includes numerous illustrations to help you visualize and understand the concepts and vocabulary of physics. The illustrations and graphs are similar to the types you will be required to interpret in Regents Examination questions. You should carefully read the illustration captions and explanations within the text.

- *Vocabulary Words:* You will need to know the definitions of the vocabulary words listed at the beginning of each topic in order to answer many Regents Examination questions. These words are shown in bold type within the topic where they are first defined. Each bold word is accompanied by a simple definition in the text. These words also may appear in other topics, where they are underlined. Vocabulary words are also defined in the glossary at the back of the book.

- *Underlined Words:* Words that are underlined in the text are either words that appear in vocabulary lists in other topics or are other words that you need to know to understand basic physics concepts. Although you are not likely to be tested on the specific definitions of non-vocabulary underlined words, these words may be used in Regents Examination questions. Underlined words are defined in the glossary.

- *Sample Problems:* Numerous solved sample problems appear throughout this book to provide you with examples of typical problems found on the Regents Examination. The step-by-step detailed solutions are designed to guide you in the problem-solving process and help reinforce content knowledge.

- *Review Questions:* Review questions appear frequently throughout each topic to help you clarify and reinforce your understanding of the content. The questions, totaling more than 600, are similar to the types of questions that may appear on the Regents Examination. Many of the questions have appeared on previous Regents Exams.

- *Questions for Regents Practice:* These questions, totaling more than 530, appear at the end of each topic. Many of the questions have appeared on previous Regents Exams. These practice questions are written and organized in the format of the Regents Examination, with Part A, Part B, and Part C questions. In many Part B and Part C questions you will notice a number in brackets. This number indicates how many points the question is worth on a Regents Examination.

- Part A questions are entirely multiple-choice and test your knowledge of concepts from the core curriculum.

- Part B questions test skills and understandings of concepts outlined in the core curriculum and include both multiple-choice and constructed-response questions.

- Part C questions are based on content and skills and require an extended constructed response. For these questions you will often need to provide a more detailed answer, supported with applications or examples. You may be asked to analyze a laboratory situation or data, or how to investigate something in the laboratory.

The back of this book contains several appendices and other items that you will find useful.

- *Appendix 1:* You will need to make use of the *Reference Tables for Physical Setting/Physics* in most of the topics in this book. When a reference table is useful, the text will refer to the *Reference Tables for Physical Setting/Physics* in italic type. A list of all of the reference tables can be found in Appendix 1 on page 187.

- *Appendix 2:* This appendix provides strategies for answering the types of questions typically found on the Regents Examination. It includes strategies for answering multiple-choice and constructed-response questions, and for using the *Reference Tables for Physical Setting / Physics*.

- *Regents Examinations:* Sample Regents Examinations are reproduced near the end of the book to provide practice in taking a Regents Examination.

- *Glossary:* All bold vocabulary words and underlined words appearing in the topics are defined in the glossary.

- *Index:* The index will enable you to find any topic that you need to review.

Many individuals not acknowledged on page ii have helped make this book a reality. I would like to thank the following people.

- My parents who instilled in me the value of education and believed that I could do anything I set my mind to.

- My sister, Juliann Hladik Albini, who assisted with preparation of art work and proofreading.

- Russell V. Pollard and Charles Derwin, retired secondary teachers, who introduced me to the wonders of physics and fostered my growth as a student.

- Edward T. Lalor, retired NYSED Assistant Commissioner for Curriculum, Instruction, Assessment, and Innovation and former Chief of the Bureau of Science Education, who afforded me the opportunity as a novice teacher to participate on a physics examination committee.

- The administration of the Greater Johnstown School District, who have supported and encouraged my professional growth throughout my teaching career.

Bernadine Hladik Cook

Measurement and Mathematics

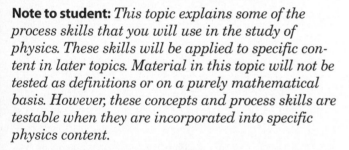

VOCABULARY

absolute error	force	range
accepted value	fundamental unit	scalar
accurate	independent variable	scientific notation
constant proportion	indirect squared proportion	SI prefix
dependent variable		SI system
derived unit	inversely proportional	significant figures
direct squared proportion	line of best fit	slope
	mass	standard deviation
directly proportional	mean	unit
experimental value	percent error	variance
extrapolation	precise	vector

Note to student: *This topic explains some of the process skills that you will use in the study of physics. These skills will be applied to specific content in later topics. Material in this topic will not be tested as definitions or on a purely mathematical basis. However, these concepts and process skills are testable when they are incorporated into specific physics content.*

Physics is based on observations and measurements of the physical world. Consequently, scientists have developed tools for measurement and adopted standard conventions for describing natural phenomena. These conventions are reviewed below.

Units

A **unit** is a standard quantity with which other similar quantities can be compared. All measurements must be made with respect to some standard quantity. For example, it makes no sense to say the distance between two cities is 26. Distance must be stated in terms of a standard unit. The distance between the cities might be 26 miles or 26 kilometers.

The SI System

The **SI system** provides standardized units for scientific measurements. All quantities measured by physicists can be expressed in terms of the seven **fundamental units** listed in Table 1-1 on the following page. **Derived units** are combinations of two or more of the fundamental units and are used to simplify notation. Other systems of units are sometimes used when they are more appropriate because of the size of the quantity being measured.

SI Prefixes

SI prefixes are prefixes combined with SI base units to form new units that are larger or smaller than the base units by a multiple or submultiple of 10. The symbol for the new unit consists of the symbol for the prefix followed by the symbol for the base unit. Table 1-2 on the next page lists some common SI prefixes. For example, 1000 meters can be expressed as 1 kilometer or 1 km, and 0.01 meter can be expressed as 1 centimeter or 1 cm.

SYMBOLS FOR UNITS AND QUANTITIES

Symbols for SI units are printed in normal type. For example, m is the symbol for meters, and A is the symbol for amperes. Letter symbols are also used for the names of quantities in equations. These symbols are printed in *italic* type. For example, *m* is the symbol for mass, and *A* is the symbol for area. Be careful not to confuse these different meanings of the same letters.

Table 1-1. Units of Measure

Kind of Unit	Quantity Being Measured	Name of Unit	Symbol
Fundamental SI	length	meter	m
	mass	kilogram	kg
	time	second	s
	electric current	ampere	A
	temperature	kelvin	K
	amount of substance*	mole	mol
	luminous intensity*	candela	cd
Derived SI	frequency	hertz	Hz
	force	newton	N
	energy, work	joule	J
	quantity of electric charge	coulomb	C
	electric potential, potential difference	volt	V
	power	watt	W
	magnetic flux	weber	Wb
	electrical resistance	ohm	Ω
	resistivity	ohm · meter	Ω · m
Non-SI	length	angstrom	Å
	mass	gram	g
	mass	universal mass unit	u
	time	hour	h
	energy, work	electronvolt	eV
	angle size	degree	°

*These quantities are not treated in this review.

Table 1-2. Prefixes for Powers of 10

Prefix	Symbol	Notation
tera-	T	10^{12}
giga-	G	10^{9}
mega-	M	10^{6}
kilo-	k	10^{3}
deci-	d	10^{-1}
centi-	c	10^{-2}
milli-	m	10^{-3}
micro-	μ	10^{-6}
nano-	n	10^{-9}
pico-	p	10^{-12}

DIMENSIONAL ANALYSIS Analyzing units can help in solving problems. The units on the left side of an equation must always be equivalent to the units on the right side of the equation. Quantities can be added or subtracted only if they have the same units. These facts can be used to check whether an answer is reasonable. For example, the formula for the period of a simple pendulum is as follows:

$$T = 2\pi\sqrt{\frac{\ell}{g}}$$

T is the period of the pendulum, ℓ is the length, and g is the acceleration due to gravity. Because the period represents time, the expression on the right side of the equation must also have the dimension time. The units of the acceleration due to gravity, m/s^2, can be expressed as length ℓ in meters divided by T^2 in seconds squared, or $\frac{\ell}{T^2}$. Thus, dimensionally the equation can be written as follows:

$$T = \sqrt{\frac{\ell}{\frac{\ell}{T^2}}}$$

The units of length divide out and $T = \sqrt{T^2}$. The factor 2π has no units so it is not considered in the analysis.

Review Questions

1. Which is not a fundamental unit? (1) kilogram
   (2) meter (3) second (4) watt

2. Which is not a unit of length? (1) angstrom (2) hertz
   (3) kilometer (4) meter

3. Which of these units for power is the smallest?
   (1) gigawatt (2) kilowatt (3) megawatt (4) watt

4. Which of these units for length is the smallest?
   (1) μm (2) mm (3) nm (4) pm

5. Continental drift speed is 1×10^{-9} meter per second.
   This is equivalent to a speed of (1) 1 Tm/s (2) 1 Gm/s
   (3) 1 nm/s (4) 1 pm/s

6. The diameter of 12-gauge wire is 2.053×10^{-3}
   meter. This is equivalent to 2.053 (1) km (2) mm
   (3) μm (4) nm

7. The energy in half a tank of gasoline is 1,000,000,000
   joules. Express this value in gigajoules.
   1 Gjoule

8. The mean radius of Earth is 6,000,000 meters. Express
   this value in kilometers.

9. Which of these lengths is 10^6 times greater than a
   nanometer? (1) μm (2) mm (3) cm (4) km

10. The period of rotation of the sun is 2.125×10^6
    seconds. This is equivalent to 2.125 (1) μs (2) ms
    (3) Ms (4) Ts

11. Human hair grows at the rate of 3 nanometers per
    second. This rate is equivalent to (1) 3×10^{-3} m/s
    (2) 3×10^{-6} m/s (3) 3×10^{-9} m/s (4) 3×10^{-12} m/s

12. The wavelength of red light is 7×10^{-7} meter.
    Express this value in nanometers.

13. If m represents mass in kg, v represents speed in m/s,
    and r represents radius in m, show that the force F in
    the equation $F = \dfrac{mv^2}{r}$ can be expressed in the unit
    $kg \cdot m/s^2$. $F = \dfrac{(kg)(m/s^2)}{m}$

14. If PE_s represents the potential energy stored in a
    spring in $kg \cdot m^2/s^2$, and x represents the elongation
    of the spring in m, what is the unit for the spring
    constant k in the equation $PE_s = \frac{1}{2}kx^2$?

15. If F_e represents the electric force between two point
    charges in N, q_1 and q_2 represent the charges in C,
    and r represents the distance between the charges in
    m, what is the unit for k in the formula $F = \dfrac{kq_1 q_2}{r^2}$?
    (1) $N \cdot m^2/C^2$ (2) $N \cdot m^2$ (3) $N \cdot C^2/m^2$ (4) $N \cdot m^2/C$

Tools for Measurement

In most laboratory investigations, you will make
observations and measurements of physical quantities. You will be expected to select the appropriate
piece of equipment, determine its scale, and make
measurements to the proper number of significant
figures.

Measuring Length

The length of an object or the total length of a path
an object moves is measured with a metric ruler or
meter stick. Path length is usually measured in
meters, but occasionally centimeters are more
appropriate. You can convert a measurement in
centimeters to meters by dividing by 100. The piece
of wire in Figure 1-1 has a length of 5.2 cm or
0.052 m.

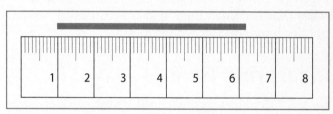

Figure 1-1. Metric ruler: The length of the wire is 5.2 cm.

Measuring Mass

The **mass,** or amount of matter contained in an
object, can be measured with a triple-beam or electronic balance. It is important that the balance be
zeroed before determining the mass of an object.
   The steel ball on the electronic balance in
Figure 1-2 has a mass of 115.2 g or 0.1152 kg.

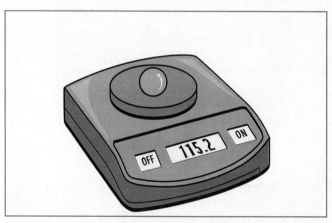

Figure 1-2. Electronic balance: The steel ball has a mass of
115.2 g.

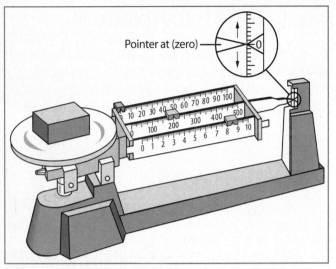

Pointer at (zero)

Figure 1-3. Triple-beam balance: The beam must be at zero when a reading of the mass is made.

The block of wood on the triple-beam balance in Figure 1-3 has a mass of 208.5 g or 0.2085 kg. A mass that is determined in grams can be converted to kilograms by dividing by 1000.

Measuring Time

Elapsed time can be measured with a clock or stopwatch. As you know, one hour equals sixty minutes and one minute equals sixty seconds. Because many of the events you will be measuring in physics occur quickly, you may be asked to record elapsed time to the nearest hundredth of a second. The stopwatch in Figure 1-4 shows an elapsed time of 37.08 s.

Measuring Force

A push or pull on a mass is called a **force.** Forces are measured with a spring scale. Ranges on spring scales typically vary from 2.5 newtons to 20.0 newtons. Figure 1-5 shows a spring scale recording a force of 4.5 N as a block is lifted at constant speed.

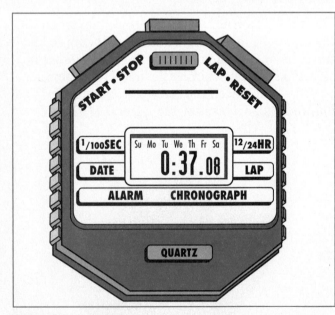

Figure 1-4. Stopwatch: Minutes are recorded to the left of the colon. Seconds (to the one-hundreth place) are recorded to the right of the colon. The elapsed time is 37.08 s.

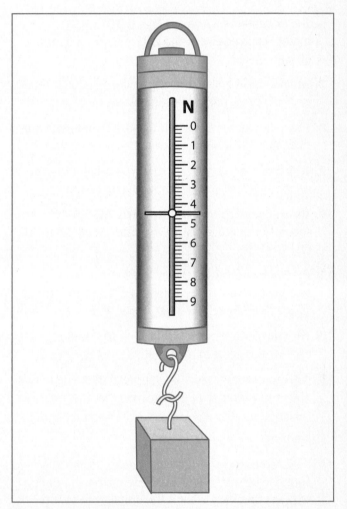

Figure 1-5. Spring scale: Force or weight is measured with a spring scale. This scale reads 4.5 N.

Measuring an Angle

A common unit for measuring angles is the degree (°), which is one ninetieth of a right angle. The protractor is an instrument used for measuring angles in degrees. Figure 1-6 shows a protractor being used to measure angle *AOB*. The wedge point of the protractor is on *O,* and the diameter of the semicircle lies on *OA,* one side of the angle. The other side of the angle intersects the semicircle at 47°. This reading gives the number of degrees in the angle. If the sides of the angle are too short to intersect the semicircle, they can be extended.

DRAWING AN ANGLE To draw an angle of 25° with its vertex at point *P,* draw a line segment originating at *P.* Place the wedge point of the protractor on *P* and the diameter of the protractor semicircle along the line segment. Make a dot on the paper at the 25° mark on the inner set of degree readings. Draw a line from this point to *P.*

Trigonometry

The branch of mathematics that treats the relationships between the angles and sides of triangles is called trigonometry. Basic trigonometric relationships are used to solve some types of physics problems. Figure 1-7 shows a right triangle. Notice that side *a* is opposite angle *θ,* side *b* is adjacent to angle *θ,* and side *c* is the hypotenuse opposite the right angle.

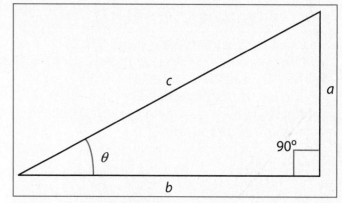

Figure 1-7. Right triangle

Important ratios of the sides of a right triangle in terms of angle *θ* include the following.

$$\sin \theta = \frac{a}{c}$$

$$\cos \theta = \frac{b}{c}$$

$$\tan \theta = \frac{a}{b}$$

If the measure of angle *θ* is 30.°, the ratio of *a* to *c* is 0.500 because sin 30.° = 0.500.

If you know the length of any two sides of a right triangle, you can find the length of the third side by using the Pythagorean theorem. The Pythagorean theorem is valid for right triangles only and has the following formula:

$$a^2 + b^2 = c^2$$

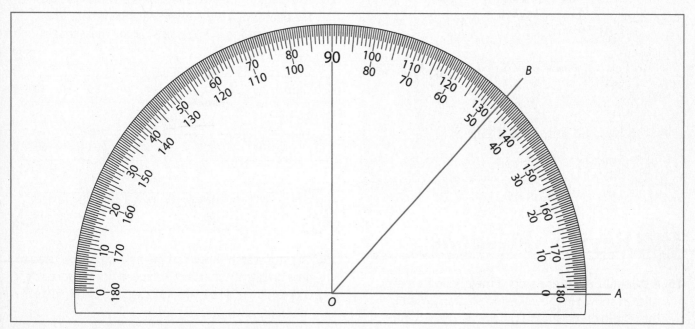

Figure 1-6. Protractor: Angle *AOB* has a measure of 47°.

SAMPLE PROBLEM

A block is displaced a vertical distance of 0.75 meter as it slides down a 1.25-meter long plane inclined to the horizontal, as shown in the following diagram.
(a) How far is the block displaced horizontally?
(b) What is the measure of the angle of inclination of the plane to the horizontal?

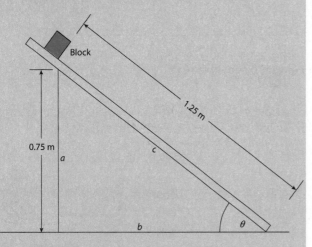

Solution: Relate the Pythagorean theorem to the diagram. Identify the known and unknown values.

Known	Unknown
$a = 0.75$ m	$b = ?$ m
$c = 1.25$ m	$\angle\theta = ?$ degrees

(a) Solve the Pythagorean theorem for the unknown, b.
$$a^2 + b^2 = c^2$$
$$b = \sqrt{c^2 - a^2}$$

Substitute the known values and solve.
$$b = \sqrt{(1.25 \text{ m})^2 - (0.75 \text{ m})^2} = 1.0 \text{ m}$$

(b) Write the formula for $\sin\theta$.
$$\sin\theta = \frac{a}{c}$$

Substitute the known values and solve for θ.
$$\sin\theta = \frac{0.75 \text{ m}}{1.25 \text{ m}}$$
$$\theta = 37°$$

Review Questions

16. A student measures a strip of metal using a metric ruler, as shown in the following diagram. What is the length of the strip? (1) 6.50 cm (2) 56.5 mm (3) 56.5 cm (4) 5065 mm

17. The following diagram shows the cross-sectional area of a dowel. Use your ruler to determine the diameter of the dowel to the nearest tenth of a centimeter.

18. Express a length of 52.5 centimeters in meters.

19. The following diagram shows an enlarged view of the beams on a triple-beam balance. What is the correct reading for the mass that is being measured? (1) 251.0 g (2) 524.5 g (3) 5245 g (4) 5,002,045 g

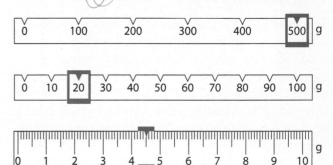

20. The diagram that follows shows an enlarged view of the beams of a triple beam balance. What is the correct reading in kilograms for the mass that is being measured?

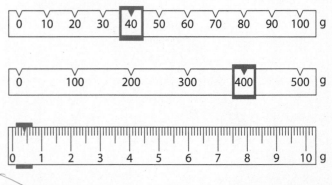

21. The stopwatch shown on the next page was used to time an event. What is the elapsed time in seconds? (1) 24.450 s (2) 154.50 s (3) 234.50 s (4) 23,450 s

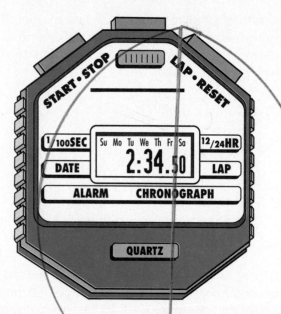

22. Each small division on the clock below represents 0.1 second. How much elapsed time is shown on the clock?

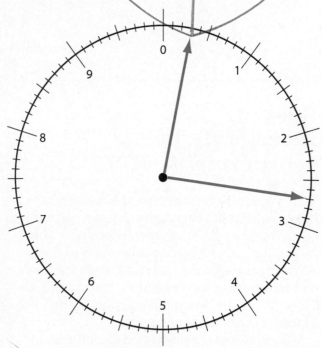

23. An electric light bulb operates for 1 hour 15 minutes. For how many seconds does the light bulb operate?

4500 s

24. An electric iron is operated for 18 minutes at 120 volts. For how many seconds is the iron operated?

25. The following diagram shows a spring scale being used to pull a wooden block up a wooden incline. What is the magnitude of the force recorded on the spring scale?

2.4N

26. The diagram that follows shows a spring scale attached to a wooden block as it is being pulled across a horizontal surface. What is the magnitude of the force recorded on the spring scale?

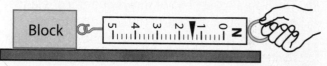

27. The following diagram represents a ramp inclined to the horizontal at angle θ. The upper end of the ramp is 30. centimeters above the horizontal. (a) What is the measure of the angle of inclination θ? (b) What is the length of the ramp?

$\theta = 25°$

$\tan 25 = \frac{30}{A}$

$\sin 25 = \frac{30}{H}$

64cm

71cm

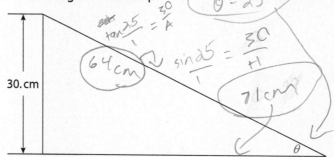

28. The following diagram represents a ramp inclined at angle θ to the horizontal. (a) What is the measure of angle θ to the nearest degree? (b) What is sin θ? (c) What is cos θ?

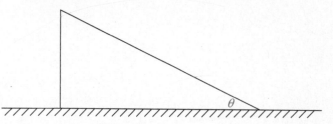

29. On the diagram that follows, use a protractor to construct an angle of 40.° with the normal to the surface at point P.

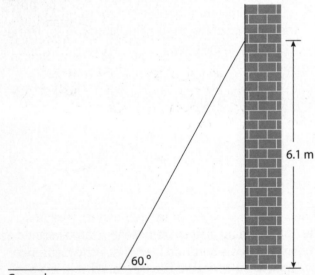

30. The diagram that follows shows one end of a ladder resting against the side of a building 6.1 meters above the level ground. The other end of the ladder makes an angle of 60.° with the ground. (a) What is the length of the ladder? (b) How far is the base of the ladder from the building?

31. A child flying a kite lets out 50. meters of string. The string makes an angle of 30.° with the ground, as shown in the following diagram. Approximately how high is the child's kite?

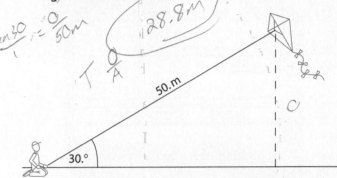

32. A forest ranger, 35 meters above the ground in a tower, observes a blazing fire. The angle of depression to the base of the fire is 20.°, as shown in the following diagram. How far from the tower is the fire?

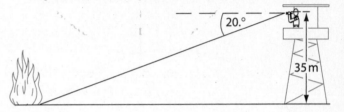

Uncertainty in Measurement

When a quantity is measured, the measurement always consists of some digits that are certain plus one digit whose value has been estimated. Thus, every measurement has an experimental uncertainty. The uncertainty can result from the quality and limitations of the measuring instrument, the skill of the person using the instrument, and the number of measurements made.

If several measurements taken of the same event are nearly identical, the measurements are said to be **precise.** If a measurement is very close to the accepted value found in a handbook, the measurement is said to be **accurate.** For example, the accepted value for the acceleration due to gravity near Earth's surface is 9.81 m/s^2. If a student measures this quantity as 9.98 m/s^2, 9.98 m/s^2, and 9.99 m/s^2, the measurements are precise, but not accurate.

Significant Figures (Significant Digits)

In a measured value, the digits that are known with certainty plus the one digit whose value has been estimated are called **significant figures** or significant digits. The greater the number of significant digits in a measurement, the greater the accuracy of the measurement.

Nonzero digits in a measurement are always significant. Zeroes appearing in a measurement may or may not be significant. The following rules should be applied *in order* to the zeroes in a measured value:

1. Zeros that appear *before* a nonzero digit are *not* significant. Examples: 0.002 m (1 significant figure) and 0.13 g (2 significant figures)

2. Zeroes that appear *between* nonzero digits are significant. Examples: 0. 705 kg (3 significant figures) and 2006 km (4 significant figures)

3. Zeroes that appear *after* a nonzero digit are significant *only* if (a) followed by a decimal point. Examples: 40 s (1 significant figure) and 20. m (2 significant figures); *or* if (b) they appear to the right of the decimal point. Examples: 37.0 cm (3 significant figures) and 4.100 m (4 significant figures)

A measurement of 0.040 900 kg utilizes all of the rules for zeroes and contains 5 significant digits.

If a whole-number measurement ends in two or more zeroes, it is not possible to indicate that some, but not all, of the zeroes are significant. For example, a measurement of 5200 m is interpreted to have only two significant figures, although it could actually represent a measurement to the nearest 10 meters. This situation is avoided by the use of scientific notation, which will be discussed later in this topic.

Addition and Subtraction with Measured Values

Measured values must have the same units before they are added or subtracted. For example, if the dimensions of a rectangle are recorded as 4.3 cm and 0.085 m, both measurements must be expressed either in centimeters or in meters before they can be combined by addition to find the perimeter of the rectangle. After adding or subtracting measured values expressed in the same units, the sum or difference is rounded to the same decimal place value as the least sensitive measurement. For example,

$$\begin{array}{r} 31.1 \ \text{m} \\ - \ 2.461 \ \text{m} \\ \hline 28.639 \ \text{m} = 28.6 \ \text{m} \end{array}$$

The example shows that subtracting a measurement known to the nearest thousandth of a meter from a measurement known to the nearest tenth of a meter produces a difference known to the nearest tenth of a meter.

Similarly, in the following example, adding measurements to the nearest hundredth of a centimeter, tenth of a centimeter, and centimeter produces a sum to the nearest centimeter.

$$\begin{array}{r} 24.82 \ \text{cm} \\ 4.7 \ \ \text{cm} \\ + \ 2 \ \ \ \ \text{cm} \\ \hline 31.52 \ \text{cm} = 32 \ \text{cm} \end{array}$$

ROUNDING CALCULATED ANSWERS The preceding examples of subtraction and addition illustrate the rules for rounding calculated answers. If the digit to the right of the last significant digit is less than 5, the last significant digit remains unchanged. If the digit to the right of the last significant digit is 5 or greater, the last significant digit is increased by 1.

Multiplication and Division with Measured Values

When multiplying or dividing measured values, the operation is performed and the answer is rounded to the same number of significant figures as appears in the value having the lowest number of significant figures. In the example that follows, 2.6 cm has two significant figures, whereas 200.0 cm has four. Thus, the product of the two values can have only two significant figures.

$$(200.0 \ \text{cm})(2.6 \ \text{cm}) = 520 \ \text{cm}^2$$

Notice that although both measurements are accurate to the nearest tenth of a centimeter, the last significant figure in the product is in the tens place. Thus, the product of a measurement with four significant figures and a measurement with two significant figures has only two significant figures.

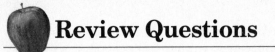

Review Questions

33. A student measures the speed of yellow light in water to be 2.00×10^8 m/s, 1.87×10^8 m/s, and 2.39×10^8 m/s. If the accepted value for the speed is 2.25×10^8 m/s, which best describes the student's measurements? (1) accurate only (2) precise only (3) both precise and accurate (4) neither precise nor accurate

34. A student measures the length of a quarter-mile lap around the school's track to be 402.3 m, 402.3 m, and 402.5 m. If the accepted value for the path length is 402.3 m, which best describes the student's measurements? (1) accurate only (2) precise only (3) both precise and accurate (4) neither precise nor accurate

35. Which length measurement contains three significant figures? (1) 0.203 m (2) 0.54 m (3) 34.70 km (4) 570 cm

36. How many significant figures are in a measurement of 14,020 g? (1) 5 (2) 2 (3) 3 (4) 4

37. What is the area of a rectangle having dimensions of 9.8 m and 12.7 m? (1) 100 m^2 (2) 120 m^2 (3) 124 m^2 (4) 124.46 m^2

38. Which mass measurement contains two significant figures? (1) 0.040 kg (2) 0.4 kg (3) 40 kg (4) 405 kg

39. How many significant figures are in a measurement of 7002 m? (1) 1 (2) 2 (3) 3 (4) 4

40. A car travels 685 meters in 27 seconds. What is the average speed of the car? (1) 25.370 m/s (2) 25.37 m/s (3) 25.4 m/s (4) 25 m/s

41. A radar signal traveling at 3.00×10^8 m/s is sent from Earth to the moon and is received back at Earth in 2.56 s. What is the distance from Earth to the moon? (1) 7.68×10^8 m (2) 3.84×10^8 m (3) 8×10^8 m (4) 4×10^8 m

42. What is the sum of 3.04 m + 4.134 m + 6.1 m?

43. What is the sum of 0.027 kg and 0.0023 kg?

44. How many significant figures are in the measurement 0.705 m?

45. How many significant figures are in the measurement 470 m?

46. Express forty meters with four significant figures.

47. Determine the area of a rectangle having a length of 41.6 cm and a width of 2.3 cm.

48. Safety guidelines recommend an area of 5.6 m^2 per student in a laboratory setting. Would a room having dimensions of 13.2 m and 10.6 m accommodate 24 students and comply with these guidelines? Justify your answer.

Scientific Notation

Measurements that have very large or very small values are usually expressed in scientific notation. **Scientific notation** consists of a number equal to or greater than one and less than ten followed by a multiplication sign and the base ten raised to some integral power. The general form of a number expressed in scientific notion is $A \times 10^n$. All of the digits in A are significant. For numbers having an absolute value greater than one, n is positive; for numbers having an absolute value less than one, n is negative. For example, the mean radius of Earth is 6,370,000 m or 6.37×10^6 m (3 significant figures). The universal gravitational constant is 0.000 000 000 066 7 N·m^2/kg^2 or 6.67×10^{-11} N·m^2/kg^2 (3 significant figures).

ADDITION AND SUBTRACTION Measurements written in scientific notation can be added or subtracted only if they are expressed in the same units and to the same power of ten. Sometimes, as in the example below, the power of ten must be changed first before adding or subtracting.

$$3.2 \times 10^2 \text{ m} + 4.73 \times 10^3 \text{ m} =$$
$$0.32 \times 10^3 \text{ m} + 4.73 \times 10^3 \text{ m} = 5.05 \times 10^3 \text{ m}$$

MULTIPLICATION AND DIVISION The commutative and associative laws for multiplication are used to find products and quotients of physical quantities written in scientific notation. Recall that the exponents are added when like bases are multiplied and the exponents are subtracted when like bases are divided. The general rule is as follows.

$$(A \times 10^n)(B \times 10^m) = (A \times B)(10^{n+m})$$
$$\text{and}$$
$$\frac{(A \times 10^n)}{(B \times 10^m)} = \frac{A}{B} \times 10^{n-m}$$

When multiplying and dividing measured values, the rules for significant figures apply to values expressed in scientific notation. Some examples follow.

$$(1.3 \times 10^5 \text{ m})(3.47 \times 10^2 \text{ m}) = 4.5 \times 10^7 \text{ m}^2$$

$$(1.3 \times 10^{-5} \text{ m})(3.47 \times 10^2 \text{ m}) = 4.5 \times 10^{-3} \text{ m}^2$$

$$(4.73 \times 10^5 \text{ m})(5.2 \times 10^2 \text{ m})$$
$$= 25 \times 10^7 \text{ m}^2 = 2.5 \times 10^8 \text{ m}^2$$

$$(8.4 \times 10^5 \text{ m}) \div (2.10 \times 10^2 \text{ m}) = 4.0 \times 10^3$$

$$(8.4 \times 10^5 \text{ m}) \div (2.10 \times 10^{-2} \text{ m}) = 4.0 \times 10^7$$

$$(2.10 \times 10^2 \text{ m}) \div (8.4 \times 10^5 \text{ m})$$
$$= 0.25 \times 10^{-3} = 2.5 \times 10^{-4}$$

Estimation and Orders of Magnitude

The technique of estimating the answer to a problem before performing the calculations makes it possible to quickly verify the procedures to be used and determine the reasonableness of the answer.

SAMPLE PROBLEM

Estimate the magnitude of the gravitational force between Earth and the moon and compare it with the actual value.

Solution: Use the formula for the gravitational force and the known values of the masses, the distance of separation, and the universal gravitational constant.

Known

$F = \dfrac{Gm_1m_2}{r^2}$

$G = 6.67 \times 10^{-11} \text{ N} \cdot \text{m}^2/\text{kg}^2$

$m_1 = 7.35 \times 10^{22} \text{ kg}$

$m_2 = 5.98 \times 10^{24} \text{ kg}$

$r = 3.84 \times 10^8 \text{ m}$

Unknown

estimated $F = ?$ N

Substitute the known values in the formula for gravitational force.

$$F = \frac{(6.67 \times 10^{-11} \text{ N} \cdot \text{m}^2/\text{kg}^2)(7.35 \times 10^{22} \text{ kg})(5.98 \times 10^{24} \text{ kg})}{(3.84 \times 10^8 \text{ m})^2}$$

Estimate the answer by rounding off each value to the nearest whole number and combining them.

$$F = \frac{(7 \times 10^{-11})(7 \times 10^{22})(6 \times 10^{24})\text{N}}{16 \times 10^{16}}$$

$F \text{ (estimated)} = 20 \times 10^{19} \text{ N} = 2 \times 10^{20} \text{ N}$

Use a calculator to determine the actual force.

$F \text{ (calculated)} = 1.99 \times 10^{20} \text{ N}$

The estimated value is close to the calculated value.

Estimating answers using orders of magnitude also helps in evaluating the reasonableness of an answer, as illustrated in the following Sample Problem.

SAMPLE PROBLEM

As the Voyager spacecraft passed the planet Uranus, it sent signals back to Earth. Determine the order of magnitude of the time in seconds for a signal to reach Earth. The distance from Earth to Uranus is 2.71×10^{12} m. The speed of light in a vacuum is 3.00×10^8 m/s

Solution: Identify the known and unknown values.

Known

$d = 2.71 \times 10^{12}$ m

$v = 3.00 \times 10^8$ m/s

Unknown

$t = ?$ s

Round the known values to the nearest whole numbers and substitute them in the equation relating distance, time, and average velocity.

$$t = \frac{d}{v} = \frac{3 \times 10^{12} \text{ m}}{3 \times 10^8 \text{ m/s}} = 10^4 \text{ s}$$

The order of magnitude is 10^4.

Review Questions

49. Express the diameter of a nickel, 0.021 m, in scientific notation.

50. Express the mass of a car, 1500 kg, in scientific notation.

51. The jet engines of a 747 exert a force of 770,000 N. Express this value in scientific notation.

52. Divide 1.49457×10^{11} m, the average distance from the sun to Earth, by 3.00×10^8 m/s, the speed of light in a vacuum. Write your answer in scientific notation with the correct units and the appropriate number of significant figures.

53. The height of a doorknob above the floor is approximately (1) 1×10^2 m (2) 1×10^1 m (3) 1×10^0 m (4) 1×10^{-2} m

54. The length of a high school classroom is probably closest to (1) 10^{-2} m (2) 10^{-1} m (3) 10^1 m (4) 10^4 m

55. The thickness of a dollar bill is closest to (1) 1×10^{-4} m (2) 1×10^{-2} m (3) 1×10^{-1} m (4) 1×10^1 m

56. Which measurement of an average classroom door is closest to 10^0 m? (1) thickness (2) width (3) height (4) surface area

57. What is the approximate mass of a chicken egg? (1) 1×10^1 kg (2) 1×10^2 kg (3) 1×10^{-1} kg (4) 1×10^{-4} kg

58. A mass of one kilogram of nickels has a monetary value in United States dollars of approximately (1) $1.00 (2) $0.10 (3) $10.00 (4) $1000.00

59. The mass of a physics textbook is closest to (1) 10^3 kg (2) 10^1 kg (3) 10^0 kg (4) 10^{-2} kg

60. Approximately how many seconds are in three hours? (1) 10^2 s (2) 10^3 s (3) 10^4 s (4) 10^5 s

61. The weight of an apple is closest to (1) 10^{-2} N (2) 10^0 N (3) 10^2 N (4) 10^4 N

62. Which object weighs approximately 1 newton? (1) dime (2) paper clip (3) physics student (4) golf ball

63. The speed of a rifle bullet is 7×10^2 m/s and the speed of a snail is 1×10^{-3} m/s. How many times faster than the snail does the bullet travel?

64. The power of sunlight striking Earth is 1.7×10^{17} watts. How many 100-watt light bulbs would produce this amount of power?

Note: Use information found on the first page of the *Reference Tables for Physical Setting/Physics* in answering questions 65 through 68.

65. The acceleration due to gravity is approximately (1) 10^{-1} m/s² (2) 10^0 m/s² (3) 10^1 m/s² (4) 10^3 m/s²

66. What is the order of magnitude of the ratio of the charge on an electron to the mass of an electron?

67. What is the order of magnitude of the ratio of the speed of light in a vacuum to the speed of sound in air at STP?

68. What is the order of magnitude of the ratio of the mass of an electron to the mass of a proton?

Evaluating Experimental Results

Experimental measurements made in any laboratory must be evaluated before they can be published in a scientific journal. An evaluation procedure has been developed for this purpose.

Data Analysis

In an experiment, for example to determine the relationship between the period of a simple pendulum and its length, multiple measurements are made of a given or identical event. Although there is a **range** of measurements or difference between the highest and lowest value in the data set, most of the measurements are close to the mean.

The notation $\sum_{i=1}^{n}$ is used to represent the sum of related terms. The index i is replaced by consecutive integers starting with the lower limit of summation written below the summation symbol Σ and ending with the upper limit of summation written above. Therefore, the **mean** or average $\bar{x}$ of a set of n measurements, where x_i is the individual measurement and f_i is the frequency of occurrence of that measurement, can be represented by this expression.

$$\bar{x} = \frac{\sum_{i=1}^{n} x_i f_i}{\sum f_i}$$

The **variance** v is the sum of the squares of the differences of the measurements from the mean, divided by the number of measurements.

$$v = \frac{\sum_{i=1}^{n} f_i (x_i - \bar{x})^2}{\sum f_i}$$

The **standard deviation** σ is the square root of the variance.

$$\sigma = \sqrt{v} = \sqrt{\frac{\sum_{i=1}^{n} f_i (x_i - \bar{x})^2}{\sum f_i}}$$

In a normal distribution, 68% of the data values lie between $\bar{x} - \sigma$ and $\bar{x} + \sigma$; 95% lie between $\bar{x} - 2\sigma$ and $\bar{x} + 2\sigma$; and 99.5% lie between $\bar{x} - 3\sigma$ and $\bar{x} + 3\sigma$.

SAMPLE PROBLEM

A student made seven measurements of the period of a simple pendulum of constant length: 1.34 s, 1.28 s, 1.26 s, 1.28 s, 1.33 s, 1.33 s, and 1.28 s. Determine the range, mean, variance and standard deviation for the data.

Solution: Identify the known and unknown values.

Known	Unknown
$T_1 = 1.34$ s	range $= ?$ s
$T_2 = 1.28$ s	mean $\bar{x} = ?$ s
$T_3 = 1.26$ s	variance $v = ?$ s²
$T_4 = 1.28$ s	standard deviation $\sigma = ?$ s
$T_5 = 1.33$ s	
$T_6 = 1.33$ s	
$T_7 = 1.28$ s	

Determine the range by subtracting the smallest measurement from the largest.

1.34 s $- 1.26$ s $= 0.08$ s

Set up a chart to simplify finding the mean, variance, and standard deviation.

Write in column 1 the four values of T (x_i) that are different.

Write the frequency of each value of T in column 2.

Find the sum of the frequencies, Σf_i, and record it in column 2.

$\Sigma f_i = 1 + 3 + 2 + 1 = 7$

Multiply the values in column 1 (x_i) by the values in column 2 (f_i). Record the results in column 3.

$x_i f_i = (1.26$ s$)(1) = 1.26$ s
$x_i f_i = (1.28$ s$)(3) = 3.84$ s
$x_i f_i = (1.33$ s$)(2) = 2.66$ s
$x_i f_i = (1.34$ s$)(1) = 1.34$ s

Calculate the sum of all the $x_i f_i$ values, $\Sigma x_i f_i$, by adding the values in column 3.

$\Sigma x_i f_i = 1.26$ s $+ 3.84$ s $+ 2.66$ s $+ 1.34$ s $= 9.10$ s

Determine the mean, $\bar{x}$, by dividing $\Sigma x_i f_i$ by Σf_i.

$$\bar{x} = \frac{\sum_{i=1}^{4} x_i f_i}{\sum f_i} = \frac{9.10 \text{ s}}{7} = 1.30 \text{ s}$$

Subtract the mean from each value in column 1 and record the values in column 4.

1.26 s $- 1.30$ s $= -0.04$ s
1.28 s $- 1.30$ s $= -0.02$ s
1.33 s $- 1.30$ s $= +0.03$ s
1.34 s $- 1.30$ s $= +0.04$ s

Square the values in column 4 and record the results in column 5.

$(-0.04$ s$)^2 = 0.0016$ s²
$(-0.02$ s$)^2 = 0.0004$ s²
$(+0.03$ s$)^2 = 0.0009$ s²
$(-0.04$ s$)^2 = 0.0016$ s²

Multiply the values in column 5 by the frequencies in column 2. Record these products in column 6.

$(0.0016$ s²$)(1) = 0.0016$ s²
$(0.0004$ s²$)(3) = 0.0012$ s²
$(0.0009$ s²$)(2) = 0.0018$ s²
$(0.0016$ s²$)(1) = 0.0016$ s²

Add the values in column 6.

$\Sigma (x_i - \bar{x})^2 f_i = 0.0016$ s² $+ 0.0012$ s² $+ 0.0018$ s² $+ 0.0016$ s² $= 0.0062$ s²

Determine the variance using the following formula.

$$v = \frac{\sum_{i=1}^{4} f_i (x_i - \bar{x})^2}{\sum f_i} = \frac{0.0062 \text{ s}^2}{7} = 8.9 \times 10^{-4} \text{ s}^2$$

Determine the standard deviation using the following formula.

$$\sigma = \sqrt{v} = \sqrt{\frac{\sum_{i=1}^{4} f_i (x_i - \bar{x})^2}{\sum f_i}}$$

$$= \sqrt{8.9 \times 10^{-4} \text{ s}^2} = 0.030 \text{ s}$$

x_i (s)	f_i	$x_i f_i$ (s)	$x_i - \bar{x}$ (s)	$(x_i - \bar{x})^2$ (s²)	$(x_i - \bar{x})^2 f_i$ (s²)
1.26	1	1.26	−0.04	0.0016	0.0016
1.28	3	3.84	−0.02	0.0004	0.0012
1.33	2	2.66	+0.03	0.0009	0.0018
1.34	1	1.34	+0.04	0.0016	0.0016
	$\Sigma f_i = 7$	$\Sigma x_i f_i = 9.10$ s			$\Sigma (x_i - \bar{x})^2 f_i = 0.0062$ s²

Percent Error

Measurements made during laboratory work may stand alone or be incorporated into one or more formulas to yield an **experimental value** for a physical quantity. In some instances, scientists have determined the most probable value or **accepted value** for quantities and published them in reference books. The difference between an experimental value and the published accepted value is called the **absolute error**. The **percent error** of a measurement can be calculated by dividing the absolute error by the accepted value and multiplying the quotient by 100.

$$\text{Percent Error} = \frac{\text{absolute error}}{\text{accepted value}} \times 100$$

SAMPLE PROBLEM

In an experiment, a student determines that the acceleration due to gravity in the laboratory is 9.98 m/s². Determine the percent error. (According to the *Reference Tables for Physical Setting/Physics,* the accepted value for the acceleration due to gravity is 9.81 m/s².)

Solution: Identify the known and unknown values.

Known	Unknown
Experimental value of	percent error = ? %
$g = 9.98$ m/s²	
Accepted value of	
$g = 9.81$ m/s²	

Determine the absolute error by finding the difference between the experimental measurement and the accepted value.

Absolute error = 9.98 m/s² − 9.81 m/s² = 0.17 m/s²

Use the following formula to determine percent error.

$$\text{Percent error} = \frac{\text{absolute error}}{\text{accepted value}} \times 100$$

Substitute the known and calculated values and solve.

$$\text{Percent error} = \frac{0.17 \text{ m/s}^2}{9.81 \text{ m/s}^2} \times 100 = 1.7\%$$

Review Questions

69. In an experiment, a student measures the speed of sound in air to be 318 m/s at STP. If the accepted value for the speed of sound under those conditions is 331 m/s, what is the student's percent error? (1) 3.9% (2) 3.93% (3) 4.09% (4) 4.1%

70. In an experiment, a student measures the speed of yellow light in water to be 2.00×10^8 m/s. The accepted value for the speed is 2.25×10^8 m/s. Determine the student's percent error.

71. In an experiment to determine the acceleration due to gravity, a student obtained a value of 9.6 m/s². According to the *Reference Tables for Physical Setting/Physics,* the accepted value is 9.81 m/s². Determine the student's percent error.

Base your answers to questions 72 through 74 on the table below, which lists winning times to the nearest hundredth of a minute for the women's 400.-meter freestyle race at the Olympics.

Year	Time (min)
1960	4.66
1964	4.73
1968	4.51
1972	4.32
1976	4.17
1980	4.15
1984	4.12
1988	4.07

72. Find the range.

73. Determine the mean to the nearest hundredth of a minute.

74. Determine the standard deviation of these times to the nearest hundredth of a minute.

Base your answers to questions 75 through 77 on the data table below, which shows the frequency of the average daily temperatures during the month of June.

Temperature (°F)	Frequency
63	5
70.	3
78	4
79	3
80.	6
84	4
96	5

75. Find the range.

76. Determine the mean to the nearest tenth of a degree.

77. Determine the standard deviation to the nearest tenth of a degree.

Base your answers to questions 78 through 80 on the data table below, which shows the average snowfall in centimeters recorded one winter at a ski resort over a period of days.

Snowfall (cm)	Frequency
18	6
19	4
20.	4
21	3
24	5
26	3

78. Find the range.

79. Determine the mean to the nearest tenth of a centimeter.

80. Determine the standard deviation to the nearest tenth of a centimeter.

Graphing Data

The data collected in a physics experiment are often represented in graphical form. A graph makes it easier to determine whether there is a trend or pattern in the data.

Making a Graph

By convention, the **independent variable,** the one the experimenter changes, is graphed on the *x*- or horizontal axis. The **dependent variable,** the one that changes as a result of the changes made by the experimenter, is graphed on the *y*- or vertical axis. The axes are labeled with the quantities and their units are given in parenthesis. An appropriate, linear scale that accommodates the range of data is determined for each axis. It is not necessary to label every grid line. The graph should be titled

as the dependent variable versus the independent variable. After the data points are plotted, a smooth line of best fit is drawn. The **line of best fit** is a straight or curved line which approximates the relationship among a set of data points. This line usually does not pass through all measured points. Sometimes the line of best fit is extrapolated. **Extrapolation** means extending the line beyond the region in which data was taken. This is important because the point where the extended line intersects the horizontal or vertical axis has physical significance.

The slope, or inclination of a graphed line, often has a physical meaning. On an *x*-*y* coordinate system, the slope of a line is defined as the ratio $\frac{\Delta y}{\Delta x}$ for any two points on the line. That is:

$$\text{slope} = \frac{\Delta y}{\Delta x} = \frac{\text{vertical change}}{\text{horizontal change}}$$

or

$$\text{slope} = \frac{\text{change in dependent variable}}{\text{change in independent variable}}$$

In determining the slope of a line, you can use points directly from the data table only if those points lie on the line of best fit.

SAMPLE PROBLEM

The position of a moving car was measured at one-second intervals and recorded in the following table. Graph the data on the grid provided and draw the line of best fit. Determine the slope of the line.

Time (s)	Position (m)
0.0	0
1.0	18
2.0	40.
3.0	62
4.0	80.
5.0	100.

Solution: Using the data in the table, plot the graph and draw the line of best fit.

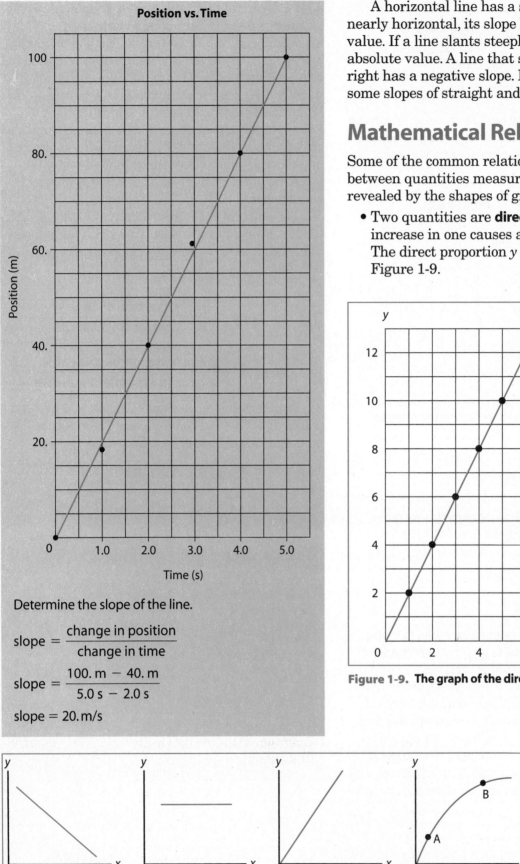

Position vs. Time

Position (m) / Time (s)

Determine the slope of the line.

$$\text{slope} = \frac{\text{change in position}}{\text{change in time}}$$

$$\text{slope} = \frac{100.\,\text{m} - 40.\,\text{m}}{5.0\,\text{s} - 2.0\,\text{s}}$$

$$\text{slope} = 20.\,\text{m/s}$$

A horizontal line has a slope of zero. If a line is nearly horizontal, its slope has a small absolute value. If a line slants steeply, its slope has a large absolute value. A line that slopes downward to the right has a negative slope. Figure 1-8 illustrates some slopes of straight and curved lines.

Mathematical Relationships

Some of the common relationships that exist between quantities measured in physics are revealed by the shapes of graphs.

- Two quantities are **directly proportional** if an increase in one causes an increase in the other. The direct proportion $y = 2x$ is illustrated in Figure 1-9.

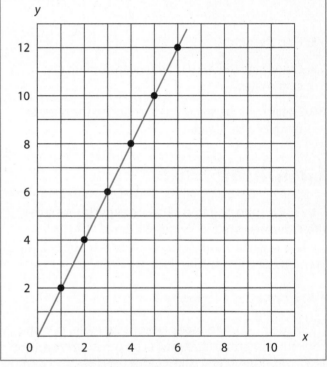

Figure 1-9. The graph of the direct proportion $y = 2x$

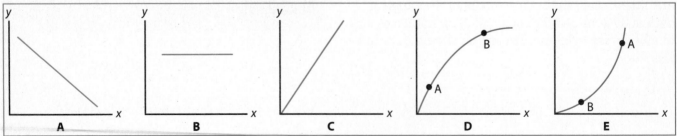

Figure 1-8. Slopes of common curves: The slope of the graph in A is negative. Graph B has a slope of zero. Graph C has a positive slope. In graphs D and E, the slope at point A is greater than at point B.

- Two quantities are **inversely proportional** if an increase in one causes a decrease in the other. The equation $y = \frac{12}{x}$ or $xy = 12$ expresses the inverse proportion shown in Figure 1-10.

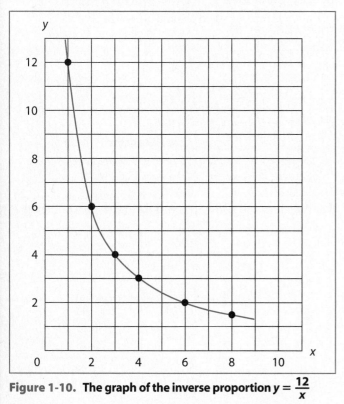

Figure 1-10. The graph of the inverse proportion $y = \frac{12}{x}$

- Two quantities have a **constant proportion** if an increase in one causes no change in the other. The equation $y = 6$, illustrated in Figure 1-11, is a constant proportion.

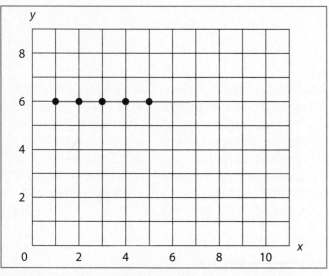

Figure 1-11. The graph of the constant proportion $y = 6$

- Two quantities have a **direct squared proportion** if an increase in one causes a squared

increase in the other. The direct squared proportion $y = x^2$ is shown in Figure 1-12.

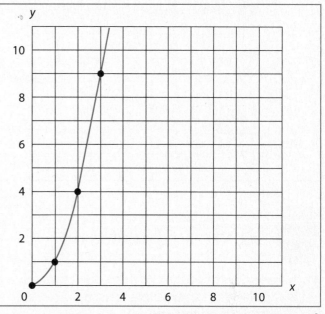

Figure 1-12. The graph of the direct squared proportion $y = x^2$

- Two quantities have an **indirect squared proportion** if an increase in one causes a squared decrease in the other. The equation $y = \frac{12}{x^2}$ expresses the indirect squared proportion illustrated in Figure 1-13.

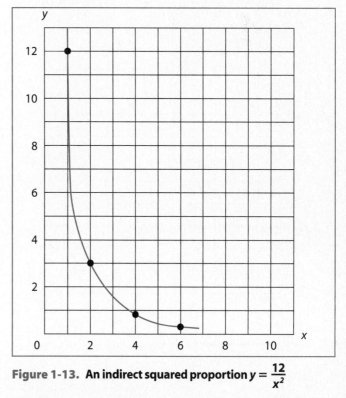

Figure 1-13. An indirect squared proportion $y = \frac{12}{x^2}$

- Figure 1-14 on the next page represents the equation $y = \sqrt{x}$.

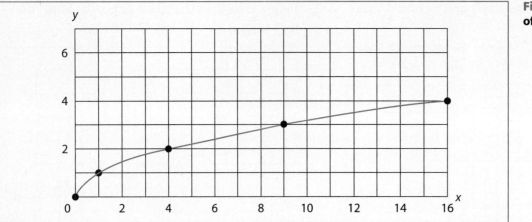

Figure 1-14. The graph of $y = \sqrt{x}$

Review Questions

81. A student prepared the grid that follows to graph data collected in an experiment. List the errors the student made on the grid.

Time vs. Position

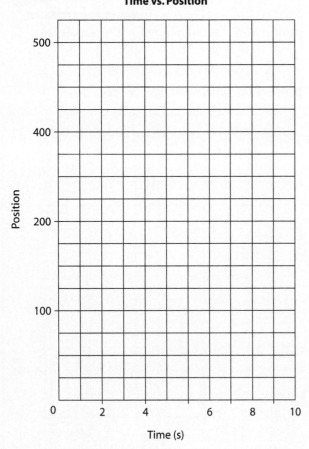

82. Which graph shows a properly drawn line of best fit?

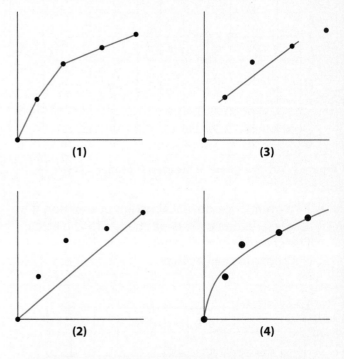
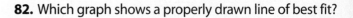

(1)

(3)

(2)

(4)

83. A student varied the length of a simple pendulum and measured its period, which is the time required for one complete vibration. In this experiment, time represents the variable that is (1) dependent and graphed on the horizontal axis (2) independent and graphed on the horizontal axis (3) dependent and graphed on the vertical axis (4) independent and graphed on the vertical axis

84. What is the slope of the line in the following graph?

Position vs. Time

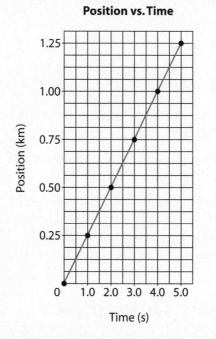

(1) 0.25 m/s (2) 1.5 m/s (3) 0.25 km/s (4) 1.5 km/s

85. The graph that follows represents the relationship between light intensity and distance from a light source. What kind of proportion exists between light intensity and distance? (1) constant (2) direct (3) direct squared (4) indirect squared

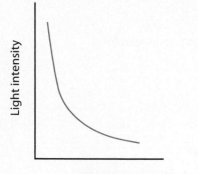

86. Which graph best represents the relationship between the cross-sectional area of a wire and its radius?

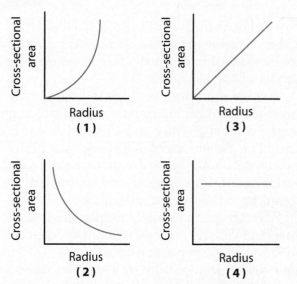

87. Vince Lombardi said, "The quality of a person's life is in direct proportion to their commitment to excellence regardless of their chosen field of endeavor." Which graph best represents this relationship?

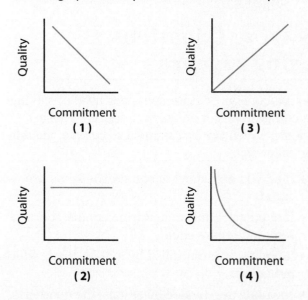

88. Sketch a graph that represents the relationship between the radius of a circle and its circumference.

89. According to Kepler's laws of planetary motion the ratio of the mean radius of the orbit of a planet cubed to the period of revolution of the planet squared is constant for all planets orbiting the sun. Sketch a graph representing this relationship.

Scalar and Vector Quantities

Physical quantities can be categorized as either scalar or vector quantities. As physical quantities are introduced in this text, their scalar or vector nature will be indicated.

A **scalar** quantity has magnitude only, with no direction specified. Time and mass are scalar quantities. For example, 30 s and 45 kg are scalar quantities. The measurement of a scalar quantity is indicated by a number with an appropriate unit. Scalar quantities are added and subtracted according to the rules of arithmetic.

A **vector** quantity has both magnitude and direction. Velocity is a vector quantity because it must be described not only by a number with an appropriate unit, but also by a specified direction. For example, the velocity of a car might be described as 25 m/s, due north. Vector quantities are added and subtracted using geometric or algebraic methods. These methods will be illustrated later in the text.

Solving Equations Using Algebra

Several axioms or statements are used in solving an equation for an unknown quantity. These axioms, which can be assumed to be true, include the following.

- If equals are added to equals, the sums are equal.
- If equals are subtracted from equals, the remainders are equal.
- If equals are multiplied by equals, the products are equal.
- If equals are divided by equals, the quotients are equal.
- A quantity may be substituted for its equal.
- Like powers or like roots of equals are equal.

You should make use of these axioms to isolate the unknown on the left side of an equation before substituting known values. Always include the units with the values in an equation. Although it is not necessary to align equal signs in the solution of an equation, it may help you keep your work orderly.

Mathematicians have agreed on the following order to be used in performing a series of operations:

1. Simplify the expression within each set of parentheses.

2. Perform exponents.

3. Perform the multiplications and divisions in order from left to right.

4. Do the additions and subtractions from left to right.

"*P*lease *e*xcuse *m*y *d*ear *A*unt *S*ue" is a useful memory device for this order: *p*arentheses, *e*xponents, *m*ultiplication and *d*ivision in order, and finally *a*ddition and *s*ubtraction in order.

Review Questions

90. Solve the following equations for *r*.

(a) $F = \dfrac{mv^2}{r}$

(b) $A = \pi r^2$

(c) $C = 2\pi r$

(d) $F = G\dfrac{m_1 m_2}{r^2}$

91. Solve the following equations for *d*.

(a) $\bar{v} = \dfrac{d}{t}$

(b) $P = \dfrac{Fd}{t}$

(c) $v_f^2 = v_i^2 + 2ad$

92. Solve the following equations for *v*.

(a) $KE = \dfrac{1}{2}mv^2$

(b) $p = mv$

(c) $n = \dfrac{c}{v}$

Mechanics

VOCABULARY

acceleration	horizontal component	resolution of forces
centripetal acceleration	impulse	resultant
	inertia	second
centripetal force	instantaneous velocity	speed
closed system	kinetic friction	static friction
coefficient of friction	kilogram	tangent
displacement	law of conservation of momentum	unbalanced force
distance		uniform circular motion
equilibrium	linear motion	
free fall	mechanics	uniform motion
free-body diagram	meter	vacuum
friction	momentum	vector component
gravitational field	net force	velocity
gravitational field strength	newton	vertical component
	normal force	weight
gravitational force	pendulum	
gravity	period (of a pendulum)	

Kinematics

The branch of physics that deals with forces and the way they produce and change motion is called **mechanics.** Kinematics is the mathematical treatment of the motions of bodies without regard to the forces that produce the motion.

Distance and Displacement

When an object moves from one point to another, it experiences a change in position relative to some arbitrary reference point. **Distance** is the total length of a path that an object travels. Distance is a scalar quantity, which means it has magnitude but not direction. **Displacement** is the change in the position of an object described by a vector that begins at the initial position of the object and ends at its final position. Because it is a vector, displacement has both magnitude and direction. Distance and displacement are usually measured in meters, centimeters, or kilometers. The **meter,** m, is the fundamental SI unit of length.

The following example illustrates the difference between distance and displacement. A car is driven on the NYS Thruway from Buffalo to Albany to New York City. The distance traveled by the car is approximately 418 miles or 673 kilometers. The magnitude of the total displacement of the car, however, is only the length of the vector connecting Buffalo and New York City—approximately 313 miles or 504 kilometers. Two or more displacement vectors can be combined to obtain the vector sum, or resultant, as the following sample problem shows.

SAMPLE PROBLEM

A student walks 5.0 meters due east and then 12.0 meters due north. Determine the magnitude and direction of the student's resultant displacement, R.

Solution: Identify the known and unknown values.

Known	Unknown
$\vec{d}_1 = 5.0$ m east	$\vec{R} = ?$ m at ?°
$\vec{d}_2 = 12.0$ m north	

Make a sketch of the situation.

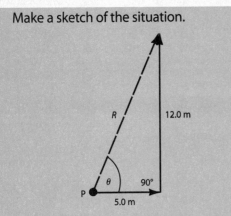

Write the equation for the Pythagorean theorem.

$c^2 = a^2 + b^2$

Substitute R for c, then substitute the known values and solve for R.

$R^2 = (5.0\,\text{m})^2 + (12.0\,\text{m})^2 = 25\,\text{m}^2 + 144\,\text{m}^2 = 169\,\text{m}^2$
$R = 13\,\text{m}$

Use the sine function to determine θ.

$$\sin \theta = \frac{\text{opposite}}{\text{hypotenuse}} = \frac{12\,\text{m}}{13\,\text{m}} = 0.92$$

$\theta = 67°$

The resultant is 13 m at 67° north of east.

Displacements along the same straight line can be combined by simple addition or subtraction to find the resultant. If the successive displacements in the previous problem had been 5.0 meters east and 12.0 meters east, the resultant would have been 17.0 meters east. Also, if the student had walked 5.0 meters east, and then 12.0 meters west, the resultant would have been 7.0 meters west.

When successive displacements are not along the same straight line, the resultant can be found either graphically, by making a scaled vector diagram using a metric ruler and a protractor, or algebraically using the law of cosines and the law of sines. Because the laws of cosines and sines are not provided in the *Reference Tables for Physical Setting/Physics*, this type of algebraic solution is not required, but it is acceptable unless a problem specifically states that the only acceptable solution is a graphical one.

SAMPLE PROBLEM

A person walks 5.0 meters due east and 12.0 meters at 60.° north of east. Find the magnitude and direction of the person's resultant displacement.

Graphic Solution: Identify the known and unknown values.

Known
$\vec{d}_1 = 5.0\,\text{m east}$
$\vec{d}_2 = 12.0\,\text{m at } 60.°\text{ north of east}$

Unknown
$\vec{R} = ?\,\text{m at } ?°$

Construct a scale drawing. A scale of 1.0 cm = 4.0 m is used, but a scale of 1.0 cm = 2.0 m would provide more accurate results.

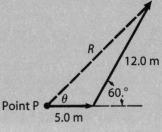

Scale: 1.0 cm = 4.0 m

Use a ruler to measure the length of the resultant vector.

Resultant vector R measures 3.75 cm.

Use the scale of the drawing to convert R in centimeters to actual meters.

$R = (3.75\,\text{cm})(4.0\,\text{m/cm}) = 15\,\text{m}$

Use a protractor to measure θ.

$\theta = 43°$. Thus, the resultant R is 15 m at 43° north of east.

Algebraic Solution: Make a sketch of the situation. Label the sides of the triangle $a, b,$ and c, and the corresponding angles $A, B,$ and C.

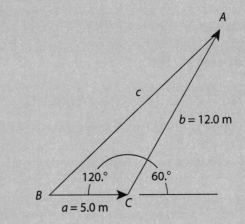

Determine the angle C between the vectors.

$180.° - 60.° = 120.°$

Write the formula for the law of cosines.

$c^2 = a^2 + b^2 - 2ab\cos \theta$

Speed and Velocity

The position of an object in motion changes with time. The **speed**, v, of an object is the distance that the object moves in a unit of time. Speed is a scalar quantity. The average speed, $\bar{v}$, of an object is given by this equation.

$$\bar{v} = \frac{d}{t}$$

Distance d is in meters and the time interval t is in seconds. The **second,** s, is the fundamental SI unit of time. Thus, the average speed $\bar{v}$ is in meters per second, or m/s, a derived SI unit. If the object's speed is constant during the entire time interval, $\bar{v}$ is its constant speed, and the object is said to be in **uniform motion.** If the speed of the object varies, the motion is nonuniform.

The **velocity** of an object is the time rate of change of its displacement. Velocity is a vector quantity having direction as well as magnitude. The magnitude of an object's velocity is its speed. For example, if one car travels at 88 kilometers per hour due east and a second car travels at 88 kilometers per hour due north, both cars have the same speed. However, the velocities of the cars differ because the direction of travel is not the same. In physics, the terms speed and velocity are not interchangeable.

Linear motion refers to an object's change of position along a straight line. On a straight path, there are only two possible directions for the velocity. One of these is called the positive direction. The opposite direction, then, is the negative direction. Depending upon the direction of the motion, changes in displacement are also positive or negative. When refer-

ring to linear motion in this text, the symbol v is used for both velocity and speed, and the symbol d is used for both displacement and distance.

GRAPHS OF LINEAR MOTION Graphs of distance versus time are commonly used to represent the linear motion of an object. The independent variable, time, is recorded on the horizontal axis, and the dependent variable, distance, is recorded on the vertical axis. Because $\bar{v} = \frac{d}{t}$, the magnitude of the slope of a distance versus time graph at any point equals the object's speed at that instant, and the algebraic sign of the slope indicates whether the velocity is in the positive or negative direction. A straight line indicates constant velocity. A straight horizontal line represents zero velocity, that is, an object at rest. If a distance-time graph is a curved line, the velocity is not constant. The slope of the tangent to the curve at any point is called the instantaneous velocity of the object. The **tangent** to a curve at any point on the curve is defined as the line passing through the point and having a slope equal to the slope of the curve at that point. **Instantaneous velocity** is the velocity of an object at any particular instant in time. The term is applied to the motion of an object that is not traveling at constant velocity. The steeper the slope of a distance versus time graph, the greater the instantaneous speed. Figure 2-1 on the next page shows examples of graphs of linear motion.

Acceleration

The time rate of change of velocity is **acceleration,** a, a vector quantity represented by this equation.

$$a = \frac{\Delta v}{t}$$

Δv is the change in velocity in meters per second and t is the time interval in seconds. Thus, acceleration can be expressed with the unit meters per second per second, or meters per second^2, m/s^2.

Note that the formula, as written without a bar over the a to indicate average, implies constant, or uniform, acceleration. This text does not address nonuniform acceleration.

The average speed $\bar{v}$ of an object accelerating uniformly from an initial speed v_i to a final speed v_f is given by this equation.

$$\bar{v} = \frac{v_i + v_f}{2}$$

This formula is valid only when the acceleration is constant.

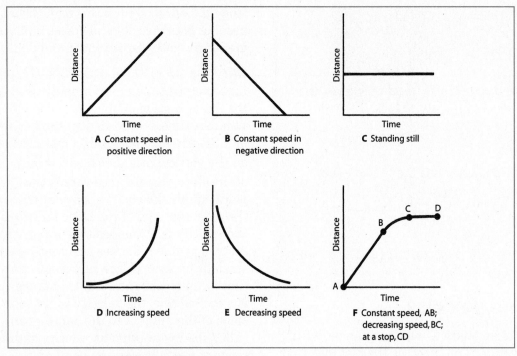

Figure 2-1. **Graphs of linear motion**

Speed versus time graphs can be used to represent accelerated linear motion, as shown in Figure 2-2. The independent variable, time, is measured on the horizontal axis, and the dependent variable, speed, is measured on the vertical axis. Because $a = \frac{\Delta v}{t}$, the magnitude of the slope of a speed versus time graph at any point equals the object's acceleration at that instant, and the algebraic sign of the slope indicates whether the acceleration is in the positive or negative direction. For example, a horizontal line with zero slope indicates constant speed or no acceleration. A straight line with a positive slope shows increasing speed or constant acceleration. A straight line with negative slope shows decreasing speed or constant negative acceleration (deceleration). A line that intersects the horizontal time axis indicates a change in direction, that is, the speed in one direction decreases to zero at the time when the graph line intersects the horizontal axis, and then the speed increases in the opposite direction. A curved speed-time line indicates that acceleration is not constant.

SAMPLE PROBLEM

The graph represents the relationship between the speed of a child coasting downhill on a skateboard and elapsed time. At 1.0 second the child is traveling at 4.0 meters per second, and at 4.0 seconds her speed is 10.0 meters per second.

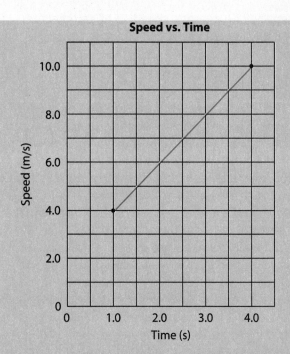

(a) Determine the magnitude of the child's acceleration. (b) Determine the average speed of the child. (c) Determine the distance traveled by the child during this 3.0-second interval.

Solution: Identify the known and unknown values.

Known	Unknown
$t_i = 1.0$ s	$a = ?$ m/s^2
$t_f = 4.0$ s	$\bar{v} = ?$ m/s
$v_i = 4.0$ m/s	$d = ?$ m
$v_f = 10.0$ m/s	

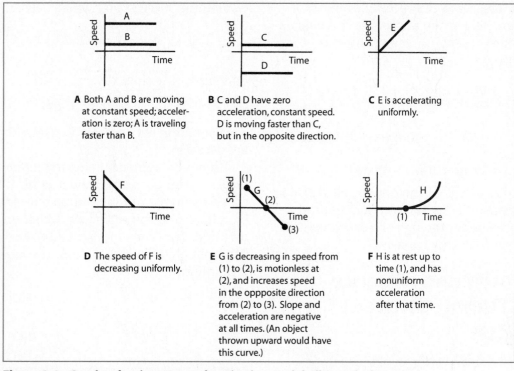

A Both A and B are moving at constant speed; acceleration is zero; A is traveling faster than B.

B C and D have zero acceleration, constant speed. D is moving faster than C, but in the opposite direction.

C E is accelerating uniformly.

D The speed of F is decreasing uniformly.

E G is decreasing in speed from (1) to (2), is motionless at (2), and increases speed in the oppposite direction from (2) to (3). Slope and acceleration are negative at all times. (An object thrown upward would have this curve.)

F H is at rest up to time (1), and has nonuniform acceleration after that time.

Figure 2-2. Graphs of various types of motion in a straight line path, drawn on speed-time axes

(a) The slope of the graph is the acceleration. Determine the slope.

$$a = \frac{\Delta v}{t} = \frac{10.0 \text{ m/s} - 4.0 \text{ m/s}}{4.0 \text{ s} - 1.0 \text{ s}} = 2.0 \text{ m/s}^2$$

(b) Write the equation for average speed.

$$\bar{v} = \frac{v_i + v_f}{2}$$

Substitute the known values and solve.

$$\bar{v} = \frac{4.0 \text{ m/s} + 10.0 \text{ m/s}}{2} = 7.00 \text{ m/s}$$

(c) Write the equation that relates distance, average speed, and time.

$$d = \bar{v}t$$

Substitute the known values and solve.

$$d = (7.00 \text{ m/s})(3.0 \text{ s}) = 21 \text{ m}$$

In the sample problem, the distance traveled by the child could have been found by determining the area under the graph line. That area has the shape of a trapezoid, which can be separated into a rectangle and a triangle, as shown in Figure 2-3.

Recall that the area of a rectangle is given by $A = bh$ and that the area of a triangle is given by $A = \frac{1}{2}bh$. Thus, the area under the line is given

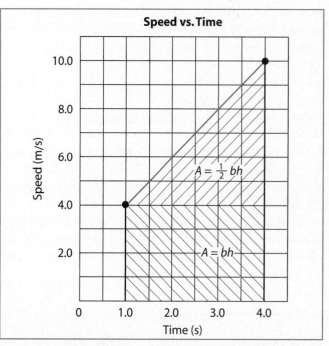

Figure 2-3. The area under a speed vs. time graph: The magnitude of the area of the rectangle is 12 and the magnitude of the area of the triangle is 9. The magnitude of the total area is 21, which is the total distance in meters traveled by the child.

by the sum of the area of the rectangle and the area of the triangle. For the purpose of this calculation, these quantities may be represented as meters. That is,

$$A_{\text{rectangle}} = bh = (3.0 \text{ s})\left(4.0 \, \frac{\text{m}}{\text{s}}\right) = 12 \text{ m}$$

$$A_{\text{triangle}} = \frac{1}{2}bh = \frac{1}{2}(3.0 \text{s})\left(6.0 \, \frac{\text{m}}{\text{s}}\right) = 9 \text{ m}$$

$$A_{\text{total}} = 12 \text{ m} + 9 \text{ m} = 21 \text{ m}$$

The total distance is 21 meters, as calculated in the sample problem. Thus, the physical significance of the area under the line of a speed versus time graph is the distance traveled.

Final Velocity and Distance Traveled During Constant Acceleration

Acceleration is defined by the equation $a = \frac{\Delta v}{t}$. Because Δ always represents a change in a variable, that is, final conditions minus initial conditions, it follows that $a = \frac{v_f - v_i}{t}$. Solving for the final speed v_f yields this equation.

$$v_f = v_i + at$$

This expression can be combined with $d = \bar{v}t$ and $\bar{v} = \frac{v_i + v_f}{2}$ to obtain a useful expression for displacement d that involves the initial velocity v_i, the acceleration a, and the time t.

$$d = \bar{v}t = \left(\frac{v_i + v_f}{2}\right)t = \frac{1}{2}(v_i + v_f)t = \frac{1}{2}(v_i + v_i + at)t$$

Thus, the equation becomes the following.

$$d = v_i t + \frac{1}{2}at^2$$

The expression is valid only when acceleration is constant.

The velocity of an object as a function of its displacement can be determined without knowing the elapsed time. From the previous derivation, the following equation can be written.

$$d = \frac{1}{2}(v_i + v_f)t$$

Solving the equation $v_f = v_i + at$ for t yields

$$t = \frac{v_f - v_i}{a}$$

Combining these expressions yields

$$d = \frac{1}{2}(v_f + v_i)\left(\frac{v_f - v_i}{a}\right) = \frac{v_f{}^2 - v_i{}^2}{2a}$$

Solving for the final velocity yields

$$v_f{}^2 = v_i{}^2 + 2ad$$

This equation is valid only for constant acceleration.

In many problems involving motion, the object is initially at rest and v_i is zero. In such cases, terms containing v_i drop out of the motion equations and the equations are simplified. In addition, the symbol for v_f can be written as v. Thus, for objects starting from rest and accelerating uniformly,

$$a = \frac{v}{t} \qquad d = \frac{1}{2}at^2$$

$$\bar{v} = \frac{v}{2} \qquad v^2 = 2ad$$

SAMPLE PROBLEM

A car is originally traveling at 15.0 meters per second (approximately 34 miles per hour) on a straight, horizontal road. The driver applies the brakes, causing the car to decelerate uniformly at 4.00 meters per second² until it comes to rest. Determine the car's stopping distance.

Solution: Identify the known and unknown values.

Known	Unknown
$v_i = 15.0$ m/s	$d = ?$ m
$v_f = 0.0$ m/s	
$a = -4.00$ m/s²	

Write the equation that relates initial and final velocities, acceleration, and distance.

$$v_f^2 = v_i^2 + 2ad$$

Solve the equation for distance, d.

$$d = \frac{v_f^2 - v_i^2}{2a}$$

Substitute the known values and solve.

$$d = \frac{(0.0 \text{ m/s})^2 - (15.0 \text{ m/s})^2}{2(-4.00 \text{ m/s}^2)}$$

$$d = \frac{-225 \text{ m}^2/\text{s}^2}{-8.00 \text{ m/s}^2} = 28.1 \text{ m}$$

Alternate Solution: Write the equation that defines acceleration.

$$a = \frac{\Delta v}{t}$$

Solve the equation for t.

$$t = \frac{\Delta v}{a}$$

Substitute the known values and solve.

$$t = \frac{0.0 \text{ m/s} - 15.0 \text{ m/s}}{-4.00 \text{ m/s}^2} = 3.75 \text{ s}$$

Write the equation that relates distance, initial velocity, acceleration, and time.

$$d = v_i t + \frac{1}{2}at^2$$

Substitute the known values and solve for *d*.

$$d = (15.0 \text{ m/s})(3.75 \text{ s}) + \tfrac{1}{2}(-4.00 \text{ m/s}^2)(3.75 \text{ s})^2$$

$$d = 56.2 \text{ m} + (-28.1 \text{ m}) = 28.1 \text{ m}$$

If the initial speed was doubled to 30.0 meters per second (or 67 miles per hour), the stopping distance would quadruple!

Freely Falling Objects

In a **vacuum,** which is a space in which there is no matter, a coin and a feather fall with the same acceleration due to gravity, *g*. **Gravity** is the force between the mass of Earth and the mass of any object in the vicinity of Earth. According to the *Reference Tables for Physical Setting/Physics,* near the surface of Earth *g* is a constant 9.81 meters per second². The ideal falling motion of an object acted upon only by the force of gravity is called **free fall.**

Although the acceleration due to gravity is the same for all objects in a vacuum, in air the acceleration of the feather is less than that of the coin because the shape and exposed area of the feather result in greater air resistance.

If an object falls freely from rest (air resistance is neglected), its speed and position at any instant in time are given by $v = gt$ and $d = \frac{1}{2}gt^2$. Table 2-1

shows the speed and distance traveled by an object falling freely from rest near Earth's surface in the absence of air resistance.

 # Review Questions

1. If a boy runs 125 meters north, and then 75 meters south, his total displacement is (1) 50. m north (2) 50. m south (3) 200. m north (4) 200. m south

2. A student walks 3 blocks south, 4 blocks west, and 3 blocks north. What is the displacement of the student? (1) 10. blocks east (2) 10. blocks west (3) 4 blocks east (4) 4 blocks west

3. A girl attempts to swim directly across a stream 15 meters wide. When she reaches the other side, she is 15 meters downstream. Determine the magnitude of her displacement.

4. What is the average speed of an object that travels 6.00 meters north in 2.00 seconds and then travels 3.00 meters east in 1.00 second? (1) 9.00 m/s (2) 0.333 m/s (3) 3.00 m/s (4) 4.24 m/s

5. A car is traveling at 60 kilometers per hour. Determine the time required for the car to travel 12 kilometers.

6. The graph below shows the relationship between the position of an object moving in a straight line and elapsed time. What is the speed of the object during the time interval $t = 2.0$ seconds to $t = 4.0$ seconds?

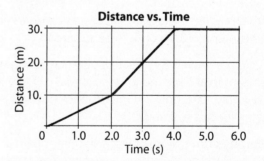

(1) 0.0 m/s (2) 5.0 m/s (3) 7.5 m/s (4) 10. m/s

Table 2-1. Free Fall of an Object Starting from Rest						
Time of fall (s)	0.00	1.00	2.00	3.00	4.00	5.00
Speed (m/s)	0.00	9.81	19.6	29.4	39.2	49.1
Distance traveled (m)	0.00	4.91	19.6	44.1	78.5	123

7. A particle is accelerated uniformly from rest to a speed of 50. meters per second in 5.0 seconds. The average speed of the particle during this 5.0-second time interval is (1) 5.0 m/s (2) 10. m/s (3) 25 m/s (4) 50. m/s

8. Which statement best describes the movement of an object with zero acceleration? (1) The object must be at rest. (2) The object must be slowing down. (3) The object may be speeding up. (4) The object may be in motion.

9. A particle has a constant acceleration of 2.0 meters per second^2. Determine the time required for the particle to accelerate from 8.0 meters per second to 28 meters per second.

10. If an object is traveling east with a decreasing speed, the direction of the object's acceleration is (1) north (2) south (3) east (4) west

Base your answers to questions 11 and 12 on the following graph, which represents the relationship between velocity and time of travel for four cars, A, B, C, and D, in straight-line motion.

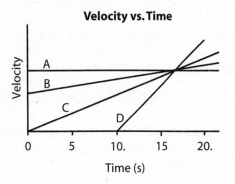

11. Which car has the greatest acceleration during the time interval 10. seconds to 15 seconds?

12. Which car travels the greatest distance during the time interval 0 second to 10. seconds? (1) A only (2) B only (3) C only (4) The distance traveled is the same for cars A, B, and C.

13. Starting from rest, an object rolls freely down a 10.-meter long incline in 2.0 seconds. The acceleration of the object is (1) 5.0 m/s (3) 10. m/s (2) 5.0 m/s^2 (4) 10. m/s^2

14. A car accelerates uniformly from rest at 3.2 meters per second^2. Determine the speed of the car when it has traveled a distance of 40. meters.

Base your answers to questions 15 through 20 on the following graph, which represents the relationship between speed and time for an object in straight-line motion.

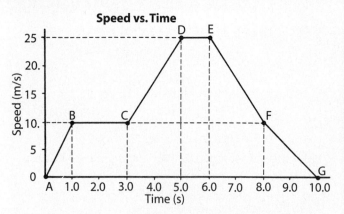

15. Determine the acceleration of the object during the time interval $t = 3.0$ seconds to $t = 5.0$ seconds.

16. Determine the average speed of the object during the time interval $t = 6.0$ seconds to $t = 8.0$ seconds.

17. Determine the total distance traveled by the object during the first 3.0 seconds.

18. During which interval is the object's acceleration greatest? (1) AB (2) CD (3) DE (4) EF

19. During the interval $t = 8.0$ seconds to $t = 10.0$ seconds, the speed of the object is (1) zero (2) increasing (3) decreasing (4) constant, but not zero

20. What is the maximum speed attained by the object during the 10.0 seconds of travel?

21. The graph below represents the relationship between distance and time of travel for an object moving in a straight line. Determine the instantaneous speed of the object at 1.5 seconds.

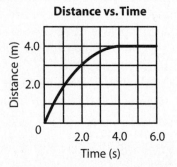

22. A boat heads directly eastward across a river at 12 meters per second. If the current in the river is flowing at 5.0 meters per second due south, what is the magnitude of the boat's resultant velocity? (1) 7.0 m/s (2) 8.5 m/s (3) 13 m/s (4) 17 m/s

23. Which pair of graphs represents the same motion?

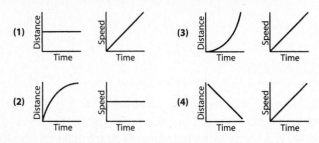

24. The graph below represents the motion of a body moving along a straight line.

Which quantity related to the motion of the body is constant? (1) speed (2) velocity (3) acceleration (4) displacement

Base your answers to questions 25 through 29 on the following four graphs, which represent the relationship between speed and time for four different objects A, B, C, and D moving in a straight line.

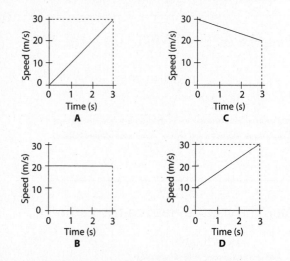

25. Which object had a retarding force acting on it?

26. Which object was neither accelerating nor decelerating?

27. Which object traveled the greatest distance in the 3.0-second time interval?

28. Which object had the greatest acceleration?

29. Compared to the average speed of object A, the average speed of object D is (1) less (2) greater (3) the same

30. As the time required for a car to accelerate from rest to 27 meters per second decreases, the acceleration of the car (1) decreases (2) increases (3) remains the same

31. An object initially traveling at 20. meters per second west decelerates uniformly at 4.0 meters per second^2 for 2.0 seconds. The displacement of the object during these 2.0 seconds is (1) 32 m east (2) 32 m west (3) 48 m east (4) 48 m west

32. An object initially traveling at 20. meters per second south decelerates uniformly at 6.0 meters per second^2 and is displaced 25 meters. The final velocity of the object is (1) 26 m/s north (2) 26 m/s south (3) 10. m/s north (4) 10. m/s south

33. The time-rate of change of displacement is (1) acceleration (2) distance (3) speed (4) velocity

Base your answers to questions 34 through 37 on the following graph, which represents the relationship between the displacement of an object and time.

Displacement vs. Time

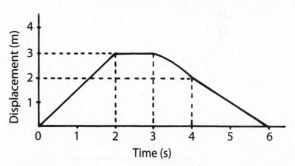

34. How far is the object from the starting point at the end of 3 seconds?

35. During which time interval is the object at rest?

36. What is the average velocity of the object from $t = 0$ to $t = 3$ seconds? (1) 1 m/s (2) 2 m/s (3) 3 m/s (4) 0 m/s

37. During which time interval is the object accelerating?

38. Which is constant for a freely falling object near Earth's surface? (1) displacement (2) speed (3) velocity (4) acceleration

39. Which graph best represents the motion of an object falling from rest near Earth's surface? (Neglect air resistance.)

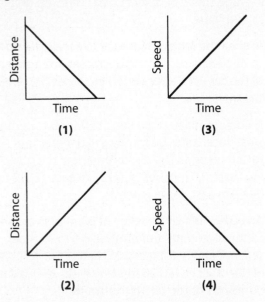

(1)

(2)

(3)

(4)

40. Approximately how far will an object near Earth's surface fall in 3.0 seconds? (1) 88 m (2) 44 m (3) 29 m (4) 9.8 m

41. An object starts from rest and falls freely near Earth's surface for 3.00 seconds. Determine the final speed of the object.

42. An object is thrown vertically upward from the surface of Earth. Which graph best represents the relationship between velocity and time for the object as it rises and then returns to Earth?

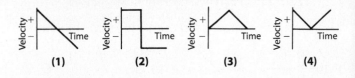

(1)

(2)

(3)

(4)

Statics

The branch of mechanics that treats forces which act on objects at rest is called <u>statics</u>. As noted in Topic 1, a force is a push or pull measured in newtons, N, a derived unit in the SI system. Force is a vector quantity. Force and the derivation of the newton will be discussed later in this text.

Concurrent Forces

Two or more forces that act on the same object at the same time are called concurrent forces. The single force that is equivalent to the combined effect of these concurrent forces is called the **resultant.** The process of combining the magnitude and direction of concurrent forces to determine their resultant is called the composition of forces.

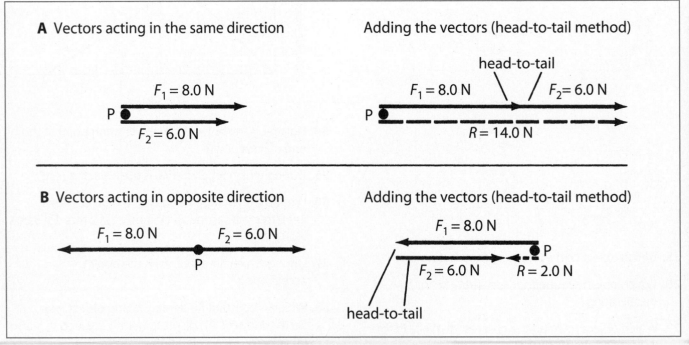

Figure 2-4. The resultants R of concurrent forces acting along the same straight line: (A) acting in the same direction, and **(B)** acting in opposite directions

If two concurrent forces F_1 and F_2 act in the same direction, the angle between the forces is 0° and the resultant force is the sum, $F_1 + F_2$, of their magnitudes acting in the same direction as the individual forces. This is the largest resultant the two forces can have. If the two forces act in opposite directions, the angle between the forces is 180.° and the resultant force is the difference, $F_1 - F_2$, between their magnitudes, acting in the direction of the larger force. This is the smallest resultant the two forces can have. Figure 2-4 on the previous page illustrates these concepts for an 8.0-newton force and a 6.0-newton force acting concurrently on point P.

TRIANGLE METHOD OF ADDING CONCURRENT FORCES The resultant of two concurrent forces F_1 and F_2 acting at an angle between 0° and 180.° can be found by the triangle method of vector addition. In this method, each force is represented by a vector drawn to scale, with its length corresponding to the magnitude of the force and its direction corresponding to the direction of the force. To add the two vectors, place the tail of the second vector F_2 at the head of the first vector F_1. The resultant is the vector drawn

from the tail of F_1 to the head of F_2, as shown in Figure 2-5.

The magnitude of the resultant is found by measuring the vector length with a ruler and then multiplying by the scale. The direction of the vector is determined by using a protractor to measure the angle of the resultant with respect to a compass point. In Figure 2-5A, the resultant has a greater magnitude than either force. In Figure 2-5B, the magnitude of the resultant is smaller than either force. Figure 2-5C correctly implies that the resultant of any number of concurrent forces acting on an object can be found by adding their vectors head to tail. The final resultant is the net force acting on the object. The net force is the single force that is equivalent to the combined effect of concurrent forces acting on an object.

If two concurrent forces act at right angles to each other, the head to tail method of vector addition produces a right triangle in which the hypotenuse is the resultant. In this case, the resultant vector is often found algebraically using the Pythagorean theorem, $c^2 = a^2 + b^2$. Figure 2-6 on the next page illustrates this method for an 8.0-newton force to the east and a 6.0-newton force to the north acting concurrently on point P.

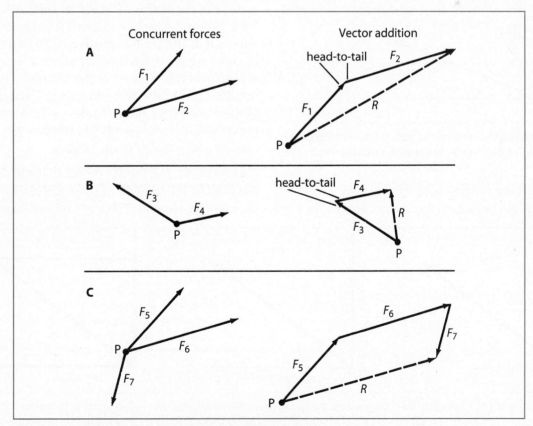

Figure 2-5. Adding force vectors by the triangle method

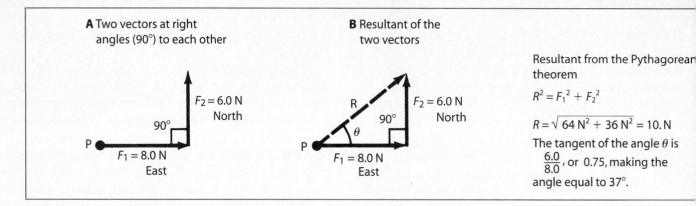

Figure 2-6. **Finding the resultant of two concurrent forces acting at right angles (90°) to each other**

Resultant from the Pythagorean theorem

$$R^2 = F_1^2 + F_2^2$$

$$R = \sqrt{64\ N^2 + 36\ N^2} = 10.\ N$$

The tangent of the angle θ is $\dfrac{6.0}{8.0}$, or 0.75, making the angle equal to 37°.

PARALLELOGRAM METHOD OF ADDING CONCURRENT FORCES

An alternate graphical method for determining the vector sum of two concurrent forces acting at any angle is the parallelogram method shown in Figure 2-7. The two vectors are drawn to scale with both tails originating at the same point. A parallelogram is then constructed with the force vectors as adjacent sides. Recall that a parallelogram is a quadrilateral having opposite sides parallel and equal in length. The diagonal of the parallelogram drawn from the vertex of the original two vector tails is the resultant.

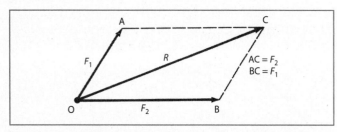

Figure 2-7. **Finding the resultant of two concurrent forces at any angle to each other using the parallelogram method**

The parallelogram method makes it obvious that as the angle between two vectors increases from 0° to 180.° the magnitude of the resultant decreases from a maximum, $F_1 + F_2$ at 0°, to a minimum, $F_1 - F_2$ at 180°.

Resolution of Forces

Just as force vectors can be added to provide the magnitude and direction of the resultant force, force vectors can be resolved or broken up into component vectors. The process of determining the magnitude and direction of the components of a force is called **resolution of forces.** Although a force vector could be resolved into any number of components, it is usually resolved into two components that are perpendicular to each other. The **vector components** of a force vector F are the concurrent forces whose vector sum is F. If the force is resolved into two components at right angles to each other, vector F is a diagonal of the rectangle formed in the parallelogram method. Perpendicular component forces are usually given directions such as east-west and north-south, perpendicular and parallel to the ground, or perpendicular and parallel to an incline.

GRAPHICAL METHOD OF RESOLVING A FORCE INTO COMPONENTS Figure 2-8 shows a 50.-newton force at 37° north of east being resolved

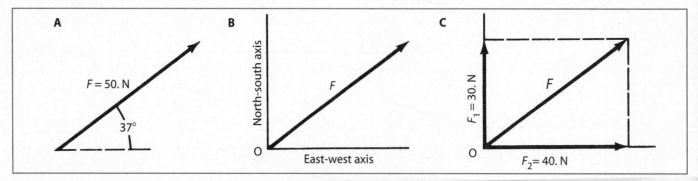

Figure 2-8. **Resolution of a force into two components at right angles (90°) to each other: (A)** The vector to be resolved is a force vector F of 50. N directed at 37° north of east. **(B)** Horizontal (east-west) and vertical (north-south) axes are constructed at the tail of the vector. **(C)** Dashed lines that start at the head of vector F and extend perpendicularly to the axes define two new vectors F_1 and F_2 that are the vertical and horizontal components of the original force vector F. To the scale of the drawing, F_1 measures 30. N north and F_2 measures 40. N east.

into two perpendicular component forces by the graphical method. Force F_1 is along the north-south axis and force F_2 is along the east-west axis. The magnitude of each force is found by drawing a perpendicular to each axis from the head end of the given vector. The line drawn from the origin, O, to each intersection with the axes determines the magnitude of each component vector. The components are measured to be $F_1 = 30.$ N north and $F_2 = 40.$ N east. Note that the vector sum of the components is equal to the original force F.

ALGEBRAIC METHOD OF RESOLVING A FORCE INTO COMPONENTS

It is also possible to determine algebraically the perpendicular components of a force or any other vector. Figure 2-9 shows how vector A, which is at an angle θ with the horizontal, can be resolved into components at right angles to each other. Recall that in a right triangle, the sine of one of the acute angles is the ratio of the side opposite the angle to the hypotenuse and that the cosine of the angle is the ratio of the adjacent side of the angle to the hypotenuse. Thus, for any vector A, making angle θ with the horizontal, the following equations apply.

$$A_x = A \cos \theta$$
$$A_y = A \sin \theta$$

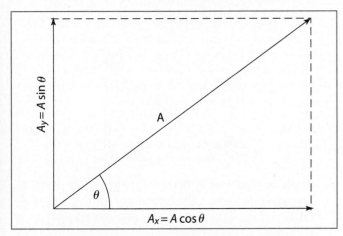

Figure 2-9. A force vector A resolved into horizontal and vertical components

Thus, the components of a vector can be readily determined without making a scale drawing.

Component forces have practical applications, such as pushing a lawnmower or pulling a suitcase by a strap at constant speed along the ground. In pulling a suitcase, the magnitude of the force that needs to be exerted depends upon the angle of the strap with the ground. The suitcase is moved only by the component of the applied force parallel to the ground. This component is a smaller fraction of the applied force when the angle the strap makes with the ground is larger. Thus, a greater force must be applied as the angle between the strap and the ground becomes larger.

Equilibrium

The vector sum of the concurrent forces acting on an object is called the **net force, F_{net}.** If the net force acting on an object is zero, the object is in **equilibrium.** An object at rest is said to be in static equilibrium.

In the example illustrated in Figure 2-6, the resultant of an 8.0-newton force to the east and a 6.0-newton force to the north is a 10.-newton force at 37° north of east. If a third force of 10. newtons acting at 37° south of west was applied, the net force would be zero. A force that is equal in magnitude and opposite in direction to the resultant of concurrent forces produces equilibrium.

Figure 2-10A shows a sign hanging from the side of a building. Because the sign is at rest, it is in static equilibrium and the net force on the sign is zero. But three forces are acting on the sign. They are its weight F_g acting perpendicular to the ground, the force exerted by the cable F_1 pulling in the direction of the cable toward the building, and the outward push F_2 of the horizontal rod.

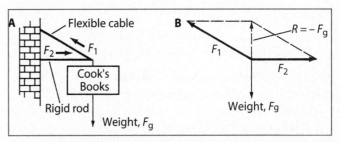

Figure 2-10. (A) The sign is supported by a flexible cable and a rigid rod. **(B)** A free-body diagram showing the relationships among the forces on the sign while it is in static equilibrium

Figure 2-10B is a free-body diagram for the sign. A **free-body diagram** is a sketch, or scale drawing, that shows all the forces acting concurrently on an object. In this example, the weight of the sign must be equal in magnitude and opposite in direction to the vector sum or resultant of the forces exerted by the rod and the cable. This diagram, drawn to scale, indicates that the weight of the sign is smaller than the magnitude of either of the forces used to support it from the building.

43. Which vector best represents the resultant of the con-current forces A and B in the diagram that follows?

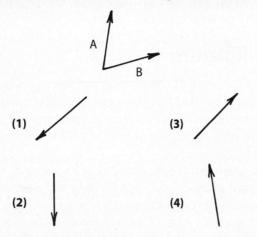

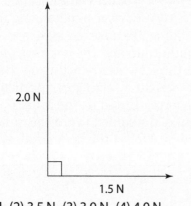

44. What is the magnitude of the vector sum of the two concurrent forces in the following diagram?

2.0 N

1.5 N

(1) 2.5 N (2) 3.5 N (3) 3.0 N (4) 4.0 N

45. The resultant of two concurrent forces is a minimum when the angle between them is (1) 0° (2) 45° (3) 90.° (4) 180.°

46. Which vector best represents the resultant of the two vectors in the following diagram?

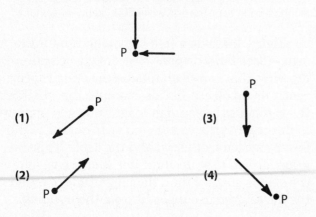

47. As the angle between two concurrent forces of 5.0 newtons and 7.0 newtons increases from 0° to 180.°, the magnitude of their resultant changes from (1) 0.0 N to 35 N (2) 2.0 N to 12.0 N (3) 12.0 N to 2.0 N (4) 12.0 N to 0.0 N

48. Which pair of concurrent forces may produce a resultant of 20. newtons? (1) 5.0 N and 10. N (2) 20. N and 20. N (3) 20. N and 50. N (4) 30. N and 5.0 N

49. In the following diagram, which force could act concur-rently with force A to produce force B as a resultant?

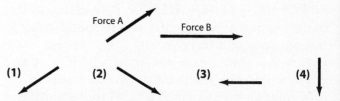

50. Three forces of 10. newtons, 8 newtons, and 6 new-tons act concurrently on an object in equilibrium. The resultant of the 6-newton and 8-newton forces has a magnitude of (1) 0.0 N (2) between 0.0 N and 10. N (3) 10. N (4) more than 10. N

51. Into how many possible components can a single force be resolved? (1) an unlimited number (2) two components (3) three components (4) four components at right angles to each other

52. A lawnmower is pushed with a constant force *F*, as shown in the following diagram.

As angle *θ* between the lawnmower handle and the horizontal increases, the horizontal component of *F* (1) decreases (2) increases (3) remains the same

53. The following diagram shows a person exerting a 300.-newton force on the handle of a shovel that makes an angle of 60.° with the horizontal ground.

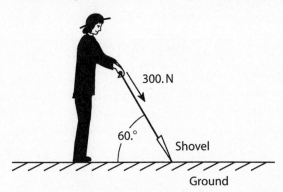

Determine the magnitude of the component of the force perpendicular to the ground.

54. In the following diagram, the numbers represent possible directions in which a force could be applied to a cart. If the magnitude of the force applied in each direction is the same, in which direction will the vertical component of the force be least?

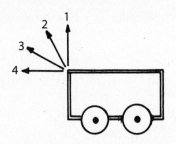

55. Which terms represent a vector quantity and the scalar quantity of the vector's magnitude, respectively? (1) acceleration and velocity (2) mass and force (3) speed and time (4) displacement and distance

56. The fundamental units for a force of one newton are (1) meters / second^2 (2) kilograms (3) meters / second^2 / kilogram (4) kilogram • meters / second^2

Dynamics

The branch of mechanics that deals with how the forces acting on an object affect its motion is called dynamics. The physical laws that govern dynamics were formulated by Isaac Newton.

Newton's Three Laws of Motion

Recall that when the net force acting on an object is zero, it is said to be in equilibrium. An object in static equilibrium is at rest. An object in dynamic equilibrium moves with a constant velocity, that is, at constant speed in a straight line.

NEWTON'S FIRST LAW According to Newton's first law, an object maintains a state of equilibrium, remaining at rest or moving with constant velocity, unless acted upon by an unbalanced force. An **unbalanced force** is a nonzero net force acting on an object. According to the first law, an unbalanced force always produces a change in an object's velocity, a vector quantity. This change in velocity produces an acceleration because the object's speed, or direction of motion, or both speed and direction are changing.

The law of inertia is another name for the first law. **Inertia** is the resistance of an object to a change in its motion. The inertia of an object is directly proportional to its mass. The fundamental SI unit of mass is the **kilogram,** kg.

Inertia can have a devastating effect on a person not wearing a seat belt in a car traveling at high speed. If the car runs off the road and collides with a tree, the force of the collision causes the car to rapidly decelerate. However, the force does not act on the passengers in the car. They continue to move with the same velocity as before the collision, until they are decelerated by colliding with the dashboard or front window. When seat belts are used, the passengers are fastened to the car and decelerate upon impact at the same rate as the car.

NEWTON'S SECOND LAW According to Newton's second law, when an unbalanced force acts on an object, the object is accelerated in the same direction as the force. The acceleration is directly proportional to the magnitude of the unbalanced force and inversely proportional to the mass of the object, as shown in this equation.

$$a = \frac{F_{net}}{m}$$

Mass m is in kilograms, acceleration a is in meters per second^2, and the net force F_{net} is in newtons. One **newton** is equal to the force that imparts an acceleration of one meter per second^2 to a one-kilogram mass. The newton, N, is the derived SI unit of force. One newton equals one kilogram • meter per second squared, kg • m/s^2.

Simple laboratory experiments can be performed to verify Newton's second law. In one experiment, the net force on a cart originally at rest on a horizontal surface is varied and the resulting acceleration calculated by timing the motion of the cart for some distance. The data is plotted with force as the independent variable on the horizontal axis and acceleration as the dependent variable on the vertical axis. Figure 2-11 shows such a graph.

The slope of the line of best fit is $\frac{\Delta a}{\Delta F}$ and is equal to $\frac{1}{m}$. Therefore, the reciprocal of the slope of the line of best fit is the mass of the object being accelerated. Sometimes the axes are reversed so that the mass of the object can be determined directly from the slope.

SAMPLE PROBLEM

A 10.-newton force gives a mass m_1 an acceleration a. A 20.-newton force gives another mass m_2 the same acceleration a. What is the ratio of m_1 to m_2?

Solution: Identify the known and unknown values.

Known

$F_1 = 10.\text{N}$

$F_2 = 20.\text{N}$

Unknown

$\dfrac{m_1}{m_2} = ?$

Write the equation that defines acceleration.

$$a = \frac{F_{net}}{m},$$

Solve the equation for m.

$$m = \frac{F_{net}}{a}.$$

Substitute the known values for each mass.

$$m_1 = \frac{10.\,\text{N}}{a} \quad \text{and} \quad m_2 = \frac{20.\,\text{N}}{a}$$

Divide the first equation by the second.

$$\frac{m_1}{m_2} = \frac{10.\,\text{N}/a}{20.\,\text{N}/a} = \frac{1}{2}$$

SAMPLE PROBLEM

Two forces F_1 and F_2 are applied to a 2.0-kilogram box originally at rest on a horizontal frictionless surface, as shown in the diagram. Determine the magnitude and direction of the acceleration of the box.

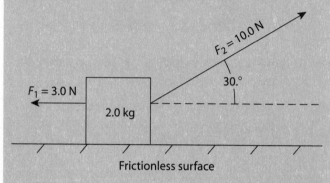

Solution: Identify the known and unknown values.

Known

$m = 2.0 \text{ kg}$

Unknown

$a = ?\text{ m/s}^2$

From the diagram:

$F_1 = 3.0$ N to the left

$F_2 = 10.0$ N to the right at 30.° above the horizontal

Determine the horizontal component of F_2.

$$F_{2_x} = F_2 \cos\theta = (10.0\text{ N})(\cos 30.°) = 8.66\text{ N}$$

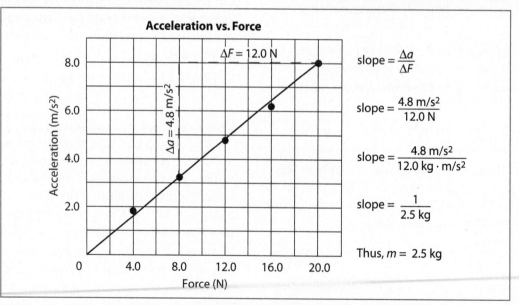

Figure 2-11. The slope of the line on an acceleration-force graph gives the reciprocal of the mass of the object being accelerated. Note in the calculation that the newton, N, is equivalent to a kilogram · meter per second².

Determine the net force in the horizontal direction.

$$F_{net_x} = F_{1_x} + F_{2_x} = -3.0\,\text{N} + 8.66\,\text{N} = 5.7\,\text{N}$$

Write the equation that defines Newton's second law.

$$a = \frac{F_{net}}{m}$$

Substitute the known quantities and solve.

$$a = \frac{5.7\,\text{N}}{2.0\,\text{kg}} = 2.9\,\text{m/s}^2 \text{ to the right}$$

NEWTON'S THIRD LAW According to Newton's third law, when one object exerts a force on a second object, the second object exerts a force on the first that is equal in magnitude and opposite in direction. The two equal and opposing forces constitute an action/reaction pair. The third law indicates that for every action force there is an equal and opposite reaction force. This means that a single force cannot be generated in nature. When one force is generated, another force of equal magnitude and opposite direction must also be generated.

A baseball bat striking a ball is an example of an action-reaction pair. If the bat exerts a 50.-newton force on the baseball, the ball exerts a 50.-newton force on the bat in the opposite direction. Each member of the action/reaction pair of forces acts on a different object; one force acts on the ball and the other on the bat. If no other forces are present, the objects are accelerated in opposite directions as long as the forces are applied.

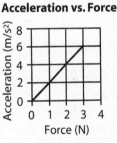 **Review Questions**

57. As the mass of an object decreases, its inertia (1) decreases (2) increases (3) remains the same

58. Compared to the inertia of a 0.10-kilogram steel ball, the inertia of a 0.20-kilogram Styrofoam ball is (1) one-half as great (2) twice as great (3) the same (4) four times as great

59. A ball rolls through a hollow semicircular tube lying flat on a horizontal tabletop. On the following diagram, draw a line with an arrowhead to represent the path of the ball after emerging from the tube, as viewed from above.

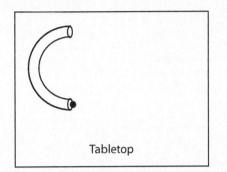

Tabletop

60. An unbalanced force of 10.0 newtons acts on a 20.0-kilogram mass for 5.0 seconds. Determine the acceleration of the mass.

61. The following graph shows the relationship between the acceleration of an object and the net force on the object. What is the mass of the object?

Acceleration vs. Force

(graph: y-axis Acceleration (m/s²) from 0 to 8; x-axis Force (N) from 0 to 4)

(1) 1 kg (2) 2 kg (3) 0.5 kg (4) 0.2 kg

62. A cart is uniformly accelerating from rest. The net force acting on the cart is (1) decreasing (2) zero (3) constant (4) increasing

63. An 8.0-kilogram block and a 2.0-kilogram block rest on a horizontal frictionless surface. When horizontal force F is applied to the 8.0-kilogram block, it accelerates at 5.0 meters per second². If the same force was applied to the 2.0-kilogram block, it would accelerate at (1) 1.3 m/s² (2) 2.5 m/s² (3) 10. m/s² (4) 20. m/s²

64. A 6-newton force and an 8-newton force act concurrently on a box located on a frictionless horizontal surface. Which top-view diagram shows the forces producing the smallest magnitude of acceleration of the box?

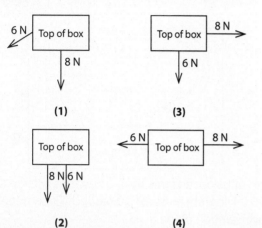

65. Two forces are applied to a 2.0-kilogram block on a frictionless, horizontal surface, as shown in the following diagram.

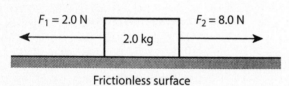

The acceleration of the block is (1) 5.0 m/s² to the right (2) 5.0 m/s² to the left (3) 3.0 m/s² to the right (4) 3.0 m/s² to the left

66. Which graph best represents the motion of an object on which the net force is zero?

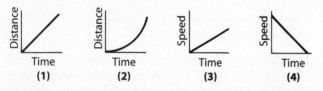

67. Which pair of concurrent forces would produce equilibrium when added to the force acting on point P in the following diagram?

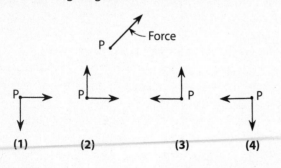

68. As the vector sum of all the forces acting on a moving object increases, the acceleration of the object (1) decreases (2) increases (3) remains the same

69. Which graph best represents the motion of an object that has no unbalanced force acting on it?

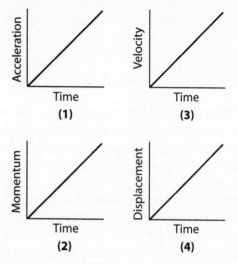

70. Four forces act on an object, as shown in the following diagram. If the object is moving with a constant velocity, what is the magnitude of force *F*?

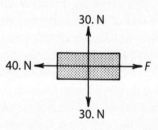

71. The following graph represents the net force acting on an object as a function of time. During which time interval is the velocity of the object constant?

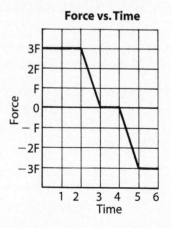

72. A 1.0-kilogram book rests on a horizontal tabletop. The magnitude of the force of the tabletop on the book is (1) 1.0 kg (2) 9.8 kg (3) 1.0 N (4) 9.8 N

73. In the following diagram, an inflated balloon released from rest moves horizontally with velocity v. What is the most likely cause of this velocity?

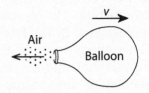

Two-Dimensional Motion and Trajectories

The motion of an object traveling in a two-dimensional plane can be described by separating its motion into the horizontal (x) and vertical (y) components of its displacement, velocity, and acceleration. A component parallel to the horizon is a **horizontal component** and a component at right angles to the horizon is a **vertical component.** If air resistance is neglected, an example of two-dimensional motion is the motion of a cannonball projected near the surface of Earth at an angle to the horizontal. If gravity is the only unbalanced force acting on the cannonball, the vertical component of the ball's motion is identical to that of a freely falling body, and the horizontal component is uniform motion. Although the two motions occur simultaneously, the two components of the motion are independent. Thus, if the object's initial velocity is known, the motion of the object in Earth's gravitational field can be described by the superposition of the two motions.

A Projectile Fired Horizontally

An object projected horizontally from some height above Earth's surface obeys Newton's laws of motion. If air resistance is neglected, the horizontal component of the velocity of the object remains constant. The initial vertical velocity of the object is zero but the vertical velocity increases as the object accelerates downward due to gravity. Figure 2-12A shows a ball falling freely straight downward from rest. Figure 2-12B shows a ball that has a horizontal component of velocity as it falls downward.

Whether an object is dropped from rest or projected horizontally, the vertical distance fallen by the object is the same at any particular instant of time, as can be seen by comparing the vertical position of the ball at 1.00-second intervals in Figure 2-12A and B. This example illustrates that a ball

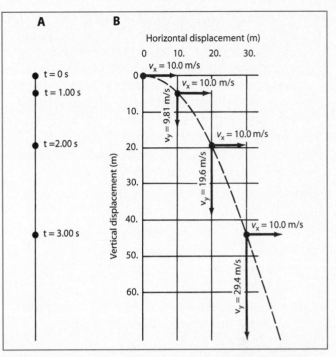

Figure 2-12. (A) The position of a ball at 1.00-second intervals as it falls from rest in a vacuum near Earth's surface. The vertical scale in drawing B also applies to drawing A. **(B)** The position of the same ball at 1.00-second intervals after it has been rolled off the edge of a building with an initial horizontal velocity of 10.0 m/s. The arrows are velocity vectors giving the horizontal and vertical components of the velocity when the ball is at each position. Note that the horizontal component of the ball's velocity is the same after each second but the vertical component increases with time as the ball is accelerated by gravity. Note also that in both A and B, the vertical distance the ball has fallen at the end of each second is the same.

thrown horizontally at 10.0 meters per second from a height of 44.1 meters above level ground, will hit the ground at the same time as another ball dropped from the same height at the same time.

In addition to showing the positions of the ball after an elapsed time of 1.00, 2.00, and 3.00 seconds, Figure 2-12B shows (by means of velocity vectors) the vertical and horizontal components of the velocity. At any particular time after the ball is released, the vertical component of velocity of an object projected horizontally is the same as the vertical component of velocity of an object dropped from rest.

When air resistance is neglected, there is no acceleration or change in velocity in the horizontal direction. In Figure 2-12B, the horizontal displacement of the ball is a constant 10.0 meters in each 1.00-second interval. If the horizontal velocity of the ball had been greater, the object would have traveled a greater horizontal distance in the first 3.00 seconds of travel.

SAMPLE PROBLEM

A plane flying horizontally at an altitude of 490 meters and having a velocity of 250 meters per second east, drops a supply packet to a work crew on the ground. It falls freely without a parachute. Assume no wind and negligible air resistance. (a) Determine the time required for the packet to hit the ground. (b) Determine the horizontal distance from the target area that the plane must drop the packet.

Solution: Identify the known and unknown values.

Known	Unknown
$d_y = 490$ m	$t = ?$ s
$v_x = 250$ m/s	$d_x = ?$ m
$v_{i_y} = 0.0$ m/s	
$g = 9.81$ m/s^2	

Write an equation that relates the distance, acceleration, and time for motion in the vertical direction.

$$d_y = v_{i_y}t + \frac{1}{2}a_yt^2$$

Because v_{i_y} is zero, the equation becomes

$$d_y = \frac{1}{2}a_yt^2$$

Solve the equation for t and substitute g for acceleration.

$$t = \sqrt{\frac{2d_y}{g}}$$

Substitute the known values and solve.

$$t = \sqrt{\frac{2(490 \text{ m})}{9.81 \text{ m/s}^2}} = 10. \text{ s}$$

(b) Write an equation that relates the distance, acceleration, and time for motion in the horizontal direction.

$$d_x = v_{i_x}t + \frac{1}{2}a_xt^2$$

The horizontal speed is constant, so $a_x = 0.0$ m/s^2. Substitute the known values in the equation and solve.

$$d_x = \bar{v}_{i_x}t = (250 \text{ m/s})(10. \text{ s}) = 2.5 \times 10^3 \text{ m}$$

The plane must drop the packet 2.5×10^3 meters west of the target.

A Projectile Fired at an Angle

A golf ball is an example of an object that is projected with an initial velocity at an angle to the horizontal. Such a projectile rises to some height above Earth and then falls back to the ground. The projectile's motion can be studied by resolving the initial velocity into its horizontal and vertical components and then calculating the motions resulting from the two components. If air resistance is ignored, the horizontal component of the velocity remains constant. The object's vertical motion will be accelerated by the force of gravity.

If a golf ball is projected with initial velocity v_i at an angle θ with the horizontal, v_i can be separated into perpendicular components, as shown in Figure 2-13.

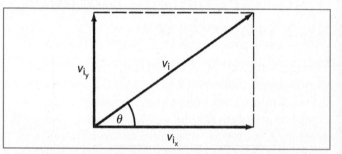

Figure 2-13. An initial velocity vector resolved into horizontal and vertical components

Recall that the two components can be determined by these equations.

Horizontal component: $v_{i_x} = v_i \cos \theta$
Vertical component: $v_{i_y} = v_i \sin \theta$

The vertical component of the velocity gradually decreases to zero as the golf ball reaches the highest point in its trajectory. When the vertical component of the velocity is zero, all of the velocity is in the horizontal. Then the vertical component gradually increases along the ball's downward path due to the constant acceleration of gravity. See Figure 2-14.

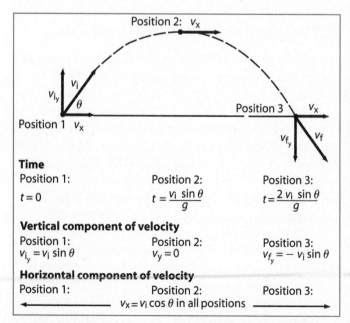

Figure 2-14. The motion of a projectile fired at an angle θ with the horizontal

To find the time t for the projectile to reach its maximum height, solve the equation $v_f = v_i + at$ for t.

$$t = \frac{v_f - v_i}{a}$$

Then, substitute the appropriate values for the vertical velocity and acceleration. If upward in the vertical direction is considered positive, then g, a downward acceleration, is negative. At the highest point, the vertical velocity of the projectile is zero. Thus $t = \frac{v_i \sin \theta}{g}$. It can be shown that the time for the projectile to reach its maximum height is the same as the time to fall back to the ground from that height. Therefore the total time of travel to return to ground level is $\frac{2v_i \sin \theta}{g}$.

The horizontal distance traveled by a projectile is called its <u>range</u>. For any given initial velocity, the range is a maximum when $\theta = 45°$. The actual range of a projectile (when air resistance is present) is shorter than the calculated ideal range.

SAMPLE PROBLEM

A small missile is fired with a velocity of 300. meters per second at an angle of 30.0° with the ground. After a total flight time of 30.6 seconds, the missile returns to the level ground. (Neglect air resistance.) (a) Determine the initial horizontal and vertical components of the velocity. (b) Determine the maximum height of the missile above the ground. (c) Determine the horizontal range of the missile.

Solution: Identify the known and unknown values.

Known	Unknown
$v_i = 300.$ m/s	$v_{i_x} = ?$ m/s
$\theta = 30.0°$	$v_{i_y} = ?$ m/s
$t = 30.6$ s	$d_y = ?$ m
$g = 9.81$ m/s²	$d_x = ?$ m

(a) Write the equations that resolve the initial velocity vector into horizontal and vertical components.

$$v_{i_x} = v_i \cos \theta$$
$$v_{i_y} = v_i \sin \theta$$

Substitute the known values and solve.

$$v_{i_x} = (300.\,\text{m/s})(\cos 30.0°) = 260.\,\text{m/s}$$
$$v_{i_y} = (300.\,\text{m/s})(\sin 30.0°) = 150.\,\text{m/s}$$

(b) Find the time for the missile to reach its highest point.

Because the total time of flight is 30.6 s, the time to reach the maximum height is $\frac{1}{2}(30.6\,\text{s}) = 15.3$ s.

Write the equation that relates distance, average velocity, and time in the vertical direction.

$$d_y = \bar{v}_y t_{rise}$$

At the highest point, velocity in the vertical direction is zero. Average velocity $= \frac{1}{2}(v_i + v_f) = \frac{1}{2}(150.\,\text{m/s} + 0$ m/s$) = 75.0$ m/s. Substitute the known values and solve.

$$d_y = (75.0\,\text{m/s})(15.3\,\text{s}) = 1150\,\text{m}$$

(c) Write the equation that relates distance, velocity, and time in the horizontal direction.

$$d_x = \bar{v}_x t_{total}$$

Substitute the known values and solve.

$$d_x = (260.\,\text{m/s})(30.6\,\text{s}) = 7960\,\text{m}$$

Review Questions

Base your answers to questions 74 through 82 on the following information.

A ball of mass m is thrown horizontally with speed v from a height h above level ground. (Neglect air resistance.)

74. If the height above the ground from which the ball is thrown was increased, the initial vertical velocity of the ball would (1) decrease (2) increase (3) remain the same

75. If the height above the ground from which the ball is thrown was increased, the time of flight of the ball would (1) decrease (2) increase (3) remain the same

76. If the initial speed of the ball was increased, the time of flight of the ball would (1) decrease (2) increase (3) remain the same

77. If the initial speed of the ball was increased, the horizontal distance traveled by the ball would (1) decrease (2) increase (3) remain the same

78. If the initial speed of the ball was increased, the vertical acceleration of the ball would (1) decrease (2) increase (3) remain the same

79. If the ball was replaced with a ball of mass $2m$, the horizontal distance traveled by the ball would (1) decrease (2) increase (3) remain the same

80. If the ball was replaced with a ball of mass $2m$, the vertical acceleration of the ball would (1) decrease (2) increase (3) remain the same

81. As time elapses before the ball strikes the ground, the horizontal velocity of the ball (1) decreases (2) increases (3) remains the same

82. Compared to the total horizontal distance traveled by the ball in the absence of air resistance, the total horizontal distance traveled by the ball with air resistance is (1) shorter (2) longer (3) the same

83. A ball rolls down a curved ramp, as shown in the following diagram. Which dotted line best represents the path of the ball after leaving the ramp?

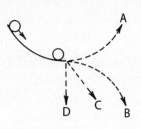

84. Above a flat horizontal plane, arrow A is shot horizontally from a bow at a speed of 20 meters per second, as shown in the following diagram. A second arrow B is dropped from the same height and at the same instant as A is fired.

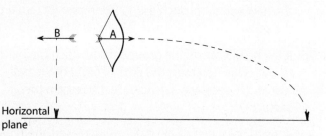

Neglecting air resistance, compared to the amount of time A takes to strike the plane, the amount of time B takes to strike the plane is (1) less (2) more (3) the same

85. A rock is thrown horizontally from the top of a cliff at 12 meters per second. Determine the time required for the rock to fall 45 meters vertically.

86. The following diagram shows the muzzle of a cannon located 50. meters above the ground. When the cannon is fired, a ball leaves the muzzle with an initial speed of 250 meters per second. (Neglect air resistance). Which action would most likely increase the time of flight of a ball fired by the cannon?

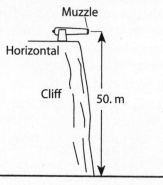

(1) pointing the muzzle of the cannon toward the ground (2) moving the cannon closer to the edge of the cliff (3) positioning the cannon higher above the ground (4) giving the ball a greater initial horizontal velocity

87. The path of a projectile fired at an angle of 30.° to the horizontal is best described as (1) parabolic (2) linear (3) circular (4) hyperbolic

88. A football player kicks a ball with an initial velocity of 25 meters per second at an angle of 53° above the horizontal. The vertical component of the initial velocity of the ball is (1) 25 m/s (2) 20. m/s (3) 15 m/s (4) 10. m/s

89. A projectile is fired with a velocity of 150. meters per second at an angle of 30.° with the horizontal. Determine the magnitude of the horizontal component of the velocity at the time the projectile is fired.

90. Projectile A is fired with a velocity v at an angle of 30.° with the horizontal. Projectile B is fired with velocity v at an angle of 40.° with the horizontal. Compared to the magnitude of the horizontal component of v at the time projectile A is fired, the magnitude of the horizontal component of v at the time projectile B is fired is (1) smaller (2) larger (3) the same

91. A projectile is launched at an angle of 60.° above the horizontal. Compared to the vertical component of the initial velocity of the projectile, the vertical component of the projectile's velocity when it has reached its maximum height is (1) smaller (2) larger (3) the same

92. A projectile is launched at an angle of 30.° above the horizontal. Neglecting air resistance, what are the projectile's horizontal and vertical accelerations when it reaches its maximum height?

Uniform Circular Motion

According to Newton's first law of motion, an unbalanced force acting on an object always produces a change in the object's velocity. If the force has a component in the direction of the object's motion, the magnitude of the velocity changes. However, if the force is applied perpendicular to the direction of motion, only the direction of the velocity changes; its magnitude remains the same. In both instances, the object accelerates because velocity changes with time. If the force has a constant magnitude and always acts perpendicular to the direction of the velocity vector, the object moves in a circular path at constant speed, experiencing **uniform circular motion.**

Centripetal Acceleration

An object moving uniformly in a circular path always has **centripetal acceleration,** which is an acceleration directed toward the center of the circle. "Center-seeking" centripetal acceleration is a vector quantity whose magnitude is directly proportional to the square of the speed of the object and inversely proportional to the radius of the circular path in which it travels. Centripetal acceleration is represented by this equation.

$$a_c = \frac{v^2}{r}$$

The speed v of the object is in meters per second, the radius of curvature r is in meters, and the centripetal acceleration a_c is in meters per second². The centripetal acceleration of an object is independent of its mass.

Centripetal Force

The force needed to keep an object moving in a circular path is called **centripetal force,** F_c. Centripetal force is the vector, directed toward the center of curvature, that produces centripetal acceleration. Newton's second law, $F = ma$, can be rewritten for the special case of circular motion as $F_c = ma_c$. Substituting in the expression for centripetal acceleration, $a_c = \frac{v^2}{r}$ yields this formula.

$$F_c = \frac{mv^2}{r}$$

The mass m is in kilograms, the speed v is in meters per second, the radius r is in meters, and the centripetal force F_c is in kilogram·meters per second², or newtons. Figure 2-15 shows the relationship between these quantities for an object in uniform circular motion.

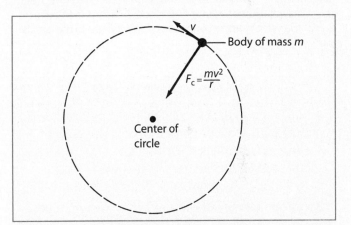

Figure 2-15. The relationship between velocity v, mass m, radius of curvature r, and centripetal force F_c for a body in uniform circular motion: The velocity vector is tangent to the circle, the centripetal force is directed toward the center of the circle, and the radius of curvature is the radius of the circle.

An object in uniform circular motion travels at constant speed in its circular path because there is no net force acting on the object in its direction of motion. That is, the object's tangential velocity is constant. However, the object is not in equilibrium because centripetal force acts perpendicular to the tangential velocity and produces a constant acceleration towards the center of curvature. Thus, although the magnitude of the object's velocity (speed) remains constant, the direction of the object's velocity is always changing, as shown in Figure 2-16.

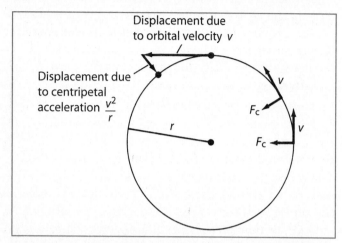

Figure 2-16. **The velocity, acceleration, and displacement of a body in uniform circular motion:** The velocity vector is always tangent to the circle and perpendicular to the centripetal acceleration. The acceleration causes a continuous change in the direction of the velocity and a continuous displacement to the circular path.

SAMPLE PROBLEM

A 1.5-kilogram cart moves in a circular path of 1.3-meter radius at a constant speed of 2.0 meters per second. (a) Determine the magnitude of the centripetal acceleration of the cart. (b) Determine the magnitude of the centripetal force on the cart.

Solution: Identify the known and unknown values.

Known	Unknown
Known	*Unknown*
$m = 1.5$ kg	$a_c = ?$ m/s^2
$r = 1.3$ m	$F_c = ?$ N
$v = 2.0$ m/s	

(a) Write the equation for centripetal acceleration.

$$a_c = \frac{v^2}{r}$$

Substitute the known values and solve.

$$a_c = \frac{(2.0 \text{ m/s})^2}{1.3 \text{ m}} = \frac{4.0 \text{ m}^2/\text{s}^2}{1.3 \text{ m}} = 3.1 \text{ m/s}^2$$

(b) Write the equation for centripetal force.

$$F_c = \frac{mv^2}{r}$$

Substitute the known values and solve.

$$F_c = \frac{(1.5 \text{ kg})(2.0 \text{ m/s})^2}{1.3 \text{ m}} = \frac{(1.5 \text{ kg})(4.0 \text{ m}^2/\text{s}^2)}{1.3 \text{ m}}$$

$$F_c = 4.6 \text{ N}$$

Another way to solve (b) is to substitute the calculated value of a_c from part (a) for v^2/r.

$$F_c = ma_c = (1.5 \text{ kg})(3.1 \text{ m/s}^2) = 4.7 \text{ N}$$

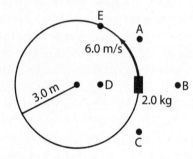

Review Questions

Base your answers to questions 93 through 101 on the following information and diagram.

A 2.0-kilogram cart travels at a constant speed of 6.0 meters per second in a horizontal circle of radius 3.0 meters.

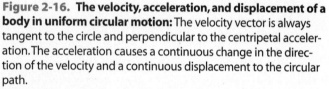

93. Determine the magnitude and direction of the centripetal acceleration of the cart.

94. Determine the magnitude of the centripetal force acting on the cart.

95. If the mass of the cart was doubled, the magnitude of the centripetal force on the cart would be (1) halved (2) doubled (3) quartered (4) quadrupled

96. If the radius of curvature of the path was doubled, the magnitude of the centripetal acceleration of the cart would be (1) halved (2) doubled (3) quartered (4) quadrupled

97. If the speed of the cart was doubled, the magnitude of the centripetal force on the cart would be (1) halved (2) doubled (3) quartered (4) quadrupled

98. If the mass of the cart was halved, the magnitude of the centripetal acceleration of the cart would (1) decrease (2) increase (3) remain the same

99. In the position shown in the diagram, towards which point is the centripetal force acting on the cart directed?

100. In the position shown in the diagram, towards which point is the velocity of the cart directed?

101. Which factor, when doubled would produce the greatest change in the magnitude of the centripetal force acting on the cart? (1) mass of the cart (2) radius of curvature of the path (3) velocity of the cart (4) weight of the cart

102. As the time taken for a car to make one lap around a circular track decreases, the centripetal acceleration of the car (1) decreases (2) increases (3) remains the same

103. Which best describes the tangential acceleration of a cart moving at constant speed in a horizontal circle? (1) 0.0 m/s^2 (2) 9.8 m/s^2 (3) constant and directed radially toward the center of curvature (4) constant and directed radially away from the center of curvature

104. Which best describes the centripetal acceleration of a ball of mass m moving at constant speed v in a horizontal circular path of radius r? (1) zero (2) constant in direction, but changing in magnitude (3) constant in magnitude, but changing in direction (4) changing in both magnitude and direction

Base your answers to questions 105 through 108 on the following information and diagram.

A 5.0-kilogram cart travels clockwise in a horizontal circle of radius 2.0 meters at a constant speed of 4.0 meters per second

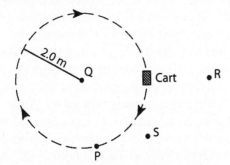

105. Towards which point is the velocity of the cart directed at the position shown?

106. Towards which point is the centripetal acceleration of the cart directed at the position shown?

107. If the mass of the cart was doubled, the magnitude of the centripetal acceleration would be (1) unchanged (2) doubled (3) halved (4) quadrupled

108. The magnitude of the centripetal force acting on the cart is (1) 8.0 N (2) 20. N (3) 40. N (4) 50. N

Newton's Universal Law of Gravitation

Every body in the universe exerts a force of attraction on every other body. According to Newton's universal law of gravitation, any two bodies attract each other with a force that is directly proportional to the product of their masses and inversely proportional to the square of the distance between them. The attractive force between two objects due to their masses is called **gravitational force,** which is given by this equation.

$$F_g = \frac{Gm_1m_2}{r^2}$$

F_g is the force due to gravity in newtons between the two objects, m_1 and m_2 are the masses of the objects in kilograms, r is the distance between the centers of the objects in meters, and G is the universal gravitational constant. G is equal to $6.67 \times 10^{-11} \text{ N} \cdot \text{m}^2 / \text{kg}^2$. The universal law of gravitation is valid only for spherical masses of uniform density and masses that are small compared to the distance separating them.

According to the law, the gravitational force that mass m_1 exerts on mass m_2 is equal in magnitude and opposite in direction to the gravitational force that mass m_2 exerts on mass m_1. If the distance between the two masses is doubled, the magnitude of the gravitational force between the masses is quartered. If one of the two masses is doubled and the distance between the masses remains constant, the gravitational force is doubled.

SAMPLE PROBLEM

Determine the magnitude of the gravitational force of attraction between Earth and the moon.

Solution: Identify the known and unknown values. Obtain needed values from the *Reference Tables for Physical Setting/Physics.*

Known	Unknown
$m_{\text{Earth}} = 5.98 \times 10^{24} \text{ kg}$	$F_g = ? \text{ N}$
$m_{\text{moon}} = 7.35 \times 10^{22} \text{ kg}$	
$r_{\text{Earth to moon}} = 3.84 \times 10^8 \text{ m}$	
$G = 6.67 \times 10^{-11} \text{ N} \cdot \text{m}^2 / \text{kg}^2$	

Write the formula for the gravitational force.

$$F_g = \frac{Gm_1m_2}{r^2}$$

Substitute the known values and solve.

$$F_g = \frac{(6.67 \times 10^{-11}\,\text{N} \cdot \text{m}^2 / \text{kg}^2)(5.98 \times 10^{24}\,\text{kg})(7.35 \times 10^{22}\,\text{kg})}{(3.84 \times 10^8\,\text{m})^2}.$$

$$F_g = 1.99 \times 10^{20}\,\text{N}$$

GRAVITATIONAL FIELD STRENGTH A region in space where a test particle would experience a gravitational force is called a **gravitational field.** Every mass is surrounded by a gravitational field. A unit test mass is used to map a gravitational field, such as the one that surrounds Earth.

Figure 2-17A shows gravitational force vectors associated with a test mass at various locations above Earth's surface. The direction of the vectors indicates that the test mass is always attracted to Earth, and the magnitude of the vectors indicates that the force on the test mass increases as it gets closer to Earth. In Figure 2-17B, the force vectors have been joined to form lines of gravitational force. The imaginary line along which a test mass would move in a gravitational field is called a line of gravitational force.

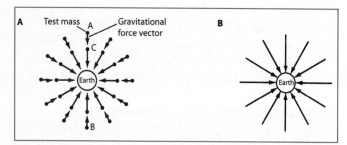

Figure 2-17. The gravitational field around Earth: (A) When the test mass is at points A or B, the gravitational force is the same because both points are the same distance from the center of Earth. At point C the gravitational force is greater than at points A and B because C is closer to the center of Earth. **(B)** The force vectors have been joined to form lines of gravitational force.

In Figure 2-17 the gravitational field lines are directed radially toward the center of Earth, that is, normal to Earth's surface. The concentration of the field lines increases as Earth's surface is approached. This indicates that gravitational field strength, a vector quantity, increases as the distance from Earth decreases. At any point in a gravitational field, **gravitational field strength,** g, equals the force per unit mass at that point. The relationship is expressed by this equation.

$$g = \frac{F_g}{m}$$

F_g is the gravitational force in newtons on a mass m in kilograms, and g is the gravitational field strength in newtons per kilogram, N/kg. Gravitational field strength has the same direction as the gravitational force acting on the mass.

The unit for gravitational field strength is the same as the unit for acceleration. Because 1 newton = 1 kilogram $\cdot$ meter / second^2, then

$$1\,\frac{\text{newton}}{\text{kilogram}} = 1\,\frac{\cancel{\text{kilogram}} \cdot \text{meter} / \text{second}^2}{\cancel{\text{kilogram}}}$$

$$= 1\,\text{meter} / \text{second}^2$$

Recall that the acceleration of an object equals the ratio $\frac{F_{net}}{m}$ from the equation $a = \frac{F_{net}}{m}$. Consequently g is the acceleration produced on a mass m by the gravitational force F_g. Therefore, the gravitational field strength g is the same as the acceleration due to gravity. For short distances near the surface of Earth, the gravitational field is considered to be uniform and g is the same for all masses:

g (gravitational field strength) = 9.81 N/kg

g (acceleration due to gravity) = 9.81 m/s^2

Weight

The gravitational force with which a planet attracts a mass is called **weight.** If M is the mass of Earth, m is the mass of an object on Earth's surface, and r is the distance from the center of Earth, it can be seen from Newton's universal law of gravitation that the weight F_g of an object on Earth's surface is directly proportional to its mass m because all the other quantities in the equation are constant. Weight is a vector quantity (force) directed toward the center of a planet and measured in newtons, whereas mass is a scalar quantity measured in kilograms. The weight of an object decreases with increasing distance from the center of a planet because the gravitational field strength decreases. But the mass of an object is constant because it is independent of its location in any gravitational field.

The weight of an object can be determined by solving the gravitational field strength equation for F_g ($F_g = mg$) and substituting values for the mass and the acceleration due to gravity. The result shows that the weight F_g of a 1.00-kilogram object on Earth's surface is 9.81 newtons. The weight of a 1.00-kilogram object on the moon is less than 9.81 newtons because the gravitational field strength on the surface of the moon is less than on Earth. The difference results from the smaller mass of the moon.

A graph of weight versus mass for a series of objects located at the same point in a gravitational field is a straight line whose slope is g, the acceleration due to gravity or gravitational field strength. Figure 2-18 shows the lines produced from data collected on the surface of Earth and the surface of the moon. The slope of the line for Earth is six times the slope of the line for the moon.

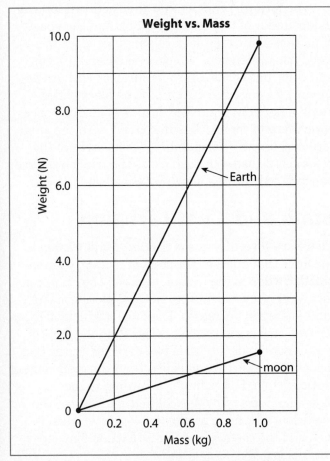

Weight vs. Mass

Figure 2-18. On a weight-mass graph the slope of the line equals the acceleration due to gravity or gravitational field strength.

If a person stands on a scale in an elevator at rest, the scale registers the downward force of the person's weight. The elevator floor exerts an upward force to balance this weight. However, when the elevator starts to rise, it must exert an additional upward force to accelerate the person's mass. By the law of action-reaction, the person's body must exert an equal force downward in addition to its weight. Thus, the scale registers an increased total force or weight. When the elevator stops accelerating and rises at constant speed,

there is no additional force and the scale reading returns to the person's weight alone. If the elevator were to accelerate downward, the reading of the scale would decrease.

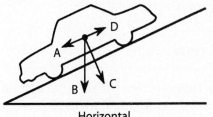

Review Questions

109. As the distance between two masses increases, the gravitational force of attraction between them (1) decreases (2) increases (3) remains the same

110. When a satellite is a distance d from the center of Earth, the gravitational force of attraction between the satellite and Earth is F. What is the gravitational force of attraction between the satellite and Earth when the satellite's distance from the center of Earth is $3d$?

111. The magnitude of the gravitational force between two objects is 20. newtons. If the mass of each object is doubled, the magnitude of the gravitational force between the objects is (1) 5.0 N (2) 10. N (3) 20. N (4) 80. N

112. Which graph best represents the gravitational force between two point masses as a function of the distance between the masses?

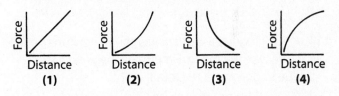

113. The following diagram represents a car stopped on a hill. Which vector best represents the weight of the car?

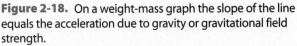

Horizontal

114. Determine the weight of a 5.00-kilogram object at the surface of Earth.

115. Compared to the mass of a 10.-newton object on Earth, the mass of the same object on the moon is (1) smaller (2) greater (3) the same

116. Which graph best represents the relationship between the mass of an object and its distance from the center of Earth?

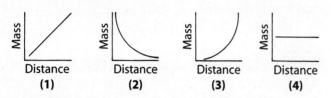

(1)   (2)   (3)   (4)

117. The following graph shows the relationship between weight and mass for a series of objects. What is represented by the slope of the graph?

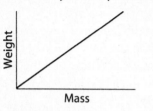

118. Which graph best represents the relationship between acceleration due to gravity for objects near the surface of Earth and the mass of the objects? (Neglect air resistance.)

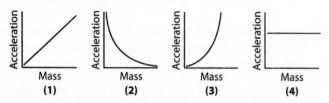

(1)   (2)   (3)   (4)

119. A 60.-kilogram astronaut weighs 96 newtons on the surface of the moon. Determine the acceleration due to gravity on the moon.

120. An 800-newton person is standing in an elevator. If the upward force of the elevator on the person is 600 newtons, the person is (1) at rest (2) accelerating upward (3) accelerating downward (4) moving downward at constant speed

Friction

The force that opposes the relative motion of two objects in contact is called **friction.** A vector quantity, friction is always parallel to the two surfaces in contact and acts in the direction that opposes the slipping motion. The force of friction, F_f, is directly proportional to the magnitude of the nor-

mal force, F_N. The **normal force** is the force pressing the two contacting surfaces together. On a horizontal surface, the normal force is equal in magnitude and opposite in direction to the weight of the object resting on the surface. The force of friction, which depends upon the nature of the two surfaces in contact, is given by this equation.

$$F_f = \mu F_N$$

The constant, μ, is the **coefficient of friction,** which is the ratio of the frictional force to the normal force, and thus has no unit.

The formula implies that the frictional force is independent of the area in contact and the speed of motion. For example, a rectangular block of wood has dimensions 4.0 cm $\times$ 6.0 cm $\times$ 10. cm, and thus, has three different surfaces with areas 24 cm², 40. cm², and 60. cm². If the block slides along a horizontal surface, it makes no difference which face of the block is in contact with the surface because the normal force (the weight of the block) is the same in each case. The frictional force depends only on the weight of the block.

Static and Kinetic Friction

There are several kinds of friction. **Static friction** is the force that opposes the start of motion, whereas **kinetic friction** is the friction between objects in contact when they are in motion. Once motion starts, kinetic friction decreases. The force of kinetic friction for two surfaces in contact is less than the force of static friction for the same two surfaces, so the coefficient of kinetic friction is less than the coefficient of static friction. For example, according to the *Reference Tables for Physical Setting/Physics,* the coefficient of kinetic friction for copper on steel is 0.36 and the coefficient of static friction for copper on steel is 0.53.

Figure 2-19 shows forces acting concurrently on a 10.0-newton wooden block in equilibrium on a wooden horizontal surface. In each case, the normal force is equal in magnitude and opposite in direction to the weight of the block. In Figure 2-19A, the applied horizontal force is equal in magnitude but opposite in direction to the maximum static friction force. In Figure 2-19B, the horizontal force applied to move the block at constant speed is equal in magnitude but opposite in direction to the force of kinetic friction.

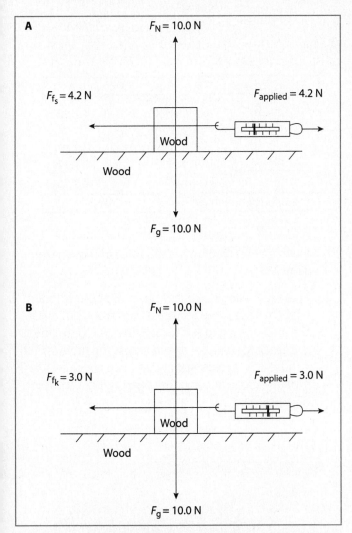

Figure 2-19. **A horizontal force is applied to a 10.0-N wooden block on a horizontal wooden surface: (A)** A maximum static friction force keeps the box from moving. **(B)** The box moves at constant speed when the applied force equals the force of kinetic friction. Note: The vectors are not drawn to scale.

Using the information in Figure 2-19, the coefficients of static and kinetic friction are

$$\mu = \frac{F_{f_s}}{F_N} = \frac{4.2 \text{ N}}{10.0 \text{ N}} = 0.42$$

and

$$\mu_k = \frac{F_{f_k}}{F_N} = \frac{3.0 \text{ N}}{10.0 \text{ N}} = 0.30$$

The values agree with those found in the *Reference Tables for Physical Setting/Physics.*

DETERMINING THE COEFFICIENT OF FRICTION

A graph of frictional force versus normal force (weight) for a wooden block in contact with a wooden horizontal surface is a straight line for both static friction and kinetic friction. (Experimentally, the weight of the block can be varied by resting masses on top it, thus keeping the nature of the two surfaces in contact the same at all times.) The slopes of the lines are the coefficient of static friction and the coefficient of kinetic friction, respectively. Figure 2-20 shows the lines that would result for data collected for a wooden block on a wooden table. The slope of the static friction line is 0.42 and the slope of the kinetic friction line is 0.30.

FRICTION ON AN INCLINED SURFACE If an object is on an inclined surface, the object's weight can be resolved into two components, one parallel to the inclined surface and the other perpendicular to the surface. The component perpendicular to the surface has no effect on the motion of the object because the object cannot move in the direction of that force. Only the component of the object's weight parallel to the inclined surface tends to accelerate

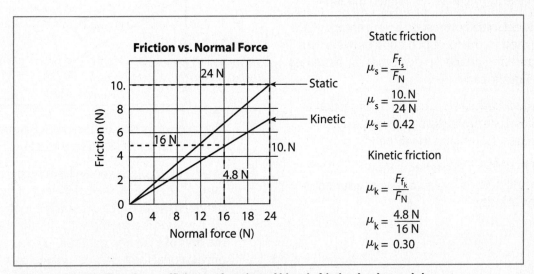

Figure 2-20. **Finding the coefficients of static and kinetic friction by determining the slopes of the lines on a friction-normal force graph**

the object down the incline. As the angle that the incline makes with the horizontal increases, the component of the weight parallel to the incline increases, and the acceleration down the incline increases. This acceleration is opposed by the friction between the object and the incline. The force of friction is directly proportional the normal force, which is equal in magnitude but opposite in direction to the perpendicular component of the object's weight. Thus, as the angle of inclination increases, the component of the weight perpendicular to the incline decreases, and the frictional force decreases. The steeper the slope of the incline, the greater the acceleration of the object down the incline.

ROLLING AND FLUID FRICTION Rolling friction, which results from the use of wheels or ball bearings, is usually less than sliding (kinetic) friction. Fluid friction, which results from an object moving through a fluid such as air or water depends upon the surface area and the speed of the object moving through the fluid. The design of race cars and bicycle helmets is influenced by the desire to reduce fluid friction.

Review Questions

121. An empty wooden crate slides across a warehouse floor. If the crate was filled, the coefficient of kinetic friction between the crate and the floor would (1) decrease (2) increase (3) remain the same

122. An empty wooden crate slides across a warehouse floor. If the crate was filled, the force of kinetic friction between the crate and the floor would (1) decrease (2) increase (3) remain the same

123. As an object initially at rest on a horizontal surface is set in motion, the force of friction between the object and the surface (1) decreases (2) increases (3) remains the same

124. As a thrown baseball is acted on by air friction, the thermal energy of the ball (1) decreases (2) increases (3) remains the same

125. Each of the following diagrams shows a different block being pushed by a force across a surface at constant velocity.

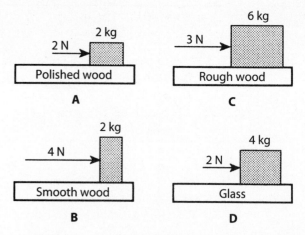

In which two diagrams is the force of friction the same?

126. In the following diagram, surface B of the wooden block has the same texture as surface A, but twice the area of surface A. If force F is required to slide the block at constant speed across the table on surface A, approximately what force is required to slide the block at constant speed across the table on surface B?

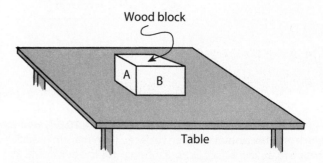

127. The following diagram represents a 10.-newton block sliding down a 30.° incline at constant speed.

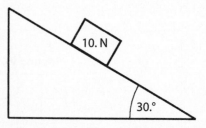

The force of friction on the block is approximately (1) 5.0 N (2) 10. N (3) 49 N (4) 98 N

128. Sand is often placed on an icy road because the sand (1) decreases the coefficient of friction between the tires of a car and the road (2) increases the coefficient of friction between the tires of a car and the road (3) decreases the gravitational force on a car (4) increases the normal force of a car on the road

Base your answers to questions 129 through 132 on the following information and diagram.

A horizontal force is used to pull a 5.0-kilogram cart at a constant speed of 5.0 meters per second across the floor. The force of friction between the cart and the floor is 10. newtons.

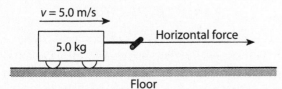

129. What is the magnitude of the horizontal force along the handle of the cart?

130. Determine the weight of the cart.

131. Compare the weight of the cart to the normal force.

132. Determine the coefficient of kinetic friction between the cart and the floor.

133. A constant horizontal force of 5.2 newtons is applied to a wooden block to slide it at constant speed across a wooden table. Determine the weight of the block.

134. A wooden block is at rest on a wooden inclined plane. As the angle the plane makes with the horizontal increases, the coefficient of static friction between the block and the plane (1) decreases (2) increases (3) remains the same

135. A wooden block is at rest on a wooden inclined plane. As the angle the plane makes with the horizontal increases, the force of static friction between the block and the plane (1) decreases (2) increases (3) remains the same

Momentum

The product of an object's mass and velocity is a vector quantity called **momentum**. It is given by this equation.

$$p = mv$$

Mass m is in kilograms, velocity v is in meters per second, and momentum p is in kilogram·meters per second. The direction of a momentum vector is the same as the direction of the velocity. The SI unit for momentum is kilogram·meters per second, kg·m/s.

Impulse and Change in Momentum

The product of the force applied to an object and the time during which the force acts is called **impulse.** Impulse, a vector quantity having the same direction as the applied force, is given by this equation.

$$J = Ft$$

F is the average force in newtons, t is the time during which the force acts in seconds, and J is the impulse in newton·seconds. The SI unit for impulse is the newton·second, N·s.

The impulse imparted to an object can be determined graphically. A horizontal force of varying magnitude is applied over time to an object on a horizontal surface and a graph of force versus time is plotted. The area under the line equals the impulse imparted to the object.

According to Newton's second law an unbalanced force acting on an object causes it to accelerate. This acceleration produces a change in the object's velocity and consequently its momentum, as shown by the following equations.

$$F = ma = m\frac{\Delta v}{t} \text{ or } Ft = m\Delta v$$

Because Ft equals the impulse and $m\Delta v$ equals the change in momentum, it follows that

$$J = \Delta p$$

The direction of the impulse is the same as the direction of the change in momentum. If an object is in equilibrium, there is no change in its momentum and, thus, no impulse imparted to it.

SAMPLE PROBLEM

A 5.0-kilogram object has a velocity of 8.0 meters per second due east. An unbalanced force acts on the object for 3.0 seconds, causing its velocity to decrease to 2.0 meters per second east. Determine the magnitude and direction of the unbalanced force.

Solution: Identify the known and unknown values.

Known	Unknown
$m = 5.0$ kg	$F = ?$ N
$v_i = 8.0$ m/s east	
$v_f = 2.0$ m/s east	
$t = 3.0$ s	

Solve the formula for impulse for force F.

$$J = \Delta p$$

$$Ft = m\Delta v$$

$$F = \frac{m\Delta v}{t}$$

Substitute the known values and solve.

$$F = \frac{(5.0\,\text{kg})(2.0\,\text{m/s} - 8.0\,\text{m/s})}{3.0\,\text{s}} = \frac{-30.\,\text{kg}\cdot\text{m/s}}{3.0\,\text{s}}$$

$$F = -10.\,\text{kg}\cdot\text{m/s}^2 = -10.\,\text{N}$$

The force is 10. N directed to the west.

In baseball, both the batter hitting the ball and the outfielder catching the ball are aware of the relationship between impulse and momentum. The batter "follows through" to keep the bat in contact with the ball as long as possible. The greater the time during which the force of impact acts on the ball, the larger the impulse imparted to it, the greater its final momentum, and the longer the distance of travel. The outfielder catching the ball tries to prolong the time of slowing the ball by moving the gloved hand back in the direction of the ball's motion. By increasing the time during which the gloved hand acts on the ball to reduce its momentum to zero, the force needed to produce the necessary impulse is reduced and the "sting" is minimized.

Conservation of Momentum

A group of objects, not acted upon by any external force, is called a **closed system.** According to Newton's third law, within such a system the force F exerted by one mass m_1 in the system on a second mass m_2 must be equal in magnitude and opposite in direction to the force that m_2 exerts on m_1. Because the force F acts on both masses for exactly the same amount of time, the magnitude of the impulse on each mass is the same. Consequently, the change in momentum for each mass has the same magnitude, but they are in opposite directions. The relationship is expressed in this way.

$$m_1\Delta v_1 = -m_2\Delta v_2,\ \text{or}$$

$$m_1\Delta v_1 + m_2\Delta v_2 = 0$$

The total change in momentum due to the interaction of masses m_1 and m_2 is zero. This relationship is summed up in the **law of conservation of momentum** which states that the total momentum

of the objects in a closed system is constant. The law is given by this equation.

$$p_{\text{before}} = p_{\text{after}}$$

Momentum p is in kilogram • meters per second, kg • m/s.

SAMPLE PROBLEM

A 1.0-kilogram cart A is initially at rest on a frictionless air track. A 0.20-kilogram cart B is moving to the right at 10.0 meters per second. Cart B collides with cart A causing cart A to move to the right at 3.0 meters per second. Determine the velocity of cart B after the collision.

Solution: Identify the known and unknown values. Let velocity to the right be positive.

Known	Unknown
$m_A = 1.0\,\text{kg}$	$v_{B_f} = ?\,\text{m/s}$
$m_B = 0.20\,\text{kg}$	
$v_{A_i} = 0.0\,\text{m/s}$	
$v_{B_i} = 10.0\,\text{m/s}$	
$v_{A_f} = 3.0\,\text{m/s}$	

Write the relationship that describes the momentum of the system before and after the collision.

$$p_{\text{after}} = p_{\text{before}}$$

$$m_A v_{A_f} + m_B v_{B_f} = m_A v_{A_i} + m_B v_{B_i}$$

Solve the equation for v_{B_f}:

$$v_{B_f} = \frac{m_A v_{A_i} + m_B v_{B_i} - m_A v_{A_f}}{m_B}$$

Substitute the known values and solve.

$$v_{B_f} =$$

$$\frac{(1.0\,\text{kg})(0.0\,\text{m/s}) + (0.20\,\text{kg})(10.0\,\text{m/s}) - (1.0\,\text{kg})(3.0\,\text{m/s})}{0.20\,\text{kg}}$$

$$v_{B_f} = -5.0\,\text{m/s}$$

The velocity of cart B after the collision is 5.0 m/s to the left.

 # Review Questions

136. As an object falls freely toward Earth, the object's momentum (1) decreases (2) increases (3) remains the same

137. What is the magnitude of the velocity of a 25-kilogram object that has a momentum of 100. kilogram · meters per second? (1) 0.25 m/s (2) 2500 m/s (3) 40. m/s (4) 4.0 m/s

138. What is the momentum of a 1,200-kilogram car traveling at 15 meters per second due east? (1) 80. kg · m/s due east (2) 80. kg · m/s due west (3) 1.8×10^4 kg · m/s due east (4) 1.8×10^4 kg · m/s due west

139. A constant unbalanced force acts on an object for 3.0 seconds, producing an impulse of 6.0 newton·seconds east. Determine the magnitude and direction of the force.

140. A 10.-newton force acts on an object for 0.010 second. What force, acting on the object for 0.050 second, would produce the same impulse? (1) 1.0 N (2) 2.0 N (3) 5.0 N (4) 10. N

141. What is the magnitude of the net force acting on a 2.0×10^3-kilogram car as it accelerates from rest to a speed of 15 meters per second in 5.0 seconds? (1) 6.0×10^3 N (2) 2.0×10^4 N (3) 3.0×10^4 N (4) 6.0×10^4 N

142. A 5.00-kilogram mass is traveling at 100. meters per second. Determine the speed of the mass after an impulse of 30.0 newton • seconds is applied.

143. A 2,400-kilogram car is traveling at a speed of 20. meters per second. Compared to the magnitude of the force required to stop the car in 12 seconds, the magnitude of the force required to stop the car in 6.0 seconds is (1) half as great (2) twice as great (3) the same (4) four times as great

144. A 2.0-kilogram cart moving due east at 6.0 meters per second collides with a 3.0-kilogram cart moving due west. The carts stick together and come to rest after the collision. Determine the initial speed of the 3.0-kilogram cart.

145. A 0.180-kilogram cart traveling at 0.80 meter per second to the right collides with a 0.100-kilogram cart initially at rest. The carts lock together upon collision. Determine the final velocity of the carts.

146. A 2.0-kilogram cart traveling north at 4.0 meters per second collides head on with a 1.0-kilogram cart traveling south at 8.0 meters per second. What is the magnitude of the total momentum of the two carts after collision? (1) 0.0 kg · m/s (2) 8.0 kg · m/s (3) 16 kg · m/s (4) 32 kg · m/s

The Simple Pendulum

A simple **pendulum** consists of a bob or mass m attached to a string of negligible mass. The length of the pendulum ℓ is measured from the pivot point at one end of the string to the center of the bob, where all the mass is assumed to be concentrated. In the equilibrium position, the string is perpendicular to the ground. To set the pendulum in motion, the bob is displaced from the equilibrium position by lifting it in the gravitational field. The angle the string makes with the equilibrium position is called the amplitude, θ. Figure 2-21 shows a simple pendulum.

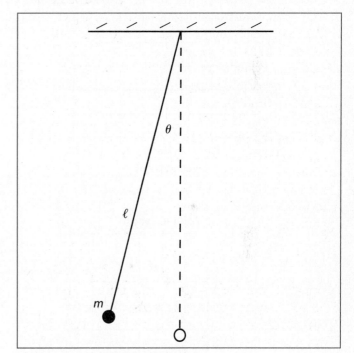

Figure 2-21. A simple pendulum

Period of a Simple Pendulum

If friction is negligible, the variables associated with a simple pendulum are mass, length, amplitude, and gravitational field strength. The time required for the displaced pendulum to complete one cycle of motion is called the **period,** T. The number of cycles the pendulum completes per unit time is called the frequency, f. The period of the pendulum is related to the frequency by the equation $T = \frac{1}{f}$ where period is in seconds and frequency is in hertz (Hz), or 1/s.

It can be found experimentally that for amplitudes less than 15°, the period of a simple pendulum is independent of the mass of the bob, and independent of the amplitude. However, the period is affected by the length of the pendulum ℓ and the acceleration due to gravity g. The period is given by this equation.

$$T = 2\pi\sqrt{\frac{\ell}{g}}$$

The length is in meters, the acceleration due to gravity is in meters per second², and the period is in seconds. Figure 2-22 shows two graphs produced as a result of varying the length of a simple pendulum and measuring its period.

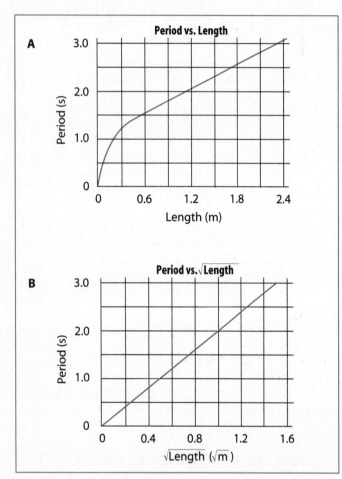

Figure 2-22. **Graphs of experimental data of the period versus the length of a pendulum:** **(A)** shows that the period is not directly proportional to the length. **(B)** confirms the equation that defines the period of a pendulum. The period is directly proportional to the square root of the length.

Equilibrium and Nonequilibrium Forces

When a pendulum is in the equilibrium position, two forces act on the bob, the weight F_g and the tension in the string F_T. The tension is equal in magnitude and opposite in direction to the weight, so there is no net force on the bob. If the bob is displaced from equilibrium and the pendulum has an amplitude θ, the pendulum is no longer in equilibrium. The tension in the string is still directed along the string, but it is not opposite in direction to the weight. If the weight of the bob is resolved into perpendicular components F_{g_x} and F_{g_y}, as shown in Figure 2-23, the tension in the string is found to be less than the weight of the bob. The net force on the bob, equal to the component of its weight, F_{g_x}, acts along the tangent to its path. This net force causes the bob to accelerate towards its equilibrium position.

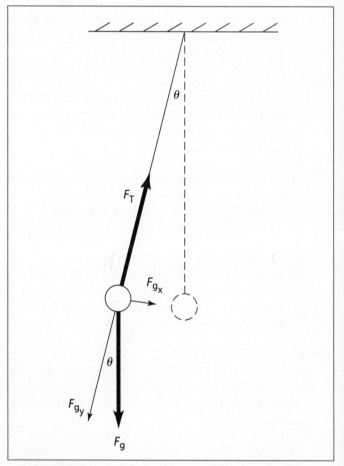

Figure 2-23. The unbalanced force F_{g_x} propels the pendulum bob along its path.

Review Questions

Base your answers to questions 147 through 149 on the following information and diagram.

A 0.65-meter-long simple pendulum consists of a 1.0-kilogram mass at the end of a string. The pendulum is released from rest at position A, 0.25 meter above its lowest point. The pendulum is timed at five positions.

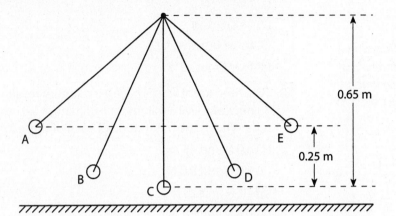

Data Table

Position	Elapsed time
A	0.00 s
B	0.20 s
C	0.40 s
D	0.60 s
E	0.80 s

147. Based on the information in the data table, what is the period of the pendulum?

148. The 1.0-kilogram mass is replaced with a 0.50-kilogram mass and the pendulum is released from rest at A. Compared to the period with the 1.0-kilogram mass, the period with the 0.50-kilogram mass is (1) shorter (2) longer (3) the same

149. The original pendulum is taken to the moon and released from rest at a position 0.25 meter above its lowest point. Compared to the period of the pendulum on Earth, the period of the pendulum on the moon is (1) shorter (2) longer (3) the same

Questions for Regents Practice

Part A

1. A student walks 1.0 kilometer due east and 1.0 kilometer due south. Then she runs 2.0 kilometers due west. The magnitude of the student's resultant displacement is

(1) 0 km

(2) 1.4 km

(3) 3.4 km

(4) 4.0 km

2. A car travels 20. meters east in 1.0 second. The displacement of the car at the end of this 1.0-second interval is

(1) 20. m

(2) 20. m/s

(3) 20. m east

(4) 20. m/s east

3. Two cars, A and B, are 400. meters apart. Car A travels due east at 30. meters per second on a collision course with car B, which travels due west at 20. meters per second. How much time elapses before the two cars collide?

(1) 8.0 s

(2) 13 s

(3) 20. s

(4) 40. s

4. A baseball pitcher throws a fastball at 42 meters per second. If the batter is 18 meters from the pitcher, approximately how much time does it take for the ball to reach the batter?

(1) 2.3 s

(2) 1.9 s

(3) 0.86 s

(4) 0.43 s

$v = 42m/s$

$d = 18m$

$\frac{42}{1} = \frac{18}{t}$

5. The velocity of an object in linear motion changes from 25 meters per second to 15 meters per second in 2.0 seconds. What is the object's acceleration during this 2.0-second interval?

(1) $-20.\,\text{m/s}^2$ (3) $-5.0\,\text{m/s}^2$

(2) $+20.\,\text{m/s}^2$ (4) $+5.0\,\text{m/s}^2$

6. An object initially traveling in a straight line with a speed of 5.0 meters per second is accelerated uniformly at 2.0 meters per second^2 for 4.0 seconds. What is the total distance traveled by the object in this 4.0-second interval?

(1) 36 m

(2) 24 m

(3) 16 m

(4) 4.0 m

$d = v_i t + \frac{1}{2} a t^2$ $v_i = 5m/s$
$t = 4s$
$a = 2m/s$
$d = ?$

7. An object initially at rest accelerates uniformly at 5.0 meters per second^2, until it attains a speed of 30. meters per second. What distance does the object move while accelerating?

(1) 180 m

(2) 150 m

(3) 3.0 m

(4) 90. m

8. A stone is dropped from a bridge 45 meters above the surface of a river. Approximately how much time is required for the stone to reach the water's surface? (Neglect air resistance.)

(1) 9.2 s

(2) 4.6 s

(3) 3.0 s

(4) 0.22 s

$d = v_i t + \frac{1}{2} a t^2$
$45 = \frac{1}{2}(9.81) t^2$ $d = 45m$
$v_i = 0$
$v_f = 9.81 m/s$

9. A ball is thrown straight up with a speed of 12 meters per second near the surface of Earth. What is the maximum height reached by the ball? (Neglect air resistance.)

(1) 15 m

(2) 7.3 m

(3) 1.2 m

(4) 0.37 m

$v_f^2 = v_i^2 + 2ad$
$v_f^2 = 2 \times 9.81 \times 4.9$

10. An object falls freely from rest near the surface of Earth. What is the speed of the object when it has fallen 4.9 meters from its rest position?

(1) 4.9 m/s   (3) 24 m/s

(2) 9.8 m/s   (4) 96 m/s

$d = 4.9 m$
$v_i = 0$
$v_f^2 = \frac{1}{2}(9.81) t^2$

11. Starting from rest, object A falls freely for 2.0 seconds and object B falls freely for 4.0 seconds. Compared with the distance fallen by object A, the distance fallen by object B is

(1) half as far

(2) twice as far

(3) three times as far

(4) four times as far

12. Two concurrent forces have a maximum resultant of 45 newtons and a minimum resultant of 5.0 newtons. What is the magnitude of each of these forces?

(1) 0.0 N and 45 N

(2) 5.0 N and 9.0 N

(3) 20. N and 25 N

(4) 0.0 N and 50. N

13. Two forces act concurrently on an object. The resultant will be greatest when the angle between the forces is

(1) 0°   (3) 90.°

(2) 60.°   (4) 180.°

14. Two concurrent forces act at right angles to each other on an object. If one of the forces is 40. newtons and the resultant of the two forces is 50. newtons, the magnitude of the other force must be

(1) 10. N   (3) 30. N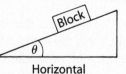

(2) 20. N   (4) 40. N

15. In the diagram below, a block is at rest on a plane inclined at an angle θ to the horizontal.

Block
θ
Horizontal

As angle θ is increased, the component of the block's weight parallel to the plane

(1) decreases

(2) increases

(3) remains the same

16. Compared to 8 kilograms of feathers, 6 kilograms of lead has

(1) less mass and less inertia

(2) less mass and more inertia

(3) more mass and less inertia

(4) more mass and more inertia

17. A box, initially at rest on a level floor, is being acted upon by a horizontal force, as shown in the following diagram.

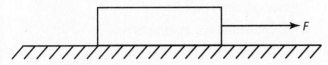

Compared to the force required to start the box moving, the force required to keep the box moving at constant speed is

(1) smaller   (3) the same

(2) greater

18. A copper coin resting on a piece of cardboard is placed on a beaker as shown in the following diagram.

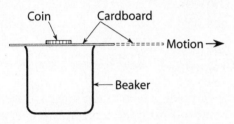

When the cardboard is rapidly removed, the coin drops into the beaker. Which two properties of the coin best explain its fall?

(1) weight and volume

(2) weight and inertia

(3) electrical resistance and volume

(4) electrical resistance and inertia

19. What is the magnitude of the force required to give an electron an acceleration of 1.00×10^2 meters per second^2?

(1) 9.11×10^{-33} N   (3) 9.11×10^{-29} N

(2) 9.11×10^{-31} N   (4) 1.10×10^{32} N

20. Two forces are applied to a 2.0-kilogram block on a frictionless horizontal surface, as shown in the following diagram.

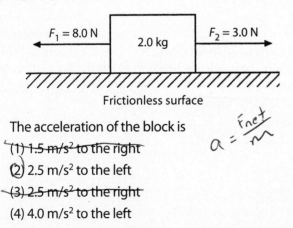

Frictionless surface

The acceleration of the block is

$a = \dfrac{F_{net}}{m}$

(1) 1.5 m/s^2 to the right

(2) 2.5 m/s^2 to the left

(3) 2.5 m/s^2 to the right

(4) 4.0 m/s^2 to the left

21. An object is moving on a horizontal frictionless surface. If the net force applied to the object in the direction of motion is doubled, the acceleration of the object is

(1) halved

(2) doubled

(3) unchanged

(4) quadrupled

22. If the sum of all the forces acting on a car is zero, the car

(1) must be at rest

(2) may be at rest

(3) must be moving at constant speed

(4) must be accelerating

23. Equilibrium exists in a system where three forces are acting concurrently on an object. If the system includes a 5.0-newton force due north and a 2.0-newton force due south, the third force must be

(1) 7.0 N south

(2) 7.0 N north

(3) 3.0 N south

(4) 3.0 N north

24. A baseball bat moving at high speed strikes a feather. If air resistance is neglected, compared to the magnitude of the force exerted by the bat on the feather, the magnitude of the force exerted by the feather on the bat is

(1) smaller

(2) larger

(3) the same

25. A baseball player throws a ball horizontally. Which statement best describes the ball's motion after it is thrown? (Neglect air resistance.)

(1) Its vertical speed remains the same and its horizontal speed increases.

(2) Its vertical speed remains the same and its horizontal speed remains the same.

(3) Its vertical speed increases and its horizontal speed increases.

(4) Its vertical speed increases and its horizontal speed remains the same.

26. A red ball and a green ball are simultaneously thrown horizontally from the same height. The red ball has an initial speed of 40. meters per second and the green ball has an initial speed of 20. meters per second. Compared to the time it takes the red ball to reach the ground, the time it takes the green ball to reach the ground will be

(1) the same   (3) half as much

(2) twice as much   (4) four times as much

27. A ball is projected horizontally to the right from a height of 50. meters, as shown in the following diagram.

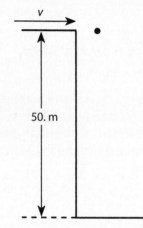

Which diagram best represents the position of the ball at 1.0-second intervals?

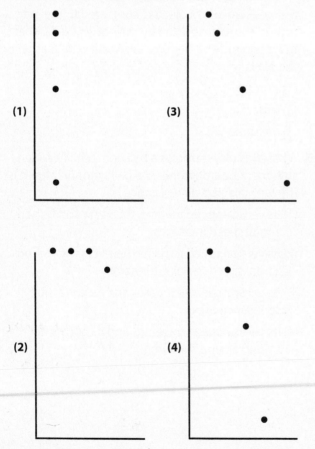

28. A student throws a stone upward at an angle of 45°. Which statement best describes the stone at the highest point that it reaches?

(1) Its acceleration is zero.

(2) Its acceleration is at a minimum.

(3) Its potential energy is at a minimum.

(4) Its kinetic energy is at a minimum.

29. A projectile is launched with an initial velocity of 200 meters per second at an angle of 30° above the horizontal. What is the magnitude of the vertical component of the projectile's initial velocity?

(1) 200 m/s × cos 30°

(2) 200 m/s × sin 30°

(3) $\dfrac{200 \text{ m/s}}{\cos 30°}$

(4) $\dfrac{200 \text{ m/s}}{\sin 30°}$

30. A convertible car with its top down is traveling at constant speed around a circular track, as shown in the following diagram.

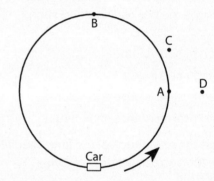

When the car is at point A, if a passenger in the car throws a ball straight up, the ball could land at point

(1) A

(2) B

(3) C

(4) D

31. An amusement park ride moves a rider at a constant speed of 14 meters per second in a horizontal circular path of radius 10. meters. What is the magnitude of the rider's centripetal acceleration in terms of g, the acceleration due to gravity?

(1) 1 g

(2) 2 g

(3) 3 g

(4) 0 g

32. As a cart travels around a horizontal circular track, the cart must undergo a change in

(1) velocity

(2) inertia

(3) speed

(4) weight

33. The diagram below represents a ball undergoing uniform circular motion as it travels clockwise on a string.

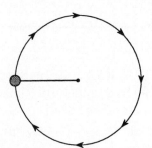

At the moment shown in the diagram, what are the correct directions of both the velocity and centripetal acceleration?

(1) $v\uparrow$ $\xrightarrow{a}$ **(3)** $v\downarrow$ $\xleftarrow{a}$

(2) $\xrightarrow{v}$ $a\uparrow$ **(4)** $\xrightarrow{v}$ $a\downarrow$

34. The following diagram shows a satellite of mass m orbiting Earth in a circular path of radius R.

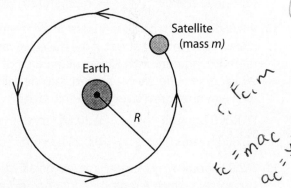

If centripetal force F_c is acting on the satellite, its speed is equal to

(1) $\sqrt{\dfrac{F_c R}{m}}$ (3) $\sqrt{\dfrac{F_c m}{R}}$

(2) $\dfrac{F_c R}{m}$ (4) $F_c mR$

35. If the mass of one of two particles is doubled and the distance between them is doubled, the magnitude of the force of attraction between the two particles will

(1) decrease   (3) remain the same

(2) increase

36. What is the magnitude of the gravitational force between two 5.0-kilogram masses separated by a distance of 5.0 meters?

(1) 5.0×10^0 N   (3) 6.7×10^{-11} N

(2) 3.3×10^{-10} N   (4) 1.3×10^{-11} N

37. Two point masses are located a distance D apart. The magnitude of the gravitational force of attraction between them can be quadrupled by changing the distance to

(1) $\frac{1}{2}D$ (3) $\frac{1}{4}D$

(2) $2D$ (4) $4D$

38. A 50-kilogram student, standing on Earth, attracts Earth with a force having a magnitude of approximately

(1) 0 N   (3) 50 N

(2) 5 N   (4) 500 N

39. An object has mass m at the surface of Earth. The mass of the object at a distance of two Earth radii from the center of Earth is

(1) m (3) $\frac{1}{2}m$

(2) $2m$ (4) $\frac{1}{4}m$

40. Which combination of units can be used to express the weight of an object?

(1) kilogram / second

(2) kilogram • meter

(3) kilogram • meter / second

(4) kilogram • meter / second^2

41. A 15-kilogram mass weighs 60. newtons on planet X. The mass is allowed to fall freely from rest near the surface of the planet. After falling for 6.0 seconds, the acceleration of the mass is

(1) 0.25 m/s^2 (3) 24 m/s^2

(2) 10. m/s^2 (4) 4.0 m/s^2

42. An object is allowed to fall freely from rest near the surface of a planet. If the object falls 54 meters in the first 3.0 seconds after it is released, what is the acceleration due to gravity on the planet?

(1) 6.0 m/s^2 (3) 12 m/s^2

(2) 9.8 m/s^2 (4) 18 m/s^2

43. The diagram below shows a student applying a 10.-newton force to slide a piece of wood at constant speed across a horizontal surface. After the wood is cut in half, one piece is placed on top of the other, as shown.

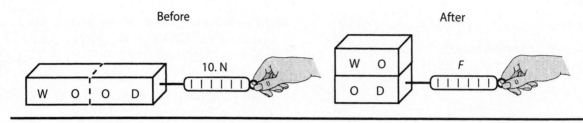

Before

After

10. N

F

W   O   O   D

W   O

O   D

Uniform horizontal surface

What is the magnitude of the force *F* required to slide the stacked wood at constant speed across the surface?

(1) 40. N   (3) 10. N

(2) 20. N   (4) 5.0 N

44. A different force is applied to each of four 1.0-kilogram blocks to slide them across a uniform steel surface at constant speed as shown. In which diagram is the coefficient of friction between the block and steel smallest?

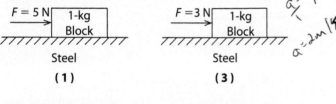

$F = 5$ N   1-kg Block

Steel

(1)

$F = 3$ N   1-kg Block

Steel

(3)

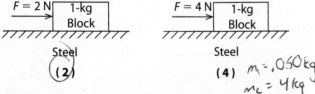

$F = 2$ N   1-kg Block

Steel

(2)

$F = 4$ N   1-kg Block

Steel

(4)

45. The magnitude of the momentum of an object is 64.0 kilogram • meters per second. If the velocity of the object is doubled, the magnitude of the object's momentum is

(1) 32.0 kg • m/s   (3) 128 kg • m/s

(2) 64.0 kg • m/s   (4) 256 kg • m/s

46. A force of 20. newtons is exerted on a cart for 10. seconds. For what period of time must a 50.-newton force act to produce the same impulse on the cart?

(1) 10. s   (3) 5.0 s

(2) 2.0 s   (4) 4.0 s

47. A bullet traveling at 5.0×10^2 meters per second is brought to rest by an impulse of 50. newton • seconds. What is the mass of the bullet?

(1) 2.5×10^4 kg   (3) 1.0×10^{-1} kg

(2) 1.0×10^1 kg   (4) 1.0×10^{-2} kg

48. A 5.0-kilogram cart traveling at 4.0 meters per second is brought to rest in 2.0 seconds. The magnitude of the average force used to stop the cart is

(1) 2.5 N   (3) 20. N

(2) 10. N   (4) 40. N

49. Two cars having different weights are traveling on a level surface at different constant velocities. Within the same time interval, greater force will always be required to stop the car that has the greater

(1) weight   (3) velocity

(2) kinetic energy   (4) momentum

50. A 0.050-kilogram bullet is fired from a 4.0-kilogram rifle which is initially at rest. If the bullet leaves the rifle with momentum having a magnitude of 20. kilogram • meters per second, the rifle will recoil with a momentum having a magnitude of

(1) 1600 kg • m/s   (3) 20. kg • m/s

(2) 80. kg • m/s   (4) 0.25 kg • m/s

51. A 2.0-kilogram toy cannon is at rest on a frictionless horizontal surface. A remote triggering device causes a 0.005-kilogram projectile to be fired from the cannon. Which equation describes the system after the cannon is fired?

(1) mass of cannon + mass of projectile = 0

(2) speed of cannon + speed of projectile = 0

(3) momentum of cannon + momentum of projectile = 0

(4) velocity of cannon + velocity of projectile = 0

52. Which pair of terms are vector quantities?

(1) force and mass

(2) distance and displacement

(3) acceleration and momentum

(4) velocity and speed

53. An ideal simple pendulum having length ℓ and bob of mass m has a period of 2.0 seconds when released from angle θ. If the bob is replaced with a bob of mass $2m$ and released from the same angle θ, the period of the pendulum is

(1) 1.0 s

(2) 2.0 s

(3) 1.4 s

(4) 4.0 s

54. For small amplitudes, the period of an ideal simple pendulum is dependent upon

(1) its length and the acceleration due to gravity only

(2) its length and the mass of the bob only

(3) the acceleration due to gravity and the mass of the bob only

(4) its length, the acceleration due to gravity, and the mass of the bob

Part B

Base your answers to questions 55 through 60 on the following diagram and information. The diagram is drawn to a scale of 1.0 centimeter = 30. meters.

A student on building X is located 240. meters from launch site B of a rocket on building Y. The rocket reaches its maximum altitude at point A. The student's eyes are level with the launch site on building Y.

55. Using the scale diagram and a protractor, measure the angle of elevation θ of the rocket and record it to the nearest degree. [1]

56. Determine the height h of the rocket above the student's eye level. [1]

57. What is the total distance the rocket must fall from its maximum altitude to reach the ground? [1]

58. Determine how much time is required for the rocket to fall freely from point A back to ground level. [2]

59. Determine the speed of the rocket as it reaches the ground after falling freely from point A. [2]

60. Which graph best represents the relationship between velocity v and time t for the rocket from the time it is launched until it hits the ground?

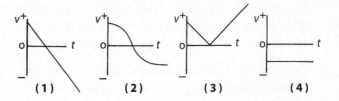

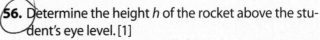

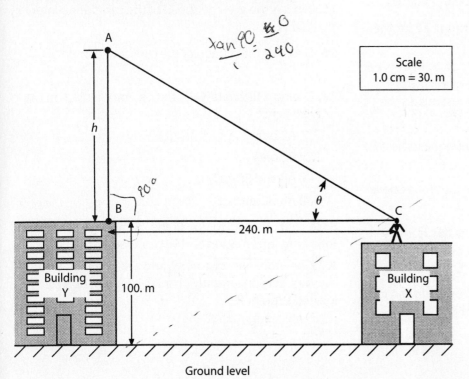

Ground level

Base your answers to questions 61 through 64 on the information that follows.

A newspaper carrier on her delivery route travels 200. meters due north and then turns and walks 300. meters due east.

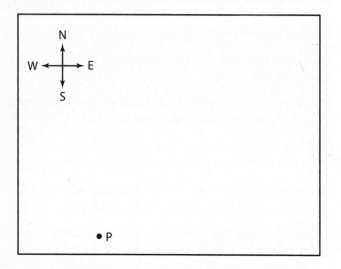

61. Using a ruler and a protractor and starting at point P, construct the sequence of two displacement vectors for the newspaper carrier's route. Use a scale of 1.0 centimeter = 50. meters. Label the vectors. [3]

62. Construct and label the vector that represents the carrier's resultant displacement from point P. [1]

63. What is the magnitude of the carrier's resultant displacement? [1]

64. What is the measure of the angle in degrees between north and the carrier's resultant displacement? [1]

Base your answers to questions 65 through 72 on the information that follows.

A stone is thrown with an initial velocity of 20. meters per second straight upward from the edge of a cliff 100. meters above a canyon floor. The stone just misses the cliff's edge on its way down.

65. Determine the time required for the stone to reach its maximum height. [2]

66. Determine the maximum height of the stone above the edge of the cliff. [2]

67. How much time elapses as the stone falls from its maximum height to the level from which it was thrown? [1]

68. What is the velocity of the stone upon returning to the level from which it was thrown? [2]

69. Determine the velocity of the stone 6.0 seconds after it is thrown. [2]

70. Determine the position of the stone 6.0 seconds after it is thrown. [2]

71. Sketch a graph to show the relationship between the stone's velocity and elapsed time from 0.0 second to 6.0 seconds. [1]

72. Sketch a graph to show the relationship between the stone's speed and elapsed time from 0.0 second to 6.0 seconds. [1]

Base your answers to questions 73 through 77 on the following speed-time graph, which represents the linear motion of a cart.

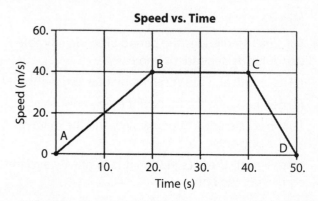

73. Determine the magnitude of the acceleration of the cart during interval AB. [2]

74. Determine the distance traveled by the cart during interval ABC. [2]

75. What is the average speed of the cart during interval CD? [1]

76. Describe the motion of the cart during interval CD. [1]

77. During which interval is the net force acting on the cart zero?

(1) AB only

(2) BC only

(3) AB and CD only

(4) AB, BC, and CD

Base your answers to questions 78 through 82 on the following information and vector diagram.

A 20.-newton force due north and a 40.-newton force due east act concurrently on a 10.-kilogram object located at point P.

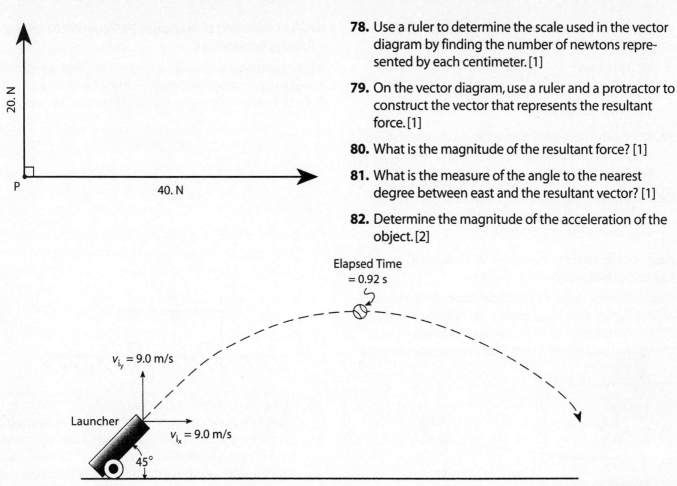

78. Use a ruler to determine the scale used in the vector diagram by finding the number of newtons represented by each centimeter. [1]

79. On the vector diagram, use a ruler and a protractor to construct the vector that represents the resultant force. [1]

80. What is the magnitude of the resultant force? [1]

81. What is the measure of the angle to the nearest degree between east and the resultant vector? [1]

82. Determine the magnitude of the acceleration of the object. [2]

Base your answers to questions 83 through 89 on the following information and the diagram above.

A machine launches a tennis ball at an angle of 45° with the horizontal, as shown. The ball has an initial vertical velocity of 9.0 meters per second and an initial horizontal velocity of 9.0 meters per second. The ball reaches its maximum height 0.92 seconds after its launch. (Neglect air resistance and assume the ball lands at the same height from which it was launched.)

83. Determine the speed of the ball as it leaves the launcher. [2]

84. Determine the total horizontal distance traveled by the ball during the entire time it is in the air. [2]

85. Compared to the vertical acceleration of the ball at the time of launch, the vertical acceleration of the ball at elapsed time 0.92 second is

(1) less

(2) greater

(3) the same

86. Which graph best represents the relationship between the horizontal speed of the ball and elapsed time. (Neglect air resistance.)

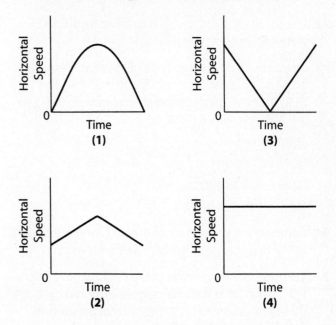

87. As the ball rises, the vertical component of its velocity

(1) decreases

(2) increases

(3) remains the same

88. On the diagram sketch an arrow to show the direction of the ball's velocity at its maximum height. Label the arrow *v*. [1]

89. On the diagram sketch an arrow to show the direction of the ball's acceleration at its maximum height. Label the arrow *a*. [1]

Base your answers to questions 90 through 95 on the following information and diagram.

A flat racetrack viewed from above has curves with radii of 50.0 meters and 100. meters. A car having a mass of 1.00×10^3 kilograms moves counterclockwise around the track at a constant speed of 20.0 meters per second.

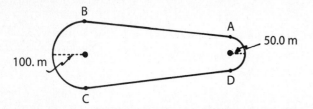

90. What is the magnitude of the net force acting on the car while it is moving from A to B? [1]

91. Determine the net force acting on the car while it is moving from B to C. [2]

92. It takes the car 20.0 seconds to travel from C to D. Determine the distance CD. [2]

93. Compared to the magnitude of the centripetal acceleration of the car while moving from D to A, the magnitude of the centripetal acceleration of the car while moving from B to C is

(1) the same

(2) twice as great

(3) one-half as great

(4) four times as great

94. Compare the magnitude of the car's momentum at D to the magnitude of the car's momentum at B. [1]

95. Compare the magnitude of the centripetal acceleration of the car at A to the magnitude of the car's centripetal acceleration at A if additional passengers were riding in the car. [1]

Base your answers to questions 96 through 101 on the following information.

A child pulls a cart with rubber wheels at constant speed across a dry, horizontal concrete surface by exerting a force of 50. newtons at an angle of 35° to the horizontal.

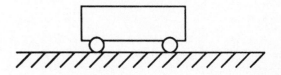

96. Using a protractor and a straightedge, construct a scaled vector showing the 50.-newton force acting on the cart at the appropriate angle. The force must be drawn to a scale of 1.0 centimeter = 10. newtons. Label the 50.-newton force and the 35° angle on the diagram. [2]

97. Construct the horizontal component of the force vector to scale on the diagram and label it *H*. [1]

98. What is the magnitude of the horizontal component of the force? [1]

99. What is the magnitude of the frictional force between the cart's rubber wheels and the concrete? [1]

100. Determine the magnitude of the normal force on the cart. [2]

101. Compared to the normal force acting on the cart, the weight of the cart is

(1) less

(2) greater

(3) the same

Base your answers to questions 102 through 106 on the following information and data table.

An astronaut on a distant planet conducted an experiment to determine the gravitational acceleration on that planet. The data table shows the results of the experiment.

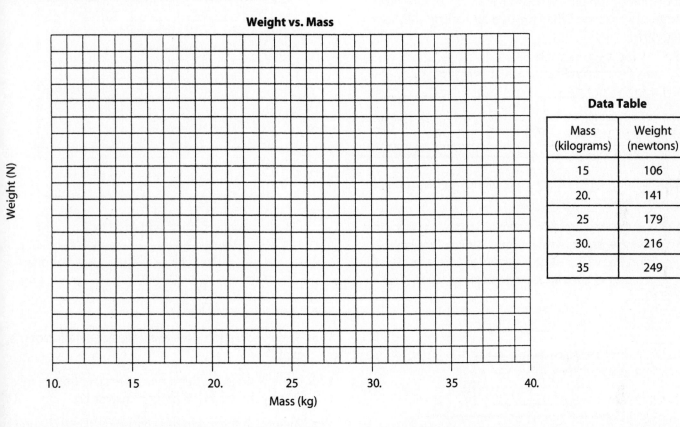

Weight vs. Mass

Data Table

Mass (kilograms)	Weight (newtons)
15	106
20.	141
25	179
30.	216
35	249

102. On the grid provided mark an appropriate scale on the axis labeled "Weight (N)." [1]

103. Plot the data points. [1]

104. Draw the best-fit line. [1]

105. Using the graph, determine the planet's gravitational acceleration. [2]

106. On the same grid sketch a line to represent Earth's gravitational acceleration. [1]

Base your answers to questions 107 through 109 on the following information.

A block weighing 4.2 newtons, sliding from left to right in a straight line on a horizontal surface, is acted upon by a 2.4-newton friction force. The block will be brought to rest by the friction force in a distance of 4.0 meters.

107. On the diagram that follows, draw an arrow to identify the direction of each force on the block while it is still moving but being slowed by the friction force. Identify each force by appropriately labeling the arrow that represents its line of direction. [3]

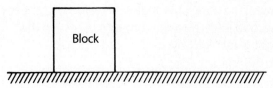

Block

108. Determine the magnitude of the acceleration of the block as it is brought to rest. [2]

109. Determine the coefficient of friction between the two surfaces in contact. [2]

Base your answers to questions 110 through 112 on the following information and diagram.

Two railroad cars, A and B, are on a frictionless, level track. Car A has a mass of 2.0×10^3 kilograms and a velocity of 4.0 meters per second toward the right. Car B has a velocity of 1.5 meters per second toward the left. The magnitude of the momentum of cart B is 6.0×10^3 kilogram · meters per second. When the two cars collide, they lock together.

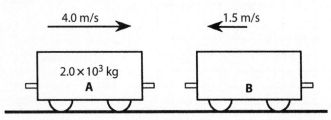

110. Determine the magnitude of the momentum of car A before the collision. [2]

111. On the diagram below, construct a scaled vector that represents the momentum of car A before the collision. The vector must be drawn to a scale of 1.0 centimeter = 1,000 kilogram · meters per second [1]

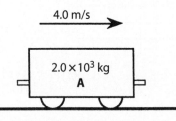

112. Describe the momentum of the two cars after the collision and justify your answer based on the initial momentum of both cars. [2]

Base your answers to questions 113 through 119 on the following information and data table.

A 1500-kilogram car is traveling due north at 24.0 meters per second when the driver sees an obstruction on the highway. The data table shows the velocity of the car at 1.0-second intervals as it is brought to rest on the straight, level highway.

Time (s)	Velocity (m/s)
0.0	24.0
1.0	19.0
2.0	14.0
3.0	10.0
4.0	4.0

113. On the grid that follows, plot the data points for velocity versus time. [1]

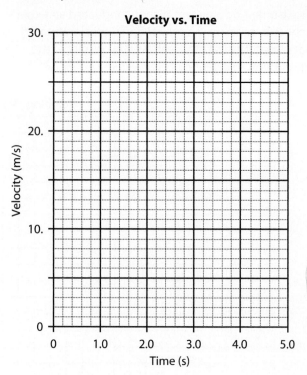

114. Draw the best-fit line. [1]

115. Using your graph, determine the acceleration of the car. [2]

116. Using your graph, determine the total distance traveled by the car as it is brought to rest. [2]

117. Determine the magnitude of the car's total change in momentum as it is brought to rest. [2]

118. Determine the magnitude and direction of the average force required to bring the car to rest. [2]

119. Compare the impulse imparted to the car to its change in momentum as it is brought to rest. [1]

Explain the statements in questions 120 through 122 on the basis of physical principles.

120. A rocket is propelled by its exhaust gases. [1]

121. A car accelerates as it travels at constant speed around a traffic circle. [1]

122. A raw egg is thrown as hard as possible against a bed sheet backdrop. The egg does not break when it hits the sheet, but the egg does break when it hits the floor below. [1]

123. The following graph represents the motion of an object traveling in a straight line as a function of time.

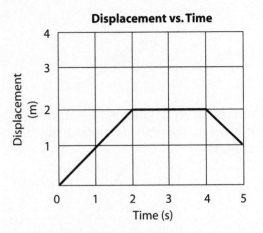

Displacement vs. Time

What is the average speed of the object during the first 4.0 seconds? [1]

124. A group of bike riders took a 4.0-hour trip. During the first 3.0 hours they traveled a total of 50. kilometers, but during the last hour they traveled only 10. kilometers. Determine the group's average speed for the entire trip. [2]

125. Which graph best represents the relationship between velocity and time for an object that accelerates uniformly for 2 seconds, then moves at constant velocity for 1 second, and finally decelerates for 3 seconds?

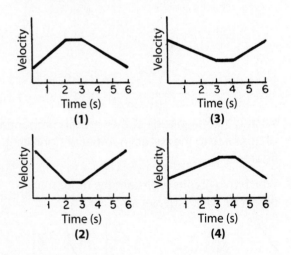

126. Which pair of graphs represents the same motion?

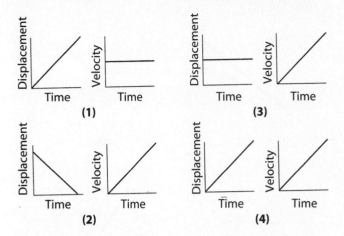

127. Which combination of graphs best describes free fall motion? (Neglect air resistance.)

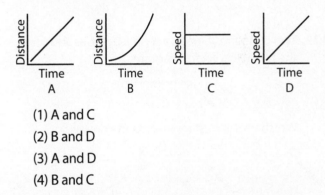

(1) A and C
(2) B and D
(3) A and D
(4) B and C

128. Two students push on a sled. One pushes with a force of 30. newtons east and the other exerts a force of 40. newtons south, as shown in the following topview diagram.

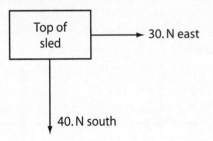

Which vector best represents the resultant of these two forces?

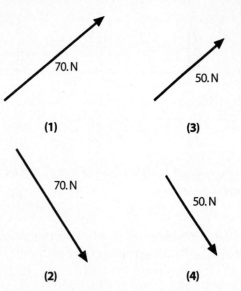

(1) 70. N

(3) 50. N

(2) 70. N

(4) 50. N

129. Two concurrent forces act on a point, as shown in the following vector diagram.

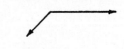

Which vector best represents their resultant?

(1)   **(2)**   **(3)**   **(4)**

130. A ball is fired with a velocity of 12 meters per second from a cannon pointing north, while the cannon is moving eastward with a velocity of 24 meters per second. Which vector best represents the resultant velocity of the ball as it leaves the cannon?

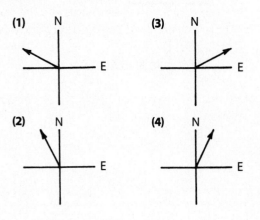

131. The vector that follows represents the resultant of two forces acting concurrently on an object at point P.

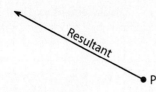

Which pair of vectors best represents two concurrent forces that combine to produce this resultant force vector?

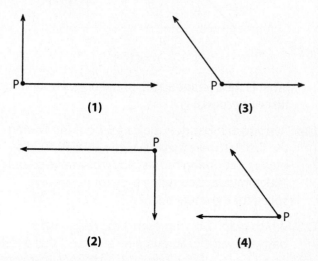

132. A 100.-newton force acts on point P as shown in the following diagram.

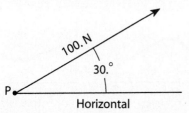

What is the magnitude of the vertical component of this force to the correct number of significant figures? [1]

133. Which two graphs represent the motion of an object on which the net force is zero?

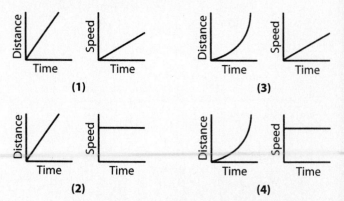

134. The following diagram represents a constant force acting on a box located on a frictionless horizontal surface.

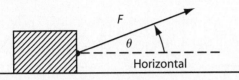

As the angle θ between the force and the horizontal increases, the acceleration of the box

(1) decreases

(2) increases

(3) remains the same

135. A series of unbalanced forces was applied to each of two blocks A and B. The following graphs show the relationship between the unbalanced force and acceleration for each block.

Unbalanced Force vs. Acceleration for Block A

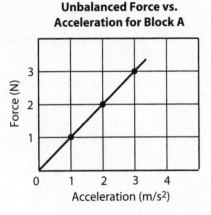

Unbalanced Force vs. Acceleration for Block B

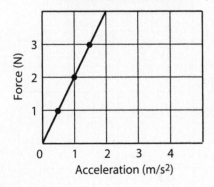

Compared to the mass of block A, the mass of block B is

(1) the same

(2) twice as great

(3) half as great

(4) four times as great

136. The following diagram shows a block on a horizontal frictionless surface. A 100.-newton force acts on the block at an angle of 30.° above the horizontal.

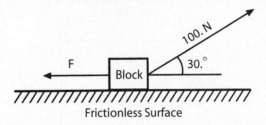

Frictionless Surface

Determine the magnitude of force F if it establishes equilibrium. [2]

137. A ball is fired vertically upward at 5.0 meters per second from a cart moving horizontally to the right at 2.0 meters per second. Which vector best represents the resultant velocity of the ball when fired?

138. In the following diagram, a cyclist traveling at constant speed to the right drops a ball from her hand.

Which pair of graphs best represents the horizontal motion of the ball relative to the ground? (Neglect air resistance.)

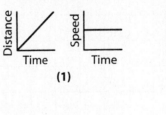

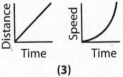

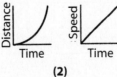

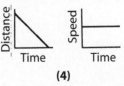

139. The following graph shows the weight of three objects on planet X as a function of their masses.

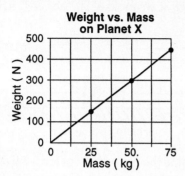

Weight vs. Mass on Planet X

What is the acceleration due to gravity on planet X?

(1) 0.17 m/s²

(2) 6.0 m/s²

(3) 9.8 m/s²

(4) 50. m/s²

140. Which graph best represents the motion of an object with no unbalanced force acting on it?

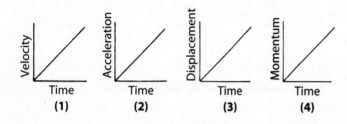

(1) (2) (3) (4)

141. Which graph best represents the relationship between the mass *m* of a satellite launched from Earth and the satellite's distance *r* from Earth?

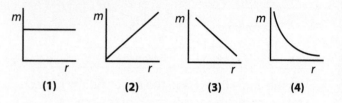

(1) (2) (3) (4)

Part C

Base your answers to questions 142 and 143 on the following information.

A student walks from her house towards the bus stop, located 50. meters to the east. After walking 20. meters, she remembers that she left her lunch at the door. She *runs* home, picks up her lunch, walks again, and arrives at the bus stop.

142. On the following grid, sketch a displacement versus time graph for the student's motion. [4]

143. Label the graph with appropriate values for time and displacement. [1]

Displacement vs. Time

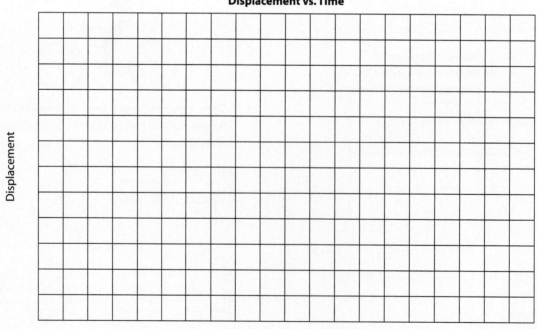

Base your answers to questions 144 through 150 on the following information and data table.

Students decided to verify the value for acceleration due to gravity found in the *Reference Tables for Physical Setting/ Physics* by performing a simple experiment. A ball bearing was dropped from the ceiling of the classroom and the time of fall measured. The twenty students took three measurements of the vertical distance and recorded an average value of 2.848 meters. Each student dropped the ball twice. The times of fall were recorded in the following tables, one showing the times as originally recorded and the other with the data sorted.

Unsorted		Sorted	
Time (s)		**Time** (s)	
0.97	0.87	0.50	0.76
0.86	0.75	0.56	0.77
1.00	0.68	0.57	0.77
0.81	0.72	0.61	0.77
0.98	0.78	0.66	0.78
0.77	0.77	0.67	0.78
0.87	0.80	0.68	0.78
0.87	0.75	0.68	0.80
0.88	0.77	0.69	0.80
0.71	0.78	0.69	0.81
0.73	0.69	0.69	0.83
0.72	0.69	0.71	0.86
0.78	0.68	0.72	0.87
0.76	0.87	0.72	0.87
0.75	0.75	0.73	0.87
0.76	0.50	0.75	0.87
0.69	0.57	0.75	0.88
0.83	0.67	0.75	0.97
0.56	0.66	0.75	0.98
0.80	0.61	0.76	1.00

144. What is the range of the data? [1]

145. What is the mean of the data, to the nearest ten thousandth of a second and to the nearest hundredth of a second? [1]

146. Determine the standard deviation of the recorded values to the nearest hundredth of a second. [2]

147. How many values are within one standard deviation from the mean? [1]

148. What percent of the data is within one standard deviation from the mean? [1]

149. Determine the acceleration due to gravity based on the students' data. [2]

150. Determine the percent error. [2]

Base your answers to questions 151 through 154 on the following information and diagram.

A block weighing 100. newtons is positioned on an incline that makes an angle of 30.° with the horizontal. The friction force between the block and the incline is 10. newtons. A force of 120. newtons is applied by pulling on a rope that makes an angle of 30.° with the incline, as shown.

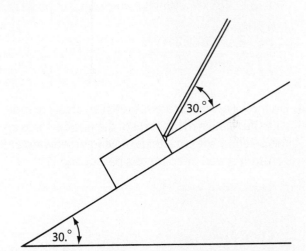

151. Draw a free-body diagram, and provide appropriate labels for each of the forces. [4]

152. Determine the components of the block's weight parallel to the incline. [2]

153. Determine the magnitude and direction of the component of the tension that is useful in moving the block up the incline. [2]

154. Determine the magnitude and direction of the block's acceleration. [3]

Base your answers to questions 155 through 158 on the following information and diagrams.

A person standing on a scale in a stationary elevator weighs 735 newtons. The net force F_{net} on the person is zero because the normal force F_N is equal in magnitude but opposite in direction to the gravitational force F_g as shown.

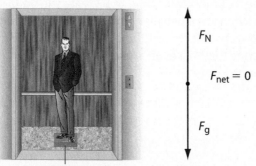

Scale

155. On the following diagram, sketch an arrow to indicate the relative magnitude of the normal force on the person if the elevator is moving downward at a constant speed of 2.5 meters per second. [1]

$F_{net} = \underline{}$

F_g

Scale

156. What is the net force on the person, when the elevator is moving at constant speed downward? [1]

157. On the following diagram, sketch an arrow to indicate the relative magnitude of the normal force on the person if the elevator is accelerating upward at 2.5 meters per second². [1]

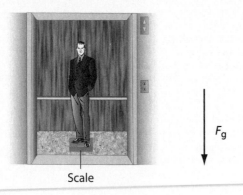

F_g

Scale

158. Compare the reading on the scale when the elevator is accelerating upward to the reading on the scale when the elevator is stationary. [1]

Base your answers to questions 159 through 163 on the following information and diagram.

Students performed an experiment to study horizontal projectile motion. A 2.00-meter-long flexible plastic track was positioned so that one end was at the edge of a lab table and the other end was elevated, as shown.

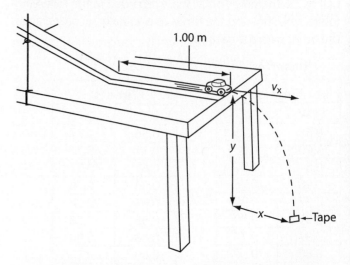

A toy car was started from rest from the elevated end of the track and the time for the car to travel the 1.00-meter horizontal distance to the edge of the table was measured. The times for three trials were 0.453 second, 0.347 second, and 0.390 second. The car was caught as it left the tabletop. Students measured the vertical distance from the bottom of the car on the horizontal track to the floor and recorded an average distance of 0.926 meter.

159. Determine the average horizontal speed of the car. [3]

160. Determine the time required for the car, initially at rest, to fall freely from the tabletop to the floor. [2]

161. Use the answers to questions 159 and 160 to determine the horizontal distance the car would travel under these conditions if it wasn't caught. [2]

162. After having performed the calculations in questions 159 and 160, students measured the distance calculated in question 161 in a straight line from the horizontal track and directly beneath it on the floor. The spot was marked with a piece of masking tape. The car was then placed at the elevated end of the track and released from rest. State two reasons why the car landed about one centimeter short of the marked target. [2]

163. The experiment was repeated with the same car, but the elevated end of the track was positioned higher. Explain what effect releasing the car from rest at a greater height above the tabletop should have on (a) the average horizontal speed of the car [1], (b) the time required for the projected car to hit the floor after leaving the edge of the table [1], (c) the horizontal distance traveled by the car after it was projected from the tabletop [1].

Base your answers to questions 164 through 167 on the following information.

A child is moving at constant speed in a vertical circle on a ferris wheel. (Assume up is positive and down is negative. The representations used for quantities should be the same as those in the *Reference Tables for Physical Setting/Physics*.)

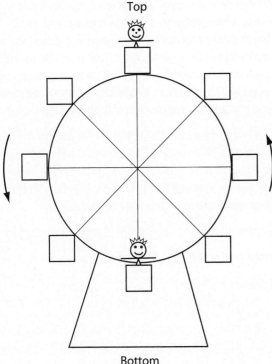
Top

Bottom

164. On the diagram, sketch labeled arrows to represent the three forces acting on the child at the bottom of the ride (centripetal force, gravitational force, and normal force). [3]

165. On the diagram, sketch labeled arrows to represent the three forces acting on the child at the top of the ride. [3]

166. Write an equation to show the relationship between the three forces acting on the child at the bottom of the ride. [1]

167. Write an equation to show the relationship between the three forces acting on the child at the top of the ride. [1]

168. The centripetal acceleration of a satellite in a circular orbit around Earth is produced by the gravitational force of attraction between the satellite and Earth. Express the tangential speed v of the satellite in terms of the mass of Earth m_E and the distance of the satellite from Earth's center R.

Base your answers to questions 169 through 171 on the information and diagram below.

A block of mass m slides at constant speed down a uniform plane inclined at an angle θ to the horizontal, as shown.

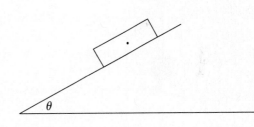

169. On the diagram, sketch and label appropriate arrows to represent the three forces acting on the block: friction, the normal force, and the force of gravity. [3]

170. Express the component of the block's weight parallel to the incline $F_\parallel$ and the component of the block's weight perpendicular to the incline $F_\perp$ in terms of F_g. [2]

171. Show that $\mu = \tan \theta$. [2]

Base your answers to questions 172 through 179 on the following information and diagram.

Two students, Julia and Tom, decided to perform an experiment to verify Newton's Second Law as applied to uniform circular motion; that is $F_c = \dfrac{mv^2}{r}$. In the lab, they collected the following materials: 15-centimeter long glass tube, fire-polished at each end and covered with rubber tubing, a piece of nylon line approximately one meter long, several two-holed rubber stoppers, a paper clip, masking tape, 36 identical iron washers, a stopwatch, and a triple-beam balance. An apparatus was assembled, with the intention of using it as shown below.

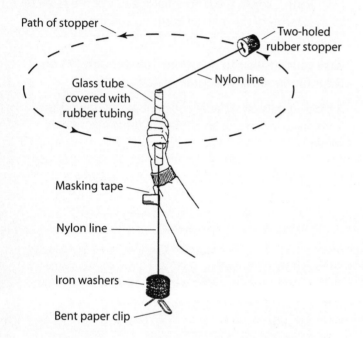

Path of stopper

Two-holed rubber stopper

Nylon line

Glass tube covered with rubber tubing

Masking tape

Nylon line

Iron washers

Bent paper clip

172. As the first objective Tom wrote: "To determine the relationship between the velocity of an object moving in a circular path and the magnitude of the centripetal force acting on the object." Julia objected stating they only could collect data that would enable them to determine the average speed of a rubber stopper in a circular path, but not its velocity. Which student was correct? Why?

173. How could the number of washers suspended at one end of the nylon cord be converted into a measurement of the magnitude of centripetal force?

174. To avoid having to use either the term velocity or speed, Tom changed their first objective to: "To determine the relationship between the period of revolution of an object moving in a circular path and the magnitude of the centripetal force acting on it." Using formulas found on the *Reference Tables for Physical Setting/Physics,* derive an expression for centripetal force in terms of r the radius of curvature of the path, m the object's mass, and T the period of revolution.

175. Name at least two *essential* pieces missing from their compilation of laboratory materials.

176. The pair decided to time the motion of the stopper for thirty revolutions instead of making three separate trials of one revolution each and calculating an average to determine its period. Provide a rationale for this decision.

177. *After securing all essential materials,* the pair proceeded with the collection of data. Julia practiced swinging the stopper overhead in a horizontal path, while keeping the radius of its path fixed. Once the technique was mastered the number of washers was varied for each trial from 36 to 4 washers in intervals of 4 washers. Tom timed each event as noted in question 176. What information should the students have recorded in their data table?

178. After the data was collected the students decided to graph their results. Sketch the general shape of the graph that should result for period of revolution versus centripetal force. Label the axis with the dependent and independent variables.

179. At the end of the lab period the pair concluded that they had not had sufficient time to verify $F_c = \dfrac{mv^2}{r}$. Explain.

Energy

VOCABULARY

battery	ideal mechanical system	nuclear energy
compression	internal energy	photocell
elastic potential energy	joule	potential energy
electromagnetic energy	kinetic energy	power
elongation	law of conservation of energy	simple pendulum
energy		spring constant
generator	mechanical energy	thermal energy
gravitational potential energy	motor	total energy
	nonideal mechanical system	watt
		work

Work and Energy

Energy is the ability to do work. Energy is a scalar quantity. When work is done on or by a system, the total energy of the system is changed.

Work

Work is the transfer of energy to an object when the object moves due to the application of a force. The force can be entirely in the direction of the object's motion or have a component in the direction of the motion. Work is a scalar quantity. The amount of work done, W, is equal to the product of the force, F, along the direction of displacement, d, of the object. The work done on the object produces a change in the object's total energy, ΔE_T:

$$W = Fd = \Delta E_T$$

The force F is in newtons and the displacement d is in meters. Thus, the work W or change in total energy ΔE_T can be expressed with the unit newton · meter. However, notice in the expressions below that 1 newton · meter equals 1 joule.

1 newton · meter = 1 kilogram · meter/second^2 · meter

1 newton · meter = 1 kilogram · meter^2/second^2 = 1 joule

The **joule,** J, is a derived unit equal to the work done on an object when a force of one newton produces a displacement of one meter. Note that the amount of work done is independent of the time the force acts on the object.

When a force is applied to a mass, but the mass does not move, no work is done. If a student was to hold an object at a constant height above the ground, no work would be done no matter how heavy the object might be and how much effort the student expended.

SAMPLE PROBLEM

A 2.3-kilogram block rests on a horizontal surface. A constant force of 5.0 newtons is applied to the block at an angle of 30.° to the horizontal, as shown in the diagram. The diagram is drawn to scale.

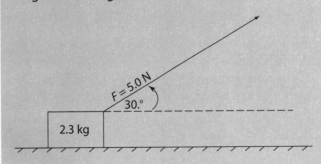

Determine the work done in moving the block a distance of 2.0 meters along the surface.

Solution: Identify the known and unknown values.

Known	Unknown
$F = 5.0$ N	$F_x = ?$ N
$m = 2.3$ kg	$W = ?$ J
$d = 2.0$ m	

Find the component of the applied force that is in the x-direction, that is, in the direction of the displacement. There are two ways to do this.

(1) Use the trigonometic relationship $F_x = F\cos\theta$. Substitute the known values and solve.

$F_x = (5.0$ N$)(\cos 30.°) = 4.3$ N

(2) Project the 5.0 N force onto the horizontal dashed line in the diagram and measure the line segment. This is the component of the applied force in the direction of motion, 4.3 N.

Use the equation that defines work to determine the work done.

$W = Fd$

Substitute the known values and solve.

$W = (4.3$ N$)(2.0$ m$) = 8.6$ J

POWER The rate at which work is done is a scalar quantity called **power.** By definition, power P is given by the equation $P = \frac{W}{t}$. However, $W = Fd$ and $\bar{v} = \frac{d}{t}$. Therefore, the equation can be rewritten as follows:

$$P = \frac{W}{t} = \frac{Fd}{t} = F\bar{v}$$

F is the force applied to an object that causes it to move with an average speed $\bar{v}$. If work W is in joules and time t is in seconds, then power can be expressed in joules per second. One joule of work done per second equals one **watt,** W, the SI derived unit for power. If 1 watt = 1 joule/second and 1 joule = 1 kilogram · meter²/second², then 1 watt = 1 kilogram · meter²/second²/second = 1 kilogram · meter²/second³.

(Do not confuse the symbol W, which is used for the *quantity* of work, with the abbreviation W for the *unit* watt.)

Because power is inversely proportional to time, the less time required to do a given amount of work, the greater the power developed. For example, as the length of time it takes a student to swim 25 meters decreases, the power developed by the student increases.

SAMPLE PROBLEM

A 7.80 × 10²-newton man does 8.58 × 10³ joules of work in 12.3 seconds by running up three flights of stairs to a landing vertically above his starting point. What power does the man develop during his run and what is his vertical displacement?

Solution: Identify the known and unknown values.

Known	Unknown
$F_g = 7.80 \times 10^2$ N	$P = ?$ J/s or W
$W = 8.58 \times 10^3$ J	$d = ?$ m
$t = 12.3$ s	

Write the equation that defines power.

$$P = \frac{W}{t}$$

Substitute the known values and solve.

$$P = \frac{8.58 \times 10^3 \text{ J}}{12.3 \text{ s}} = 698 \text{ W}$$

To find the displacement, use the equation that defines work.

$W = Fd$

Solve the equation for d.

$$d = \frac{W}{F}$$

Substitute the known values and solve.

$$d = \frac{8.58 \times 10^3 \text{ J}}{7.80 \times 10^2 \text{ N}} = 11.0 \text{ m}$$

SAMPLE PROBLEM

A constant horizontal force of 6.0 newtons is applied to a box on a counter to overcome friction. Determine how much power is dissipated in moving the box 3.0 meters along the counter in 1.5 seconds.

Solution: Identify the known and unknown values.

Known	Unknown
$F = 6.0$ N	$P = ?$ W
$d = 3.0$ m	
$t = 1.5$ s	

Use the formula that defines power.

$$P = \frac{W}{t} = \frac{Fd}{t}$$

Substitute the known values and solve.

$$P = \frac{(6.0 \text{ N})(3.0 \text{ m})}{1.5 \text{ s}} = 12 \text{ W}$$

Review Questions

1. Which combination of units can be used to express work? (1) newton · second/meter (2) newton · meter/second (3) newton/meter (4) newton · meter

2. A jack exerts a force of 4.5×10^3 newtons to raise a car 0.25 meter. How much work is done by the jack? (1) 5.6×10^{-5} J (2) 1.1×10^3 J (3) 4.5×10^3 J (4) 1.8×10^4 J

3. If a 2.0-kilogram mass is raised 0.050 meter vertically, the work done on the mass is approximately (1) 0.10 J (2) 0.98 J (3) 9.8 J (4) 40. J

4. A horizontal force of 80.0 newtons pushes a 50.0-kilogram object for 8.00 meters across a level floor. The work done in pushing the object is (1) 10.0 J (2) 400. J (3) 640. J (4) 3.20×10^5 J

5. Work is being done when a force (1) acts vertically on a cart that can only move horizontally (2) is exerted by one team in a tug of war when there is no movement (3) is exerted while pulling a wagon up a hill (4) of gravitational attraction acts on a person standing on the surface of Earth

6. In the following diagram, a 20.0-newton force is used to push a 2.00-kilogram cart a distance of 5.00 meters.

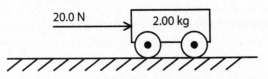

Determine the amount of work done on the cart.

7. How much work is done on a downhill skier by an average braking force of 9.8×10^2 newtons to stop her in a distance of 10.0 meters? (1) 1.0×10^1 J (2) 9.8×10^1 J (3) 1.0×10^3 J (4) 9.8×10^3 J

8. A student does 300. joules of work pushing a cart 3.0 meters due east and then does 400. joules of work pushing the cart 4.0 meters due north. The total amount of work done by the student is (1) 100. J (2) 500. J (3) 700. J (4) 2500 J

9. A constant horizontal force of 20.0 newtons applied to a box causes it to move at a constant speed of 4.0 meters per second. Determine how much work is done against friction on the box in 6.0 seconds.

10. A horizontal force of 3 newtons moves a 10-kilogram mass horizontally a distance of 3 meters at constant velocity. The work done against friction is (1) 6 J (2) 9 J (3) 3 J (4) 30 J

11. A student pulls a block along a horizontal surface at constant velocity. The following diagram shows the components of the force exerted on the block by the student.

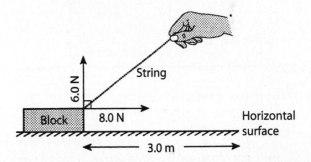

Determine how much work is done against friction.

12. A constant horizontal force of 2.0 newtons is used to push a 3.0-kilogram mass 4.0 meters across a counter top. How much work is done on the mass? (1) 6.0 J (2) 8.0 J (3) 12 J (4) 24 J

13. The diagram that follows shows a 9.8-newton cart being pulled a distance of 0.50 meter along a plane inclined at 15° to the horizontal. The amount of work required is 1.3 joules.

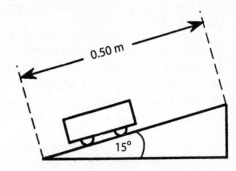

If the cart was raised 0.50 meter vertically instead of being pulled along the inclined plane, the amount of work done would be (1) less (2) more (3) the same

14. A crane raises a 200-newton weight to a height of 50 meters in 5 seconds. The crane does work at the rate of (1) 8×10^{-1} W (2) 2×10^1 W (3) 2×10^3 W (4) 5×10^4 W

15. A machine is used to move an object. As the power of the machine is increased, the time required for it to move the object a fixed distance (1) decreases (2) increases (3) remains the same

16. An engine rated at 5.0×10^4 watts exerts a constant force of 2.5×10^3 newtons on a vehicle. Determine the average speed of the vehicle.

17. The following diagram shows a 1.0×10^3-newton crate to be lifted at constant speed from the ground to a loading dock 1.5 meters high in 5.0 seconds.

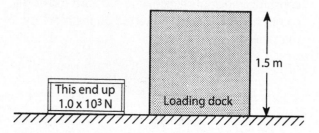

What power is required to lift the crate?
(1) 1.5×10^3 W (2) 2.0×10^2 W (3) 3.0×10^2 W (4) 7.5×10^3 W

18. As the time required to do a given quantity of work decreases, the power developed (1) decreases (2) increases (3) remains the same

19. Determine the power developed by a man weighing 6.0×10^2 newtons who climbs a rope at a constant speed of 2.0 meters per second.

20. One elevator lifts a mass a given vertical distance in 8 seconds and a second elevator does the same work in 4 seconds. Compared to the power developed by the first elevator, the power developed by the second elevator is (1) one-half as great (2) twice as great (3) the same (4) four times as great

21. A 5.0×10^2-newton girl takes 10.0 seconds to run up two flights of stairs to a landing, a total of 5.0 meters vertically above her starting point. What power does the girl develop during her run? (1) 25 W (2) 50. W (3) 250 W (4) 2,500 W

22. A motor having a maximum power rating of 8.1×10^4 watts is used to operate an elevator with a weight of 1.8×10^4 newtons. What is the maximum weight this motor can lift at an average speed of 3.0 meters per second? (1) 6.0×10^3 N (2) 1.8×10^4 N (3) 2.4×10^4 N (4) 2.7×10^4 N

23. A girl weighing 500. newtons takes 50.0 seconds to climb a flight of stairs 18 meters high. Determine the girl's vertical power output.

24. If the time required for a student to swim 500 meters is doubled, the power developed by the student will be (1) halved (2) doubled (3) quartered (4) quadrupled

25. Determine the average speed of a 4.0×10^2-newton weight being lifted vertically by a 2.00×10^3-watt motor.

Forms of Energy

As already noted, energy and work are related. The joule is the SI unit for both quantities, which are scalar. When one system does work on another system, the second system gains an amount of energy equal to the amount of work done on it. This process is called a transfer of energy.

Energy has many forms, including thermal, chemical, nuclear, electromagnetic, sound, and mechanical. Whatever its form, energy is measured by the amount of work it can do. **Thermal energy,** or heat, is the total kinetic energy possessed by the individual particles that comprise an object. (The term "thermal energy" is also used by nuclear physicists to describe the average kinetic energy, 0.025 electronvolt, possessed by neutrons at room temperature.)

Internal energy refers to the total potential energy and kinetic energy possessed by the particles that make up an object, but excludes the potential and kinetic energies of the system as a whole.

Nuclear energy is the energy released by nuclear fission, the division of a heavy atomic nucleus into parts of comparable mass, or nuclear fusion, the combining of two light nuclei to form a heavier nucleus.

Electromagnetic energy is the energy associated with electric or magnetic fields. Electromagnetic energy can take many forms, such as visible light, microwaves, and radio waves.

Potential Energy

The energy possessed by an object due to its position or condition is called **potential energy.** If there is no energy lost due to friction, the work done to bring the object to a different position or condition from its original condition or position is equal to the object's change in potential energy.

GRAVITATIONAL POTENTIAL ENERGY If an object, originally at rest on Earth's surface, is lifted to some height, work is done *against* gravitational force. The work done in lifting the object to a height above Earth's surface is equal to the object's **gravitational potential energy** relative to Earth's surface. The work done is equal to the gravitational potential energy acquired by the object. If the object falls, work is done *by* gravity on the object, and the object loses gravitational potential energy. However, the work done by gravity on the object increases its energy of motion (kinetic energy) as the object's speed increases during its fall. This kinetic energy can, in turn, do an amount of work equal to the loss in gravitational potential energy.

Recall that work is described by the formula $W = Fd$. For a falling object, F equals F_g, the weight of the object given by the formula $F_g = mg$, and the displacement d corresponds to Δh, the change in height. Thus, the change in gravitational potential energy is given by this equation:

$$\Delta PE = mg\Delta h$$

The mass m is in kilograms, g is the acceleration due to gravity in meters per second^2 (or gravitational field strength in newtons per kilogram), and Δh is the change in height of the mass in meters. Thus ΔPE, the change in potential energy, can be expressed in kilogram $\cdot$ meter^2/second^2 or joules. The change in potential energy of an object equals the product of its weight, mg, and its vertical change in height. This formula is valid only for displacements that are small compared to Earth's radius, so that g can be considered constant.

SAMPLE PROBLEM

How much potential energy is gained by an object with a mass of 2.00 kilograms that is lifted from the floor to the top of a 0.92-meter high table?

Solution: Identify the known and unknown values.

Known	Unknown
$m = 2.00$ kg	$PE = ?$ J
$h = 0.92$ m	
$g = 9.81$ m/s^2	

Substitute the known quantities and solve.

$\Delta PE = mg\Delta h = (2.00 \text{ kg})(9.81 \text{ m/s}^2)(0.92 \text{ m}) = 18$ J

Devices for Converting Energy

A **photocell** (photovoltaic cell) is a device that converts light, a form of electromagnetic radiation, into electrical energy. A **generator** is a device that converts mechanical energy into electrical energy by rotating a large coil of wire in a magnetic field. On the other hand, a **motor** is a device that converts electrical energy into mechanical energy as a result of forces on a current-carrying conductor in a magnetic field. A **battery** is a direct-current voltage source that converts chemical, thermal, nuclear, or solar energy into electrical energy.

Measuring Power

From the definition of power, $P = \frac{W}{t}$, it follows that $W = Pt$. Thus, one watt of power used for one second transfers one joule of energy or does one joule of work. One joule is equivalent to one watt $\cdot$ second, and energy can be measured in watt $\cdot$ seconds. Electric utility companies charge their customers for kilowatt $\cdot$ hours of energy rather than for watts of power.

 **Review Questions**

26. Which is a scalar quantity? (1) force (2) energy (3) displacement (4) velocity

27. Work is measured in the same units as (1) force (2) momentum (3) power (4) energy

28. Which quantity and unit are correctly paired?
    (1) velocity; m/s^2
    (2) momentum; kg $\cdot$ m/s^2
    (3) energy; kg $\cdot$ m^2/s^2
    (4) work; kg/m

29. A unit for elastic potential energy is the (1) watt (2) joule (3) newton (4) kilogram $\cdot$ meter/second

30. Which mass has the greatest potential energy with respect to the floor? (1) 50.-kg mass resting on the floor (2) 2.0-kg mass 10. m above the floor (3) 10.-kg mass 2.0 m above the floor (4) 6.0-kg mass 5.0 m above the floor

31. As an object slides across a horizontal surface, the gravitational potential energy of the object (1) decreases (2) increases (3) remains the same

32. The following diagram represents a cart traveling with initial speed *v* from left to right along a frictionless surface.

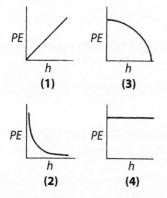

At which point is the gravitational potential energy of the cart least? (1) A (2) B (3) C (4) D

33. Determine the gain in potential energy of a 5.00-kilogram mass as it is raised 2.00 meters from the surface of Earth.

34. Which graph best represents the relationship between potential energy *PE* and height above the ground *h* for a freely falling object released from rest?

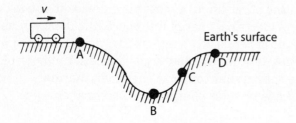

35. At the top of an incline, a 0.50-kilogram sphere has a potential energy of 6.0 joules. After rolling halfway down the incline, the sphere's potential energy is (1) 0.0 J (2) 6.0 J (3) 3.0 J (4) 12 J

36. A ball is thrown upward from Earth's surface. While the ball is rising, its gravitational potential energy is (1) decreasing (2) increasing (3) remaining the same

37. When a 5-kilogram mass is lifted from the ground to a height of 10 meters, the gravitational potential energy of the mass is increased by approximately (1) 0.5 J (2) 2 J (3) 50 J (4) 500 J

38. Three people of equal mass climb a mountain using paths A, B, and C shown in the following diagram.

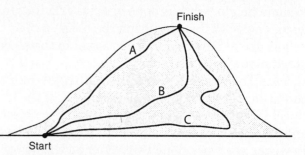

Along which path(s) does a person gain the greatest amount of gravitational potential energy from start to finish? (1) A only (2) B only (3) C only (4) The gain is the same along all paths.

Elastic Potential Energy

The energy stored in a spring, when work is done in compressing or stretching it, is called **elastic potential energy.** The **compression** or **elongation** of a spring is the change in spring length from its equilibrium position when a force is applied to it. Provided the elastic limit of the spring is not exceeded, the compression or elongation of a spring is directly proportional to the applied force. This relationship, called Hooke's law, is given by the following equation:

$$F_s = kx$$

In the equation, *k* is the **spring constant,** the constant of proportionality between the applied force F_s and the compression or elongation *x* of the spring. If F_s is in newtons and *x* is in meters, then *k* is in newtons per meter. The SI unit for the spring constant is the newton/meter, N/m.

A common laboratory activity is to vary the force applied to a spring and measure the resulting elongation or compression. Force is the independent variable and change in spring length is the dependent variable. However, force is often indicated on the vertical axis and change in spring length on the horizontal axis when the data from the experiment is graphed. If a graph of F_s versus *x* is plotted for the data collected for a given spring, the slope of the line of best fit is equal to the spring constant for that spring. For an ideal spring, the line is straight and passes through the origin. A stiff spring has a larger value of *k* than a weak spring.

SAMPLE PROBLEM

In an experiment, a student varied the force applied to a spring and measured the resulting elongation. The table shows the average elongation for three trials with each force.

Force (N)	Average Elongation (m)
0.00	0.000
1.00	0.040
2.00	0.075
3.00	0.120
4.00	0.165
5.00	0.200

Using the information in the data table and the grid provided, complete (1) through (4).
(1) Mark an appropriate scale on the axis labeled "Average elongation (m)".
(2) Plot the data points.
(3) Draw the line of best fit.
(4) Use your line to determine the spring constant k.

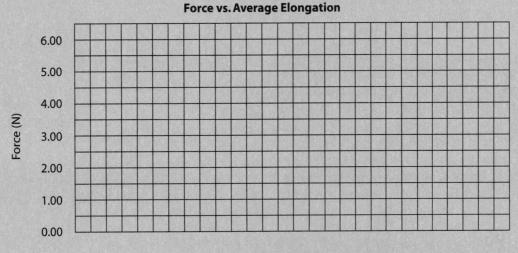

Force vs. Average Elongation

Solution: The spring constant k is the slope of the line.

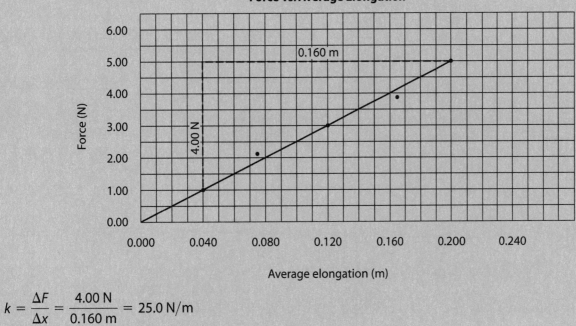

Force vs. Average Elongation

$$k = \frac{\Delta F}{\Delta x} = \frac{4.00 \text{ N}}{0.160 \text{ m}} = 25.0 \text{ N/m}$$

Potential Energy of a Spring

When no force is applied to a spring, there is no change in spring length from the equilibrium position. That is, when $F_s = 0$ N, $x = 0$ m. According to Hooke's law, as F_s increases, x increases. Because F_s increases uniformly from 0 to kx, the *average* applied force equals $\frac{1}{2}kx$. The work done in stretching the spring is equal to the product of the *average* force $\overline{F}_s$ and the elongation x.

$$W = \overline{F}_s x = \frac{1}{2} kx \cdot x = \frac{1}{2} kx^2$$

Because the work done on the spring is equal to the spring's elastic potential energy PE_s, the equation can be rewritten in this way:

$$PE_s = \frac{1}{2} kx^2$$

The spring constant k is in newtons per meter, the change in spring length from the equilibrium position x is in meters, and the potential energy stored in the spring PE_s is in newton · meters, or joules. As the following Sample Problem shows, the area under an F_s versus x curve yields a number equal to the number of joules of work done in stretching the spring, and thus, the potential energy stored in the spring.

SAMPLE PROBLEM

Determine the potential energy stored in the spring in the previous Sample Problem when a force of 2.50 newtons is applied to it.

Solution: Identify the known and unknown values.

Known	Unknown
$F_s = 2.50$ N	$PE_s = ?$ J
$k = 25.0$ N/m	

Find A_Δ, the area under the curve in the previous Sample Problem. At $F = 2.50$ N the area is a triangle with height h equal to 2.50 N and base b equal to 0.100 m. Write the formula for the area of a triangle.

$$A_\Delta = \frac{1}{2} bh$$

Substitute the known values and solve.

$$A_\Delta = PE_s = \frac{1}{2}(0.100 \text{ m})(2.50 \text{ N})$$

$$PE_s = 0.125 \text{ J}$$

An alternative solution is to use the relationship

$$F_s = kx$$

Solve the equation for x.

$$x = \frac{F_s}{k}$$

Substitute the known values and solve.

$$x = \frac{2.50 \text{ N}}{25.0 \text{ N/m}} = 0.100 \text{ m}$$

Write the formula that relates PE_s and x.

$$PE_s = \frac{1}{2} kx^2$$

Substitute the known values and solve.

$$PE_s = \frac{1}{2}(25.0 \text{ N})(0.100 \text{ m})^2$$

$$PE_s = 0.125 \text{ J}$$

Review Questions

39. A spring has a spring constant of 25 newtons per meter. Determine the magnitude of the minimum force required to stretch the spring 0.25 meter from its equilibrium position.

40. Which graph best represents the relationship between the force applied to a spring and the elongation of the spring? (Assume the spring's elastic limit has not been reached.)

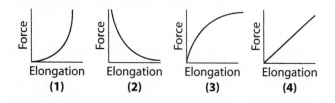

41. A 20.-newton weight is attached to a spring causing it to stretch, as shown in the following diagram.

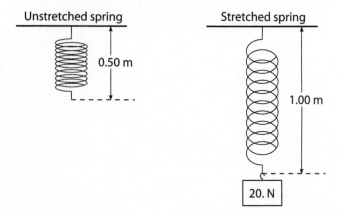

What is the spring constant of this spring?
(1) 0.050 N/m   (2) 0.25 N/m   (3) 20. N/m   (4) 40. N/m

42. The graph that follows shows the relationship between the elongation of a spring and the force applied to the spring causing it to stretch.

Elongation vs. Applied Force

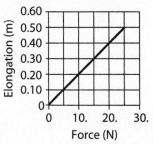

What is the spring constant for this spring?
(1) 0.020 N/m (2) 2.0 N/m (3) 25 N/m (4) 50. N/m

43. A mass hanger is attached to a spring, as shown in the following diagrams.

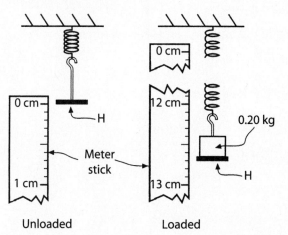

Unloaded   Loaded

What is the magnitude of the displacement of the mass hanger H after a 0.20-kilogram mass is loaded on it? (Assume the hanger is at rest in both positions.)

44. Graphs A and B represent the results of applying an increasing force to stretch a spring. The spring did not exceed its elastic limit.

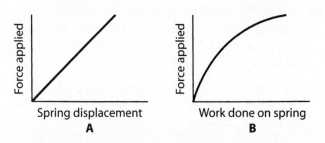

The spring constant can be represented by the
(1) slope of graph A (2) slope of graph B (3) reciprocal of the slope of graph A (4) reciprocal of the slope of graph B

45. Force *F* is applied to a spring causing it to stretch a distance *x*. If force 2*F* is applied to the spring and the elasticity of the spring is not exceeded, the spring will stretch a distance (1) *x* (2) 2*x* (3) $\frac{x}{2}$ (4) $\frac{x}{4}$

46. A spring having a spring constant *k* is cut in half. Each of the newly formed springs has a spring constant that is equal to (1) *k* (2) 2*k* (3) $\frac{k}{2}$ (4) 4*k*

47. A force is applied to a spring causing it to stretch. If the applied force is halved, the potential energy stored in the spring will be (1) halved (2) doubled (3) quartered (4) quadrupled

48. If the distance a spring is stretched is doubled and the elastic limit is not exceeded, the potential energy stored in the spring is (1) halved (2) doubled (3) quartered (4) quadrupled

49. When a spring is stretched 0.200 meter from its equilibrium position, it possesses a potential energy of 10.0 joules. What is the spring constant for this spring? (1) 100. N/m (2) 125 N/m (3) 250. N/m (4) 500. N/m

50. A spring has a spring constant of 120 newtons per meter. Determine the potential energy stored in the spring as it is stretched 0.20 meter.

51. A force of 0.2 newton is needed to compress a spring a distance of 0.02 meter. The potential energy stored in this compressed spring is (1) 8×10^{-5} J (2) 2×10^{-3} J (3) 2×10^{-5} J (4) 4×10^{-5} J

52. A spring of negligible mass with a spring constant of 2.0×10^2 newtons per meter is stretched 0.20 meter. How much potential energy is stored in the spring? (1) 8 J (2) 8.0 J (3) 4 J (4) 4.0 J

53. In the diagram below, a child compresses the spring in a pop-up toy 0.020 meter.

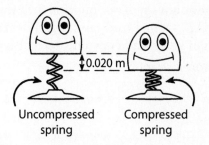

Uncompressed spring   Compressed spring

If the spring has a spring constant of 340 newtons per meter, how much energy is being stored in the spring? (1) 0.068 J (2) 0.14 J (3) 3.4 J (4) 6.8 J

Base your answers to questions 54 through 56 on the following graph, which represents the relationship between the force applied to a spring and its elongation.

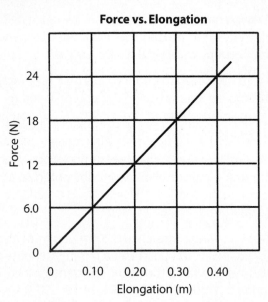

Force vs. Elongation

54. How much work must be done to stretch the spring 0.40 meter? (1) 4.8 J (2) 6.0 J (3) 9.8 J (4) 24 J

55. Determine the spring constant k for the spring.

56. On the grid, sketch a line that represents the relationship between applied force and elongation for a stiffer spring.

Kinetic Energy

When a moving object strikes another object and displaces it, the moving object exerts a force on the second object and does work on it. The moving object possesses energy due to its motion. The energy an object possesses due to its motion is called **kinetic energy.** The equation for kinetic energy is $KE = \frac{1}{2}mv^2$ and can be derived from the definition of work and Newton's second law.

$W = Fd$ and $F = ma$

$W = mad$ where $a = \dfrac{v}{t}$ from rest, $d = \bar{v}t$, and

$$\bar{v} = \frac{v}{2} \text{ from rest.}$$

$W = m \cdot \dfrac{v}{t} \cdot \bar{v}t = m \cdot \dfrac{v}{t} \cdot \dfrac{v}{2} \cdot t$

$W = \dfrac{1}{2}mv^2$

The net work done in accelerating an object from rest to some speed is equal to the kinetic energy of the object. The following equation describes the relationship:

$$KE = \frac{1}{2}mv^2$$

Mass m is in kilograms, velocity or speed v is in meters per second, and kinetic energy KE is in kilogram·meter²/second² or joules.

SAMPLE PROBLEM

How much kinetic energy is possessed by a 2.7-kilogram cart traveling at 1.5 meter per second?

Solution: Identify the known and unknown values.

Known	Unknown
m = 2.7 kg	KE = ? J
v = 1.5 m/s	

Write the equation for kinetic energy.

$KE = \dfrac{1}{2}mv^2$

Substitute the known values and solve.

$KE = \dfrac{1}{2}(2.7 \text{ kg})(1.5 \text{ m/s})^2 = 3.0 \text{ J}$

Note: If the weight of the cart had been given, it would have been necessary to use the formula

$g = \dfrac{F_g}{m}$ to determine the cart's mass.

Review Questions

57. If the speed of a car is doubled, its kinetic energy is (1) halved (2) doubled (3) quartered (4) quadrupled

58. A 1.0×10^3-kilogram car is moving at a constant speed of 4.0 meters per second. What is the kinetic energy of the car? (1) 1.6×10^3 J (2) 2.0×10^4 J (3) 8.0×10^3 J (4) 4.0×10^3 J

59. A 3.0-kilogram cart possesses 96 joules of kinetic energy. Determine the speed of the car.

60. A cart of mass m traveling at speed v has kinetic energy KE. If the mass of the cart is doubled and the speed is halved, the kinetic energy of the cart will be (1) half as great (2) twice as great (3) one-fourth as great (4) four times as great

61. Which cart has the greatest kinetic energy?

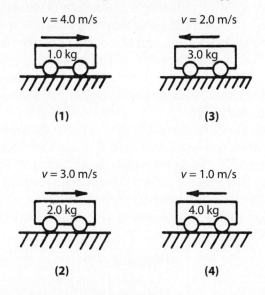

62. A 2.0-kilogram cart is initially at rest on a level floor. Determine the kinetic energy of the cart after a constant horizontal 8.0-newton force is applied to the cart over a distance of 1.5 meters.

63. A person does 100 joules of work in pulling back the string of a bow. What is the initial speed of a 0.5-kilogram arrow when it is fired from the bow? (1) 20 m/s (2) 50 m/s (3) 200 m/s (4) 400 m/s

64. An 8.0-kilogram object and a 4.0-kilogram object are released simultaneously from a height of 50. meters above the ground. After falling freely for 2.0 seconds, the objects have different (1) accelerations (2) speeds (3) kinetic energies (4) displacements

65. The work done in raising an object must result in an increase in the object's (1) internal energy (2) kinetic energy (3) gravitational potential energy (4) elastic potential energy

66. Two cars having different weights are traveling on a level surface at different constant velocities. Within the same time interval, greater force is always required to stop the car that has the greater (1) weight (2) kinetic energy (3) velocity (4) momentum

Work-Energy Relationship

If there is no friction, all the work done in lifting an object to a new height is equal to the object's increase in gravitational potential energy. The change in potential energy depends only on the change in height, not on the path taken. For example, the work done in lifting a 10.0-kilogram box from the floor to a 0.92-meter high tabletop is equal to the box's change in gravitational potential energy.

$$W = \Delta PE = mg\Delta h = (10.0 \text{ kg})(9.81 \text{ m/s}^2)(0.92 \text{ m})$$
$$W = 90. \text{ J}$$

Figure 3.1 shows that the work done in moving the box from the floor to the tabletop is the same regardless of the path taken. When work done against a force is independent of the path taken, the force is said to be a <u>conservative force</u>. Gravitation is an example of a conservative force. The elastic force of a spring is also a conservative force. Potential energy has meaning only in relation to work done against conservative forces.

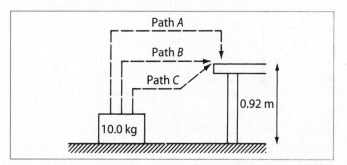

Figure 3-1. A conservative force: Because gravitation is a conservative force, the same amount of work is done when raising the box from the floor to the tabletop regardless of which path is followed.

Air resistance and friction are examples of <u>nonconservative forces</u>. The work done against a nonconservative force is dependent upon the path taken. In Figure 3-2, the same box is moved from the floor to the tabletop by sliding it along an inclined plane A. Once again, 90. joules of work is done to change the gravitational potential energy of the box, but because additional work must be done against friction, the total work done is greater than 90. joules.

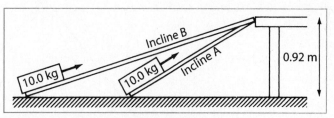

Figure 3-2. A nonconservative force: Because friction is a nonconservative force, moving the box from the floor to the tabletop requires more work on incline B than on incline A. In this case, the path makes a difference in the amount of work required. (Read the explanation in the text.)

If inclined plane B is used instead of inclined plane A, the work done against friction, $W_f = F_f d$, is greater, even though the coefficient of friction is the same for both planes. The force of friction F_f is greater when a plane is inclined at a smaller angle because the normal force F_N for the same object on the incline is larger and $F_f = \mu F_N$. In addition, the frictional force acts over a greater distance on incline B. Because friction is a nonconservative force, the work required to raise the box from the floor to the top of the table on incline B is greater than the work required to raise it on incline A.

Conservation of Energy

A closed system is one in which there are no external forces doing work on the system, no external work being done by the system, and no transfer of energy into or out of the system. In a closed system, the sum of the potential energy (gravitational and/or elastic), kinetic energy, and internal energy remains constant. Although the energy within a closed system may be transformed from one type to another, the total energy of the system always remains the same. These ideas are expressed in the **law of conservation of energy,** which states that energy cannot be created or destroyed. In other words, the sum of the *changes* in energy (potential, kinetic, and internal) within a closed system is zero.

Mechanical Systems

The sum of the kinetic and potential energies in a system is called the total **mechanical energy.** An **ideal mechanical system** is a closed system in which no friction or other nonconservative force acts. In an ideal mechanical system, the sum of the kinetic and potential energies is constant, or the sum of the *changes* in kinetic and potential energy is zero.

The relationship between potential and kinetic energy for an ideal simple pendulum is shown in Figure 3-3. A **simple pendulum** consists of a mass (bob) attached to one end of a string or wire that is attached at the other end to a pivot point.

An object falling freely from rest in a vacuum is another example of an ideal mechanical system. If a stationary object having mass m is located a vertical distance h above Earth's surface, the object has initial potential energy, $PE_i = mgh$ and kinetic energy, $KE_i = 0$. As the object falls, its potential energy decreases, but because its speed increases, the object's kinetic energy increases. These energy changes can be expressed by the law of conservation of energy:

$$\Delta PE + \Delta KE = 0$$
$$\text{or}$$
$$\Delta KE = -\Delta PE$$

As the object falls from rest, its change in potential energy is given by $\Delta PE = -mgh$, and its change in kinetic energy is $\Delta KE = \frac{1}{2}mv^2$. These expressions can be substituted into the previous equations:

$$\frac{1}{2}mv^2 - mgh = 0 \quad \text{or}$$

$$\frac{1}{2}mv^2 = mgh$$

The common factor, m, can be eliminated:

$$\frac{1}{2}v^2 = gh, \text{ so } v^2 = 2gh \text{ and } v = \sqrt{2gh}$$

The acceleration due to gravity, g, can be considered constant near Earth's surface, so the last equation can be used to determine the speed of an object falling from rest from a known height. Note that the speed of the object is independent of its mass.

Figure 3-3. The relationship between potential and kinetic energy for an ideal simple pendulum

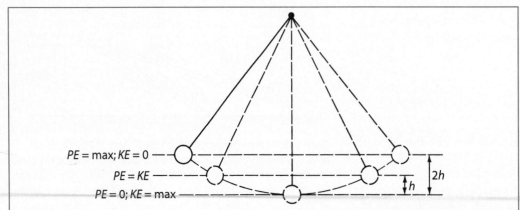

$PE = \max; KE = 0$
$PE = KE$
$PE = 0; KE = \max$
$2h$
h

Nonideal Mechanical Systems

When a system is acted upon by a nonconservative force, such as friction, it is called a **nonideal mechanical system.** In reality, friction opposes the motion of two objects in contact with each other and moving relative to each other. Frictional force converts some or all of the kinetic energy of a moving object into internal energy, that is, potential or kinetic energy of the individual particles that comprise the object. The "lost" kinetic energy usually appears as an increase in temperature of the objects in contact. For example, a simple pendulum set in motion in air does not swing back to its original release point. The pendulum experiences both friction at the pivot point and air resistance. A piece of paper dropped to the ground from some height has more initial gravitational potential energy than it has kinetic energy at the instant it reaches the ground. A lead sphere dropped from some height onto a steel surface does not bounce; all of its initial gravitational potential energy is converted into internal energy when it hits the steel.

The **total energy** of a nonideal system is given by this equation:

$$E_T = PE + KE + Q$$

E_T represents the total energy, PE is potential energy, KE is kinetic energy, and Q is internal energy. All quantities are expressed in joules.

SAMPLE PROBLEM

A 1.0-kilogram cart A and a 2.0-kilogram cart B are at rest on a frictionless table, as shown in the diagram. A cord and a spring of negligible mass join the two carts. The spring is compressed 0.060 meter between the two carts until the spring's potential energy is 12 joules. When the cord is cut, the spring will force the carts apart.

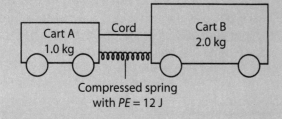

Cart A 1.0 kg — Cord — Cart B 2.0 kg

Compressed spring with $PE = 12$ J

(1) Determine the total amount of work done in compressing the spring.
(2) Determine the spring constant for the spring.

---

(3) Determine the magnitude of the average force required to compress the spring 0.060 meter.
(4) Compare the following quantities while the spring is pushing the carts apart:
 (a) the forces acting on the two carts
 (b) the change in momentum of the two carts
 (c) the total initial and final momentum of the two carts
 (d) the acceleration of the two carts
(5) Determine the final velocity of cart A.
(6) Determine the ratio of the maximum kinetic energy of cart A to the maximum kinetic energy of cart B.

Solution: Identify the known and unknown values.

Known	Unknown
$m_A = 1.0$ kg	$W = ?$ J
$m_B = 2.0$ kg	$k = ?$ N/m
$x = 0.060$ m	$F_s = ?$ N
$PE_s = 12$ J	$v_{f_A} = ?$ m/s

(1) The work done in compressing the spring is equal to the potential energy stored in the spring.

$W = PE_s = 12$ J

(2) Write the equation for the potential energy of a spring.

$$PE_s = \frac{1}{2}kx^2$$

Solve the equation for k.

$$k = \frac{2PE_s}{x^2}$$

Substitute the known values and solve.

$$k = \frac{2(12 \text{ J})}{(0.060 \text{ m})^2}$$

$k = 6.7 \times 10^3$ N/m

(3) Write the equation for the average force needed to compress the spring.

$F_s = kx$

Substitute the known values and solve.

$F_s = (6.7 \times 10^3 \text{ N/m})(0.060 \text{ m})$
$F_s = 4.0 \times 10^2$ N

(4a) The forces are equal in magnitude and opposite in direction.

(4b) Momentum must be conserved. Thus, the change in momentum is equal in magnitude and opposite in direction for the two carts at all times.

(4c) The total momentum is zero at all times, because the carts were initially at rest.

(4d) The forces on the two carts are equal in magnitude and the mass of A is one half the mass of B. Thus, the acceleration of cart A is twice that of cart B and opposite in direction.

(5) Write an equation for the relationship between the initial and final momentum of the system. Because momentum must be conserved, the initial momentum of the system, which is zero, must equal the final momentum.

$$p_i = p_f = 0$$

Write this equality in terms of mass and velocity.

$$m_A v_A + m_B v_B = 0$$

Solve the equation for v_B.

$$m_B v_B = -m_A v_A$$

$$v_B = -\frac{m_A v_A}{m_B}$$

Substitute known values and solve.

$$v_B = -\frac{(1.0 \text{ kg}) v_A}{2.0 \text{ kg}}$$

$$v_B = -\frac{1}{2} v_A$$

Recognizing that energy is conserved, write an equation that equates the total initial energy of the system and the total final energy of the system.

$$PE_i + KE_i + PE_{s_i} = PE_f + KE_f + PE_{s_f}$$

$$PE_i = PE_f, PE_{s_F} = 0, \text{ and } KE_i = 0$$

Thus, because energy is conserved, the final kinetic energy of the two carts equals the initial potential energy of the spring.

$$PE_{s_i} = KE_f$$

Write an equation in terms of mass and velocity that states this relationship.

$$PE_{s_i} = \frac{1}{2} m_A (v_A)^2 + \frac{1}{2} m_B (v_B)^2$$

Substitute known values and solve for v_A.

$$12 \text{ J} = \frac{1}{2}(1.0 \text{ kg})(v_A)^2 + \frac{1}{2}(2.0 \text{ kg})\left(-\frac{v_A}{2}\right)^2$$

$$12 \text{ J} = (0.50 \text{ kg})(v_A)^2 + (1.0 \text{ kg})\left(\frac{v_A^2}{4}\right)$$

$$12 \text{ J} = (0.75 \text{ kg})v_A^2$$

$$v_A^2 = 16 \text{ J/kg} = 16\frac{\text{kg} \cdot \text{m}^2/\text{s}^2}{\text{kg}}$$

$$v_A = 4.0 \text{ m/s}$$

(6) It has already been determined that the speed of cart B is one-half that of cart A, thus

$$\frac{KE_A}{KE_B} = \frac{\frac{1}{2} m_A v_A^2}{\frac{1}{2} m_B v_B^2} = \frac{\frac{1}{2}(1.0 \text{ kg})(4.0 \text{ m/s})^2}{\frac{1}{2}(2.0 \text{ kg})(2.0 \text{ m/s})^2} = \frac{2}{1}$$

Review Questions

67. As the speed of an object falling toward Earth increases, the gravitational potential energy of the object with respect to Earth (1) decreases (2) increases (3) remains the same

68. At what point in its fall does the kinetic energy of a freely falling object equal its potential energy? (1) at the start of the fall (2) halfway between the start and the end (3) at the end of the fall (4) at all points during the fall

69. A 2.0-kilogram mass falls freely for 10. meters near the surface of Earth. The total kinetic energy gained by the object during its free fall is approximately (1) 400 J (2) 200 J (3) 100 J (4) 50 J

70. A 20.0-kilogram object falls freely from rest and strikes the ground with 1,962 joules of kinetic energy. How far above the ground was the object when it was released?

71. A 1.0-kilogram mass gains kinetic energy as it falls freely from rest a vertical distance d. How far would a 2.0-kilogram mass have to fall freely from rest to gain the same amount of kinetic energy? (1) d (2) $2d$ (3) $\frac{d}{2}$ (4) $\frac{d}{4}$

72. A basketball player, who weighs 600 newtons, jumps 0.5 meter vertically off the floor. Determine her kinetic energy just before hitting the floor.

Base your answers to questions 73 through 75 on the following information and diagram.

A 10-kilogram block starts from rest at point A and slides along a frictionless track. (Neglect air resistance.)

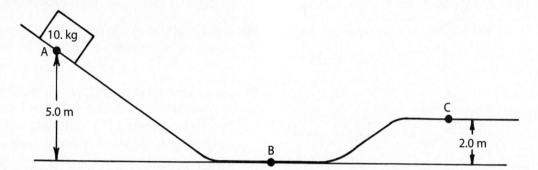

73. As the block moves from point A to point B, the total amount of gravitational potential energy that changes to kinetic energy is approximately
   (1) 5 J (2) 20 J (3) 50 J (4) 500 J

74. What is the approximate speed of the block at point B? (1) 1 m/s (2) 10 m/s (3) 50 m/s (4) 100 m/s

75. What is the approximate potential energy of the block at point C? (1) 20 J (2) 200 J (3) 300 J (4) 500 J

76. As an object falls freely in a vacuum, the total energy of the object (1) decreases (2) increases (3) remains the same

77. In the diagram that follows, an ideal pendulum released from point A swings freely through point B.

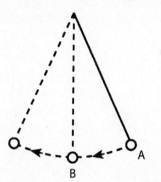

Compared to the pendulum's kinetic energy at A, its potential energy at B is (1) half as great (2) twice as great (3) the same (4) four times as great

Base your answers to questions 78 through 80 on the following information and diagram.

A 1.00-kilogram block is held at rest on a frictionless plane inclined at 30.° to the horizontal.

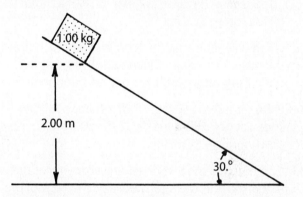

78. The block is released and slides down the length of the incline. Determine the block's kinetic energy at the bottom of the incline.

79. If the angle between the plane and the horizontal is increased, the magnitude of the force required to hold the block at rest on the incline will (1) decrease (2) increase (3) remain the same

80. As the block slides down the incline, the sum of its gravitational potential energy and kinetic energy (1) decreases (2) increases (3) remains the same

Base your answers to questions 81 through 85 on the following information and diagram.

A 2.0-kilogram mass is placed on a frictionless track at point A and released from rest. (Assume that the gravitational potential energy of the system is zero at point E.)

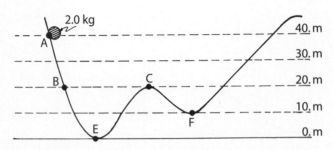

81. Determine the gravitational potential energy of the system at point A.

82. Compared to the kinetic energy of the mass at point B, the kinetic energy of the mass at point E is (1) the same (2) twice as great (3) half as great (4) four times as great

83. On the diagram, mark an X on the track to indicate the maximum height the mass will reach above point E after the object has passed through point E.

84. If the mass was released from rest at point B, its speed at point C would be (1) 0 m/s (2) 0.50 m/s (3) 10. m/s (4) 14 m/s

85. Compared to the total mechanical energy of the system at point A, the total mechanical energy of the system at point F is (1) less (2) more (3) the same

Base your answers to questions 86 through 92 on the following information and diagram.

A 10.0-kilogram box starts from rest at point A and is accelerated uniformly to point B in 4.0 seconds by the application of a constant horizontal force F. At point B, the speed of the box is 10.0 meters per second as it begins to move up a plane inclined at 30.° to the horizontal. (Neglect friction.)

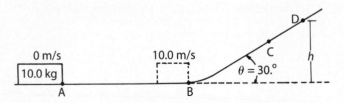

86. Determine the kinetic energy of the box at point B.

87. Determine the magnitude of force F.

88. Determine the distance the box travels in moving from point A to point B.

89. Compared to the impulse required to stop the box at point B, the impulse required to stop the box at point C is (1) less (2) greater (3) the same

90. As the mass moves up the incline, its potential energy (1) decreases (2) increases (3) remains the same

91. The box comes to rest at a vertical height of h (point D) when $\angle\theta = 30.°$. If $\angle\theta$ was increased to 40.°, the box would come to rest at a vertical height (1) less than h (2) greater than h (3) equal to h

92. On the axes below, sketch a line to represent the relationship between the kinetic energy of the box and its speed as it travels from point A to point B.

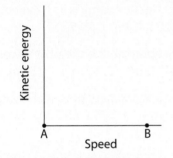

Base your answers to questions 93 through 96 on the following information and diagram.

A 1.00-kilogram sphere M, suspended by a string from point P, is lifted to a height h. The sphere is released and passes through the lowest point in its swing at a speed of 10.0 meters per second. (Neglect friction.)

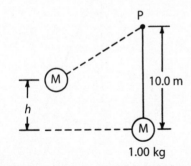

93. Determine the height from which the sphere was released.

94. Determine the magnitude of the centripetal force on the sphere as it passes through the lowest point in its swing.

95. The magnitude of the centripetal force on the sphere could be halved as it passes through the lowest point in its swing by doubling the (1) weight of the sphere only (2) length of the string only (3) height h and the weight of the sphere (4) the length of the string and height h

96. Compared to the sphere's speed through the lowest point of its swing when released from h, the sphere's speed through the lowest point when released from $2h$ would be (1) lower (2) greater (3) the same

97. In the following diagram, a toy car having a mass of 4.00×10^{-2} kilogram starts from rest at point A and travels 3.60 meters along a uniform track until coming to rest at point B.

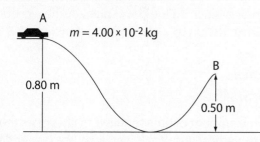

A $m = 4.00 \times 10^{-2}$ kg

0.80 m

B

0.50 m

Determine the magnitude of the frictional force acting on the car. (Assume the frictional force is constant.)

98. A car has a mass of 1.00×10^3 kilograms. Determine the work done in moving the car at constant speed a distance of 250 meters along a horizontal asphalt-paved road.

Base your answers to questions 99 and 100 on the following information and diagram.

A 20.0-newton force is needed to pull a 5.00-kilogram object up a hill at a constant speed of 2.0 meters per second.

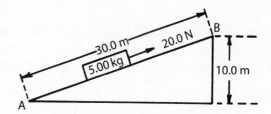

30.0 m 20.0 N B

5.00 kg

10.0 m

A

99. Determine the work done against gravity in moving the object from point A to point B.

100. Determine the work done against friction in moving the object from point A to point B.

Questions for Regents Practice

Part A

1. Which variable expression is correctly paired with its corresponding unit?

(1) $\dfrac{\text{mass} \cdot \text{distance}}{\text{time}}$ and watt

(2) $\dfrac{\text{mass} \cdot \text{distance}^2}{\text{time}}$ and watt

(3) $\dfrac{\text{mass} \cdot \text{distance}^2}{\text{time}^2}$ and joule

(4) $\dfrac{\text{mass} \cdot \text{distance}}{\text{time}^3}$ and joule

2. What is an essential characteristic of an object in equilibrium?

(1) zero velocity (3) zero potential energy

(2) zero acceleration (4) zero kinetic energy

3. A net force of 5.0 newtons moves a 2.0-kilogram object a distance of 3.0 meters in 3.0 seconds. How much work is done on the object?

(1) 1.0 J

(2) 10. J

(3) 15 J

(4) 30. J

4. A force is applied to a block causing it to accelerate along a horizontal, frictionless surface. The energy gained by the block is equal to the

(1) work done on the block

(2) power applied to the block

(3) impulse applied to the block

(4) momentum given to the block

5. A 2.2-kilogram mass is pulled by a 30.-newton horizontal force through a distance of 5.0 meters as shown in the following diagram.

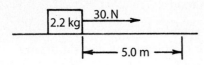

What is the total amount of work done on the mass?

(1) 11 J   (3) 150 J

(2) 66 J   (4) 330 J

6. In the following diagram, a 1.0-kilogram mass falls a vertical distance of 0.50 meter, causing a 2.0-kilogram mass to slide the same distance along a tabletop.

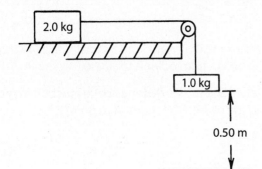

How much work is done by the falling mass?

(1) 1.5 J   (3) 9.8 J

(2) 4.9 J   (4) 15 J

7. A horizontal force of 40. newtons is used to push a block along a level table at a constant speed of 2.0 meters per second. How much work is done on the block in 6.0 seconds?

(1) 80. J

(2) 120 J

(3) 240 J

(4) 480 J

8. A force of 100. newtons is used to push a trunk to the top of an incline 3.0 meters long. Then a force of 50. newtons is used to push the trunk for 10. meters along a horizontal platform. What is the total work done on the trunk?

(1) 8.0×10^2 J

(2) 5.0×10^2 J

(3) 3.0×10^2 J

(4) 9.0×10^2 J

9. The following diagram shows two identical wooden planks, A and B, at different incline angles. The planks are used to slide concrete blocks from a truck.

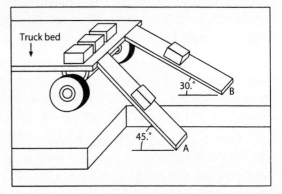

Compared to the amount of work done against friction by a block sliding down plank A, the work done against friction by a block sliding down plank B is

(1) less

(2) more

(3) the same

10. As the amount of time required to lift a mass the same vertical distance is increased, the power developed

(1) decreases

(2) increases

(3) remains the same

11. What is the minimum power required for a conveyor to raise an 8.0-newton box 4.0 meters vertically in 8.0 seconds?

(1) 260 W

(2) 64 W

(3) 32 W

(4) 4.0 W

12. A weightlifter lifts a 200-kilogram mass a vertical distance of 0.5 meter in 0.1 second. What is the lifter's power output?

(1) 1×10^{-4} W

(2) 4×10^{-4} W

(3) 1×10^4 W

(4) 4×10^4 W

13. A 4.0×10^3-watt motor applies an 8.0×10^2-newton force to move a boat at constant speed. How far does the boat move in 16 seconds?

(1) 3.2 m

(2) 5.0 m

(3) 32 m

(4) 80. m

14. As the speed of a bicycle moving along a level horizontal surface changes from 2 meters per second to 4 meters per second, the magnitude of the bicycle's gravitational potential energy

(1) decreases

(2) increases

(3) remains the same

15. An object is lifted at constant speed a distance *h* above the surface of Earth in time *t*. The total potential energy gained by the object is equal to the

(1) average force applied to the object

(2) total weight of the object

(3) total work done on the object

(4) total momentum gained by the object

16. A box weighing 1.0×10^2 newtons is dragged to the top of an incline, as shown in the following diagram.

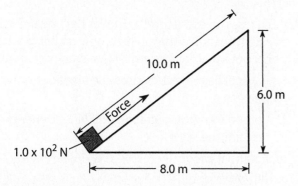

The gravitational potential energy of the box at the top of the incline is approximately

(1) 1.0×10^2 J

(2) 6.0×10^2 J

(3) 8.0×10^2 J

(4) 1.0×10^3 J

17. What is the spring constant of a spring of negligible mass that gains 6.0 joules of potential energy as a result of being compressed 0.40 meter?

(1) 2.4 N/m   (3) 38 N/m

(2) 15 N/m   (4) 75 N/m

18. Spring A has a spring constant of 140 newtons per meter and spring B has a spring constant of 280 newtons per meter. Both springs are stretched the same distance. Compared to the potential energy stored in spring A, the potential energy stored in spring B is

(1) the same

(2) twice as great

(3) half as great

(4) four times as great

Base your answers to questions 19 through 22 on the following information and diagram.

A block sliding on a frictionless, horizontal surface collides with a spring, compressing it a maximum distance *x*.

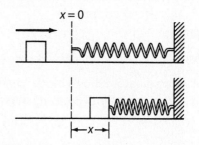

19. During the interval of collision, the potential energy of the spring

(1) decreases

(2) increases

(3) remains the same

20. As the block compresses the spring, the spring constant for the spring

(1) decreases

(2) increases

(3) remains the same

21. As the block compresses the spring, the total mechanical energy of the system

(1) decreases

(2) increases

(3) remains the same

22. If the initial speed of the block had been greater, the maximum compression of the spring would have been

(1) smaller

(2) greater

(3) the same

23. The unstretched spring in the following diagram has a length of 0.40 meter and a spring constant k. A weight is hung from the spring causing it to stretch to a length of 0.60 meter.

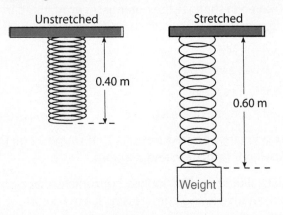

How many joules of elastic potential energy are stored in this stretched spring?

(1) $0.020 \times k$ (3) $0.18 \times k$

(2) $0.080 \times k$ (4) $2.0 \times k$

24. The following diagram shows block A having mass $2m$ and speed v, and block B having mass m and speed $2v$.

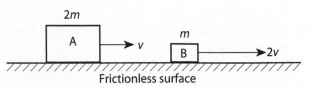

Compared to the kinetic energy of block A, the kinetic energy of block B is

(1) the same

(2) twice as great

(3) one-fourth as great

(4) four times as great

25. An object with a speed of 20. meters per second has a kinetic energy of 400. joules. The mass of the object is

(1) 1.0 kg

(2) 2.0 kg

(3) 0.50 kg

(4) 40. kg

26. A total of 10.0 joules of work is done in accelerating a 20.-newton object from rest across a horizontal frictionless table. What is the total kinetic energy gained by the object?

(1) 0.0 J

(2) 2.0 J

(3) 10. J

(4) 200 J

27. A baseball bat strikes a ball with an average force of 2.0×10^4 newtons. If the bat stays in contact with the ball for a distance of 5.0×10^{-3} meter, what kinetic energy will the ball acquire from the bat?

(1) 1.0×10^2 J

(2) 2.0×10^2 J

(3) 2.5×10^1 J

(4) 4.0×10^2 J

28. An object 8 meters above the ground has Z joules of potential energy. If the object falls freely, how many joules of kinetic energy will it have gained when it is 4 meters above the ground?

(1) Z

(2) $2Z$

(3) $\frac{Z}{2}$

(4) 0

29. A girl rides an escalator that moves her upward at constant speed. As the girl rises, how do her gravitational potential energy and kinetic energy change?

(1) Potential energy decreases and kinetic energy decreases.

(2) Potential energy decreases and kinetic energy remains the same.

(3) Potential energy increases and kinetic energy decreases.

(4) Potential energy increases and kinetic energy remains the same.

30. A 0.10-kilogram ball dropped vertically from a height of 1.00 meter above the floor bounces back to a height of 0.80 meter. The mechanical energy "lost" by the ball as it bounces is approximately

(1) 0.020 J

(2) 0.20 J

(3) 0.78 J

(4) 0.98 J

31. A stone is dropped in air from a height of 50 meters above the ground. As the stone falls, what happens to the stone's kinetic energy and internal energy?

(1) Kinetic energy decreases and internal energy decreases.

(2) Kinetic energy decreases and internal energy increases.

(3) Kinetic energy increases and internal energy decreases.

(4) Kinetic energy increases and internal energy increases.

32. An aluminum pie pan is attached to a string and suspended from a hook, as shown in the following diagram. The pan is released from rest at point A and swings through the air to point B.

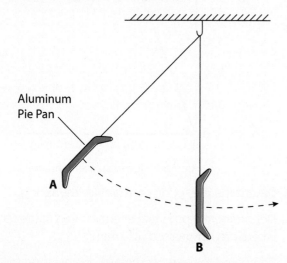

What is the relationship of kinetic energy at point B, KE_B, to potential energy at point A, PE_A?

(1) KE_B is equal to PE_A minus work done against friction.

(2) KE_B is equal to the PE_A plus work done against friction.

(3) KE_B is equal to PE_A.

(4) KE_B is equal to $2PE_A$.

33. The bottom of a heavy block is covered with sandpaper. The block is repeatedly slid 1.0 meter at constant speed across a uniform, horizontal wooden plank by the application of a constant horizontal force. As the coefficient of friction between the sandpaper and the plank decreases, the amount of work done in sliding the block 1.0 meter along the plank at constant speed

(1) decreases

(2) increases

(3) remains the same

34. In the following diagram, a box is pulled at constant speed across the floor by the application of a constant 120-newton force acting at an angle of 37° to the horizontal.

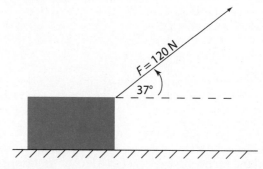

How much work is done in pulling the box a distance of 10. meters?

(1) 7.2×10^2 J

(2) 9.6×10^2 J

(3) 1.2×10^3 J

(4) 1.5×10^3 J

Part B

35. A 20.-newton block is at rest at the bottom of a frictionless incline, as shown in the following diagram.

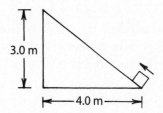

Determine how much work must be done against gravity to move the block to the top of the incline. [2]

36. A student applies a constant horizontal force having a magnitude of 20. newtons to move a crate at a constant speed of 4.0 meters per second across a rough floor. Determine how much work is done by the student on the 80.-kilogram crate in 6.0 seconds. [2]

37. A student running up a flight of stairs increases her speed at a constant rate. Which graph best represents the relationship between work and time for the student's run up the stairs?

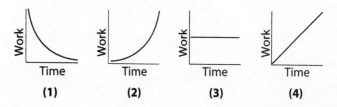

38. On the following axes, sketch a line to represent the relationship between gravitational potential energy *PE* and height *h* above the ground for an object near the surface of Earth. [1]

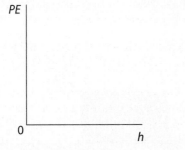

39. On the following axes, sketch a line to represent the relationship between the elongation of an ideal spring and the applied force. [1]

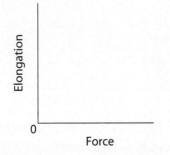

40. On the following axes, sketch a line to represent the relationship between the potential energy stored in a spring PE_s and the change in the length of the spring from its equilibrium position *x*. [1]

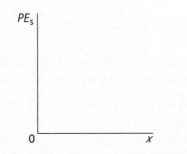

41. On the following axes, sketch a line to represent the relationship between the kinetic energy *KE* of a moving object and its speed *v*. [1]

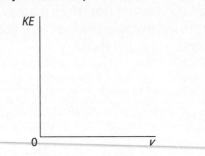

Base your answers to questions 42 through 44 on the following graph, which shows the relationship between the force applied to an ideal spring and the compression of the spring.

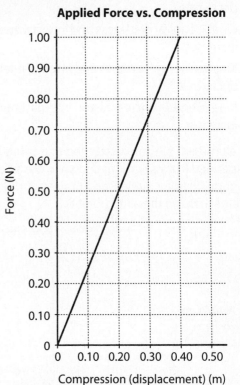

Applied Force vs. Compression

42. Determine the spring constant for the spring. [2]

43. Determine the potential energy stored in the spring when it is compressed 0.20 meter. [2]

44. Compared to the work done in compressing the spring 0.20 meter, the potential energy stored in the spring when compressed 0.20 meter is

(1) less   (3) the same

(2) greater

45. A cart of mass *M* on a frictionless track starts from rest at the top of a hill having height h_1, as shown in the following diagram.

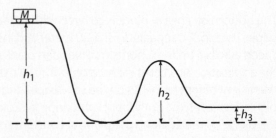

What is the kinetic energy of the cart when it reaches the top of the next hill h_2?

(1) Mgh_1 (3) $Mg(h_2 - h_3)$

(2) $Mg(h_1 - h_2)$ (4) 0

Base your answers to questions 46 through 50 on the following information and graph.

A 2.0-kilogram object moves along a horizontal frictionless surface. The graph shows the relationship between the object's velocity and elapsed time.

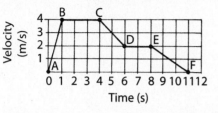

46. Determine the distance the object moves during interval EF. [2]

47. What is the net force on the object during the interval DE? [1]

48. Determine the momentum of the object during interval BC. [2]

49. The kinetic energy of the object is greatest during interval

(1) AB   (3) CD

(2) BC   (4) DE

50. Work is *not* being done on the object during interval

(1) AB   (3) CD

(2) EF   (4) DE

Base your answers to questions 51 through 55 on the following information and diagram.

A 3.0-kilogram mass is being moved at constant speed across a horizontal surface by a constant horizontal force of 6.0 newtons.

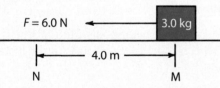

51. What is the change in kinetic energy of the mass as it is moved from point M to point N? [1]

52. Determine the amount of work done in 2.0 seconds if energy is supplied at a rate of 10.0 watts. [2]

53. What is the magnitude of the force of friction acting on the mass? [1]

54. Determine the acceleration that would be produced by the 6.0-newton force if the surface the mass slides on was frictionless. [2]

55. Determine the gravitational potential energy of the 3.0-kilogram mass relative to the horizontal surface if the mass was raised to a height of 4.0 meters. [2]

Base your answers to questions 56 through 60 on the following information and diagram.

A simple pendulum with a 2.00-kilogram bob and a length of 10.0 meters is released from rest at position 1 and swings without friction through position 4. At position 3, its lowest point, the speed of the bob is 6.00 meters per second.

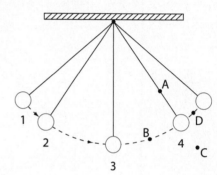

56. At which point does the bob have its maximum kinetic energy? [1]

57. Determine the potential energy of the bob at position 1 in relation to position 3. [2]

58. At position 4, toward which point, A, B, C, or D, is the centripetal force directed? [1]

59. Determine the magnitude of the centripetal acceleration of the bob at position 3. [2]

60. Compared to the sum of the kinetic and potential energies of the bob at position 1, the sum of the kinetic and potential energies of the bob at position 2 is

(1) smaller

(2) greater

(3) the same

Base your answers to questions 61 through 63 on the following information and diagram, which is drawn to a scale of 1.0 centimeter = 3.0 meters.

A 650-kilogram roller coaster car starts from rest at the top of the first hill of its track and glides freely. (Neglect friction.)

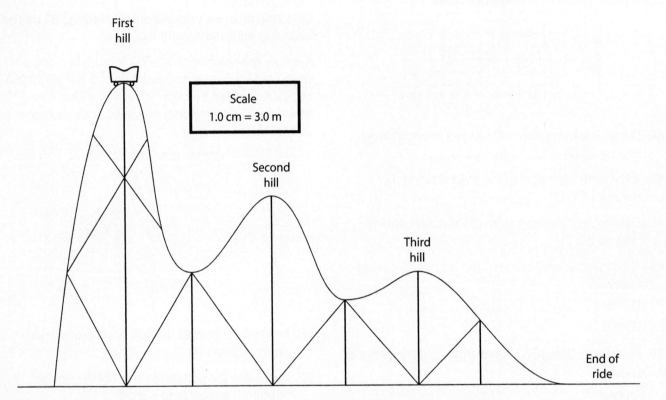

61. Using a metric ruler and the scale 1.0 cm = 3.0 m, determine the height of the first hill. [1]

62. Determine the gravitational potential energy of the car at the top of the first hill. [2]

63. Compare the kinetic energy of the car at the top of the second hill to its kinetic energy at the top of the third hill. [1]

Base your answers to questions 64 through 67 on the following information.

A 6.00-kilogram concrete block is dropped from the top of a tall building. The block falls a distance of 55.0 meters and has a speed of 30.0 meters per second when it hits the ground.

64. Determine the gravitational potential energy of the block with respect to the ground at the instant it is released. [2]

65. Determine the kinetic energy of the block at the point of impact. [2]

66. How much mechanical energy is "lost" by the block as it falls? [1]

67. Explain what happens to the mechanical energy that is "lost" by the block. [1]

Base your answers to questions 68 through 71 on the following information and data table.

A student performs a laboratory activity in which a constant 15-newton force acts on a 2.0-kilogram mass. The work done over time is summarized in the data table.

Time (s)	Work (J)
0	0
1.0	32
2.0	59
3.0	89
4.0	120.

68. Use the information in the data table to construct a graph on the following grid according to this procedure:

- Develop an appropriate scale for work. [1]

- Plot the data points. [1]

- Draw the line of best fit. [1]

Work vs. Time

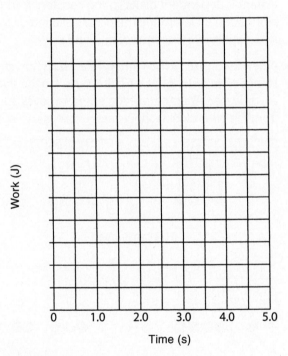

69. Determine the slope of the graph. [2]

70. What is the physical significance of the slope of the graph? [1]

71. Based on your graph, how much time did it take to do 75 joules of work? [1]

Base your answers to questions 72 through 74 on your knowledge of physics.

72. Explain why it requires more work to stop a ferry boat than a canoe if both are originally traveling with the same velocity. [1]

73. A 2.0-kilogram ball is used as the bob of a pendulum suspended from the ceiling of a classroom. The bob is drawn from its equilibrium position and released from the tip of a student's nose. Explain why, if the student does not move, there is no danger of the student being struck on the return swing. [1]

74. A 700.-newton physics teacher runs at constant speed up a flight of stairs rising 6.0 meters in 7.0 seconds. Explain why the teacher can claim he is more powerful than five 100-watt light bulbs. [1]

Part C

75. The following diagram shows a small mass sliding along a frictionless track having a loop of radius r.

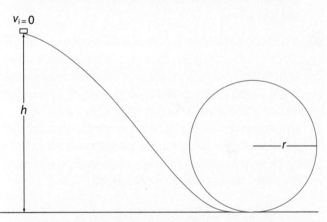

Using your knowledge of energy and circular motion, prove that if the object is to remain on the track at the top of the loop, the minimum height h from which the object must be released from rest is $\frac{5r}{2}$. [4]

Base your answers to questions 76 through 79 on the following information and diagram.

A car of mass m starts at point A with speed v_i and travels along the frictionless track. The height of hills A and B is h, the height of hill C is $\frac{h}{2}$ and the distance from point D to point E is d.

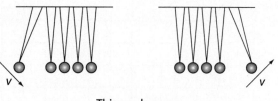

76. Determine the speed v_B of the car at point B. [1]

77. Determine the speed v_C of the car at point C. [2]

78. Determine the momentum p_D of the car at point D. [3]

79. Determine the average braking force F required to stop the car at point E if the brakes are applied at point D. [2]

80. A ballistic pendulum is a device consisting of a large block of wood having mass m_w suspended from two light-weight wires. The device is used to measure the initial speed v_{B_i} of a bullet having mass m_B. The bullet is shot into the wood and stopped. The block with embedded bullet has speed v_f immediately after the collision. As the following diagram shows, the bullet-block system swings through some vertical distance h, as mechanical energy is conserved.

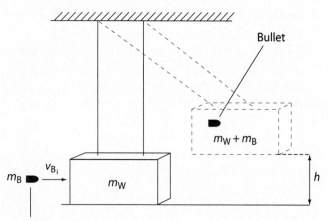

Express the vertical distance h in terms of the given quantities and other appropriate quantities. [2]

81. Determine the relationship between joules and 1.00 kilowatt·hour. [2]

82. When a mass m, hanging from a spring with spring constant k, is set into up-and-down simple harmonic motion, it has a period of vibration T, which is given by the equation $T = 2\pi \sqrt{\frac{m}{k}}$. The amount of elastic potential energy PE_s stored in this spring at any given instant is dependent on its spring constant k and its elongation x. Determine the potential energy stored in the spring, PE_s, in terms of m, T, and x. [2]

83. A device consists of five identical steel balls hung from strings of equal length. One ball is pulled to the side and released. After the collision one ball moves out from the other side, as shown in the following diagram.

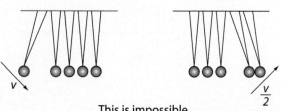

If two balls are pulled to the side and released, two balls move out from the other side. Assuming that both momentum and kinetic energy are conserved in the collision, show mathematically that one ball pulled to the side and striking four stationary balls with speed v can never result in two balls moving out from the other side, each with speed $\frac{v}{2}$. [3]

Base your answers to questions 84 through 87 on the following information and diagrams.

A block of mass m falls from rest a vertical distance h before striking a spring and compressing it a distance $-y$. The spring has spring constant k. At the point where the block first makes contact with the uncompressed spring, the block has speed v and distance is assumed to be zero. (Assume an ideal system.)

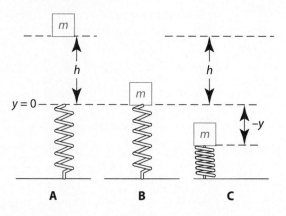

84. Write an equation that represents the gravitational potential energy of the block-spring system, as illustrated in A. [1]

85. Determine the speed v of the block in terms of h at the instant it makes contact with the uncompressed spring. [1]

86. When the block comes to rest, the spring is compressed a distance $-y$. Write an equation that represents the conservation of energy of the block-spring system in B and C in terms of the variables stated in the problem or other conventional terms. [2]

87. Determine the spring constant k in terms of $g, v, m,$ and y. [1]

Base your answers to questions 88 through 90 on the following information.

A student performed an experiment in which the force applied to a spring was varied and the resulting elongation measured. The data was graphed, as shown, and the spring constant of the spring was determined to be 60. newtons per meter.

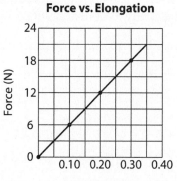

Force vs. Elongation

The equivalent spring constant for multiple springs connected in parallel is given by the following equation:

$$k_{eq\ parallel} = k_1 + k_2 + k_3 + \ldots$$

For multiple springs connected in series the equivalent spring constant is given by the equation:

$$\frac{1}{k_{eq\ series}} = \frac{1}{k_1} + \frac{1}{k_2} + \frac{1}{k_3} + \ldots$$

In these equations, $k_1, k_2,$ and k_3 are the spring constants of the individual springs.

88. On the grid provided, draw a line to represent two identical springs with a spring constant of 60. newtons per meter connected in series. Label the line $k_{eq\ series}$. [1]

89. On the grid draw a line to represent the same two springs connected in parallel. Label the line $k_{eq\ parallel}$. [1]

90. The student was given two springs A and B, having different spring constants. The student was told to perform another investigation to determine the equivalent spring constant for springs A and B combined in series and the equivalent spring constant for A and B combined in parallel. The student measured $k_{eq\ series}$ to be 30. newtons per meter and $k_{eq\ parallel}$ to be 160. newtons per meter. Using the student's data, determine the spring constants of spring A and spring B. [3]

Base your answers to questions 91 through 93 on the following information and diagram.

A simple pendulum of length ℓ has a bob of mass m. The bob is released from rest at point A and swings to point B directly below the pivot point. At B the cord comes in contact with a peg located a distance r above the center of the bob. This causes the bob to travel in a circular path to point C, as shown. (Neglect friction. Assume a gravitational potential energy of zero at point B.)

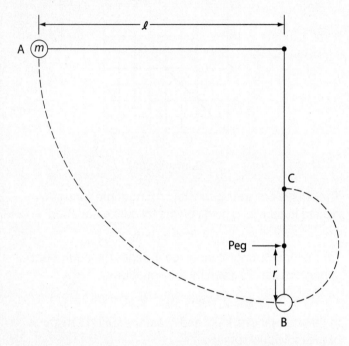

91. Express the speed v_B of the bob at point B in terms of ℓ. [1]

92. Write an expression for the gravitational potential energy of the bob at point C. [1]

93. Express the speed v_C of the bob at point C in terms of ℓ and r. [2]

Electricity and Magnetism

VOCABULARY

ammeter	electronvolt	ohm
ampere	electrostatic force	ohm · meter
battery	elementary charge	Ohm's law
cell	equivalent resistance	parallel circuit
conductivity	induced potential difference	potential difference
conductor		proton
coulomb	joule	resistance
Coulomb's law	law of conservation of charge	resistivity
current		resistor
electric circuit	magnet	series circuit
electric field	magnetic field	switch
electric field line	magnetic field strength	tesla
electric field strength		variable resistor
electrical energy	magnetic field (flux) lines	volt
electrical power	magnetic force	voltmeter
electromagnetic induction	magnetism	watt
	neutron	weber
electromagnetic wave	north magnetic pole	
electron		

Electrostatics

The study of electric charges at rest, and their electric fields and potentials, is called electrostatics. Charges are said to be "at rest" if there is no net transfer of charge.

MICROSTRUCTURE OF MATTER The smallest unit of an element is the atom. Atoms are composed of several different subatomic particles—electrons, protons, and neutrons. A typical atom consists of a cloud of electrons surrounding a central dense core known as the nucleus. The nucleus always contains protons and usually contains neutrons. The **electron** is the fundamental negatively charged ($-$) particle of matter. The **proton** is the fundamental positively charged ($+$) particle of matter. The **elementary charge,** e, is equal in magnitude to the charge on an electron ($-e$) or the charge on a proton ($+e$). Although the charge on

the proton is equal in magnitude to the charge on the electron, the mass of the proton is much greater than the mass of the electron. **Neutrons,** which are found in the nucleus, are neutral (no charge) subatomic particles that have nearly the same mass as protons. Because they contain equal numbers of protons and electrons, all atoms are electrically neutral.

CHARGED OBJECTS Protons and neutrons cannot be removed from an atom by ordinary means. Because of this, electrically charged objects are usually formed when neutral objects lose or gain electrons. Electrons are often removed from an atom when energy is imparted to the atom by friction, heat, or light. When an atom gains or loses electrons, it becomes a charged particle known as an <u>ion</u>. An object with an excess of electrons is negatively charged, and an object with a deficiency of electrons is positively charged.

Two objects with the same sign of charge (both positive or both negative) that are located near each other are repelled by an electrical force. A negatively charged object and a positively charged object that are near each other are attracted by an electrical force. As you'll learn in the next section, neutral objects and charged objects can also be attracted to each other.

TRANSFER OF CHARGE If a system consists only of neutral objects, it has a total net charge of zero. If objects in the system are rubbed together, electrons may be transferred between the objects. This, however, does not change the overall charge on the system—the system as a whole remains neutral. If one of the objects loses electrons and becomes positively charged, the object in contact with it acquires the electrons and becomes negatively charged.

If you run a plastic comb through your hair, electrons are transferred from your hair to the comb. Your hair becomes positively charged and the comb becomes negatively charged. If you then bring the comb near neutral pieces of paper on a tabletop, the charges within the paper are rearranged, as shown in Figure 4-1.

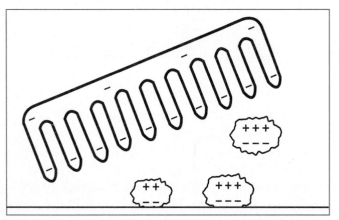

Figure 4-1. Opposite charges attract: The tiny pieces of paper are attracted to the comb by an electric force that is greater than Earth's gravitational force.

LAW OF CONSERVATION OF CHARGE The statement that in a closed, isolated system, the total charge of the system remains constant is known as the **law of conservation of charge**. Charges within the system may be transferred from one object to another, but charge is neither created nor destroyed.

SAMPLE PROBLEM

The diagram below shows the initial charges and positions of three metal spheres, R, S, and T, on insulating stands.

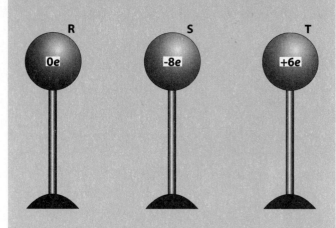

Sphere R is brought into contact with sphere S and then removed. Then sphere S is brought into contact with sphere T and removed. What is the charge on sphere T after this procedure is completed?

Solution: When spheres R and S are brought into contact, they share the $-8e$ charge equally. Thus each sphere possesses $-4e$ when they are separated. When spheres S and T are brought into contact, they also share the charge evenly.

$$\frac{-4e + 6e}{2} = \frac{+2e}{2} = +e$$

The final charge on sphere T is $+e$. Note also that charge is conserved; the initial charge of the system equals the final charge of the system.

$$-8e + 6e = -4e + e + e = -2e$$

QUANTITY OF CHARGE The SI unit of charge is the **coulomb,** C. One coulomb is equal to 6.25×10^{18} elementary charges. The charge on an electron $(-e)$ is -1.6×10^{-19} coulomb, and the charge on a proton $(+e)$ is $+1.6 \times 10^{-19}$ coulomb. The net charge on a charged object is always an integral multiple of e, that is, charge is quantized. For example, an object may have a net charge of 8.0×10^{-19} C (equivalent to $+5e$) or -1.6×10^{-18} C (equivalent to $-10e$), but it cannot have a charge of 2.4×10^{-19} C (equivalent to $\frac{3}{2}e$).

COULOMB'S LAW

COULOMB'S LAW The size or magnitude of the **electrostatic force** between two point charges is directly proportional to the product of the charges and inversely proportional to the square of the distance between them. This relationship, called **Coulomb's law,** is given by this equation.

$$F_e = \frac{kq_1q_2}{r^2}$$

F_e is the electrostatic force in newtons, q_1 and q_2 are the charges in coulombs, and r is the distance of separation in meters. The electrostatic constant, k, is equal to 8.99×10^9 N·m²/C². The electrostatic force is directed along the line joining the charges. The force that q_1 exerts on q_2 is equal in magnitude but opposite in direction to the force that q_2 exerts on q_1. The Coulomb's law equation is valid for charged objects whose dimensions are small compared with the distance separating the objects.

SAMPLE PROBLEM

What is the electrostatic force between two small spheres possessing net charges of +2.0 microcoulombs and −3.0 microcoulombs, respectively, if the distance between them is 10.0 meters?

Solution: Identify the known and unknown values.

Known
$k = 8.99 \times 10^9$ N · m²/C²
$q_1 = +2.0 \times 10^{-6}$ C
$q_2 = -3.0 \times 10^{-6}$ C
$r = 10.0$ m

Unknown
$F_e = ?$ N

Substitute the known values into the Coulomb's law equation and solve.

$$F_e = \frac{kq_1q_2}{r^2}$$

$$F_e = \frac{\left(8.99 \times 10^9 \, \frac{\text{N·m}^2}{\text{C}^2}\right)(+2.0 \times 10^{-6}\,\text{C})(-3.0 \times 10^{-6}\,\text{C})}{(1.00 \times 10^1 \,\text{m})^2}$$

$$F_e = \frac{\left(8.99 \times 10^9 \, \frac{\text{N·m}^2}{\text{C}^2}\right)(-6.0 \times 10^{-12}\,\text{C}^2)}{1.00 \times 10^2 \,\text{m}^2}$$

$$F_e = -5.4 \times 10^{-6} \,\text{N}$$

The negative sign indicates a force of attraction.

Review Questions

1. What is the charge of a proton? (1) 9.11×10^{-31} C (2) 1.67×10^{-27} C (3) 1.60×10^{-19} C (4) 6.25×10^{18} C

2. A charge of 100 elementary charges is equivalent to (1) 1.60×10^{-21} C (2) 1.60×10^{-17} C (3) 6.25×10^{16} C (4) 6.25×10^{20} C

3. Compare the sign and magnitude of the charge on a proton to the sign and magnitude of the charge on an electron.

4. Which particle has no charge? (1) neutron (2) proton (3) electron (4) ion

5. A small, uncharged metal sphere is placed near a large, negatively charged sphere. Which diagram best represents the charge distribution of the smaller sphere?

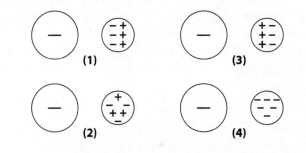

6. Which net charge could be found on an object? (1) 8.00×10^{-20} C (2) 2.40×10^{-19} C (3) 3.20×10^{-19} C (4) 6.25×10^{-18} C

7. One of two identical metal spheres has a charge of $+q$ and the other sphere has a charge of $-q$. The spheres are brought together and then separated. Compared to the total charge on the two spheres before contact, the total charge on the spheres after contact is (1) less (2) greater (3) the same

8. After two neutral solids, A and B, were rubbed together, Solid A acquired a net negative charge. Solid B, therefore, experienced a net (1) loss of electrons (2) increase of electrons (3) loss of protons (4) increase of protons

9. A rod and a piece of cloth are rubbed together. If the rod acquires a charge of $+1 \times 10^{-6}$ coulomb, the cloth acquires a charge of (1) 0 C (2) $+1 \times 10^{-6}$ C (3) -1×10^{-6} C (4) $+1 \times 10^{+6}$ C

10. Two identical spheres, A and B, carry charges of +6 microcoulombs and −2 microcoulombs, respectively. If these spheres touch, what will be the resulting charge on sphere A?

11. The diagram below shows the initial charges and positions of three identical metal spheres, X, Y, and Z, which have been placed on insulating stands.

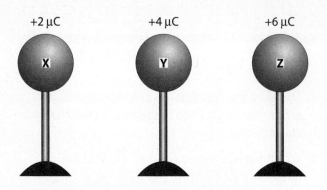

+2 μC   +4 μC   +6 μC

All three spheres are simultaneously brought into contact with each other and then returned to their original positions. Which statement best describes the charge of the spheres after this procedure is completed? (1) All the spheres are neutral. (2) Each sphere has a net charge of $+4$ μC. (3) Each sphere retains the same charge that it had originally. (4) Sphere Y has a greater charge than sphere X or sphere Z.

12. Two oppositely charged metal spheres are brought toward each other. Which graph best represents the relationship between the magnitude of the electric force between the spheres and the distance between them?

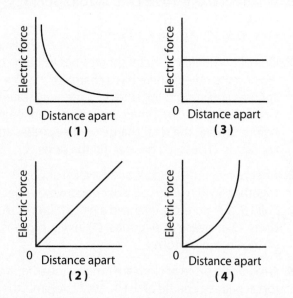

13. The electrostatic force of attraction between two small spheres that are 1.0 meter apart is F. If the distance between the spheres is decreased to 0.5 meter, the electrostatic force will be (1) $\frac{F}{2}$ (2) $2F$ (3) $\frac{F}{4}$ (4) $4F$

14. The diagram below shows two metal spheres suspended by strings and separated by a distance of 3.0 meters. The charge on sphere A is $+5.0 \times 10^{-4}$ coulomb, and the charge on sphere B is $+3.0 \times 10^{-5}$ coulomb.

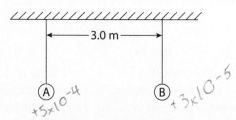

Which statement best describes the electrical force between the spheres? (1) It has a magnitude of 15 N and is repulsive. (2) It has a magnitude of 45 N and is repulsive. (3) It has a magnitude of 15 N and is attractive. (4) It has a magnitude of 45 N and is attractive.

15. Two identical small spheres possessing charges q_1 and q_2 are separated by distance r. Which change would produce the greatest increase in the electrical force between the two spheres? (1) doubling charge q_1 (2) doubling r (3) doubling r and charge q_1 (4) doubling r and charges q_1 and q_2

16. If the charge on each of two small spheres a fixed distance apart is doubled, the electrostatic force between the spheres will be (1) halved (2) doubled (3) quartered (4) quadrupled

17. A point charge of $+3.0 \times 10^{-7}$ coulomb is placed 2.0×10^{-2} meter from a second point charge of $+4.0 \times 10^{-7}$ coulomb. What is the magnitude of the electrostatic force between the charges?

Electric Fields

An **electric field** is the region around a charged particle through which a force is exerted on another charged particle. An **electric field line** is the imaginary line along which a positive test charge would move in an electric field. The direction of an electric field is the direction of the force on a stationary positive test charge located at any point on a field line. On a curved field line, the direction of the field at any point is the tangent drawn to the field line at that point. Electric field lines begin on positive charges (or at infinity) and end on negative charges (or infinity). Field lines never intersect.

Electric field strength, E, is the force on a stationary positive test charge per unit charge in an electric field. It is given by this equation.

$$E = \frac{F_e}{q}$$

F_e is the electrostatic force in newtons, q is the charge in coulombs, and E is the electric field strength in newtons per coulomb. Because it has both magnitude and direction, electric field strength is a vector quantity.

SAMPLE PROBLEM

What is the magnitude of the electric field strength at a point in a field where an electron experiences a 1.0-newton force?

Solution: Identify the known and unknown values.

Known   *Unknown*
$F_e = 1.0\ \text{N}$ $E = ?\ \text{N/C}$
$q = 1.60 \times 10^{-19}\ \text{C}$

Substitute the known values into the electric field strength equation and solve.

$$E = \frac{F_e}{q} = \frac{1.0\ \text{N}}{1.60 \times 10^{-19}\ \text{C}} = 6.3 \times 10^{18}\ \text{N/C}$$

FIELD AROUND A POINT CHARGE OR SPHERE

Field lines extend radially outward from a positive point charge and radially inward toward a negative point charge. On a sphere, charge is distributed uniformly, and electric field lines are normal (perpendicular) to the surface. According to Coulomb's law, the electric field strength around a point charge or charged sphere varies inversely with the square of the distance from the point charge or sphere. The electric field strength within a hollow, charged conducting sphere is zero.

FIELD BETWEEN TWO OPPOSITELY CHARGED PARALLEL PLATES

If the distance separating two oppositely charged parallel plates is small compared to their area, the electric field between the plates is uniform. The electric field lines are parallel to each other, so the field strength is the same at every point between the plates. Figure 4-2 shows the electric fields surrounding charged objects.

The magnitude of the electric force on an electron or a proton located at any point between two given oppositely charged parallel plates is the same. The electric force acting on either of these charged particles causes it to accelerate toward the plate of opposite sign. That is, the particle's speed increases as it approaches the plate of opposite sign.

POTENTIAL DIFFERENCE

If the direction of an electric field is such that it opposes the motion of a charged particle, work must be done to move the particle in that direction. The **potential difference** between two points in an electric field is the work done (or change in potential energy) per unit charge as a charged particle is moved between the points. The potential difference is given by this formula.

$$V = \frac{W}{q}$$

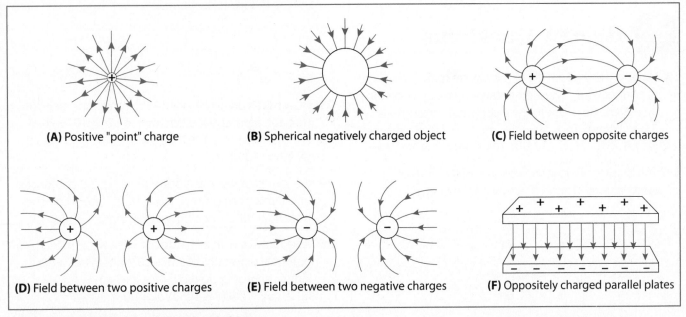

(A) Positive "point" charge

(B) Spherical negatively charged object

(C) Field between opposite charges

(D) Field between two positive charges

(E) Field between two negative charges

(F) Oppositely charged parallel plates

Figure 4-2. Fields surrounding charged objects

W is the work in joules, q is the charge in coulombs, and V is the potential difference in joules per coulomb. If one joule of work is done to move one coulomb of charge between two points in an electric field, a potential difference of one **volt** is said to exist between the two points. That is, 1 joule/coulomb = 1 volt. The volt, V, is the derived SI unit for potential difference.

If an elementary charge is moved against an electric field through a potential difference of one volt, the work done on the charge is calculated as shown below.

$$W = Vq = (1.00 \text{ V})(1.60 \times 10^{-19} \text{ C}) = 1.60 \times 10^{-19} \text{ J}$$

This amount of work $(1.60 \times 10^{-19} \text{ J})$, or gain in potential energy, is called the **electronvolt,** eV. That is, $1.00 \text{ eV} = 1.60 \times 10^{-19} \text{ J}$.

SAMPLE PROBLEM

Moving a point charge of 3.2×10^{-19} coulomb between points A and B in an electric field requires 4.8×10^{-18} joule of energy. What is the potential difference between these points?

Solution: Identify the known and unknown values.

Known	Unknown
$q = 3.2 \times 10^{-19}$ C	$V = ?$ V
$W = 4.8 \times 10^{-18}$ J	

Substitute the known values into the equation for potential difference and solve.

$$V = \frac{W}{q} = \frac{4.8 \times 10^{-18} \text{ J}}{3.2 \times 10^{-19} \text{ C}} = 15 \text{ V}$$

Review Questions

18. What is the magnitude of the electrostatic force experienced by one elementary charge at a point in an electric field where the electric field strength is 3.0×10^3 newtons per coulomb? (1) 1.0×10^3 N (2) 1.6×10^{-19} N (3) 3.0×10^3 N (4) 4.8×10^{-16} N

$E = N \cdot C$

19. The diagram below shows some of the lines of electric force around a positive point charge.

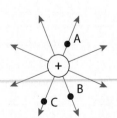

The strength of the electric field is (1) greatest at point A (2) greatest at point B (3) greatest at point C (4) equal at points A, B, and C

20. A charged particle is placed in an electric field E. If the charge on the particle is doubled, the magnitude of the force exerted on the particle by the field E is (1) unchanged (2) doubled (3) halved (4) quadrupled

21. Which diagram best illustrates the electric field around two unlike charges?

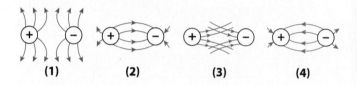

22. Which diagram best represents the electric field of a point negative charge?

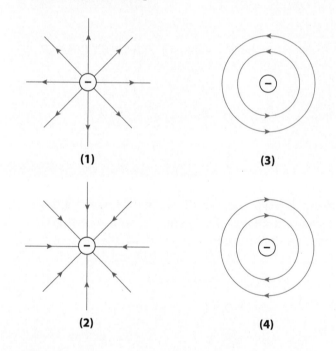

23. How much energy is needed to move one electron through a potential difference of 1.0×10^2 volts? (1) 1.0 J (2) 1.0×10^2 J (3) 1.6×10^{-17} J (4) 1.6×10^{-19} J

24. 6.0 joules of work are done to move 2.0 coulombs of charge from point A to point B. Determine the potential difference between points A and B.

25. A helium ion with a charge of $+2e$ is accelerated by a potential difference of 5.0×10^3 volts. What is the kinetic energy acquired by the ion? (1) 3.2×10^{-19} eV (2) 2.0 eV (3) 5.0×10^3 eV (4) 1.0×10^4 eV

26. If 4 joules of work are required to move 2 coulombs of charge through a 6-ohm resistor, what is the potential difference across the resistor?

27. An electron is accelerated from rest through a potential difference of 200. volts. What is the work done on the electron in electron volts?

28. The graph below shows the relationship between the work done on a charged body in an electric field and the net charge on the body.

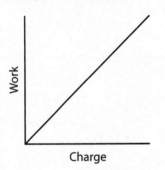

What does the slope of the graph represent?

Electric Current

Electric **current** is the rate at which charge passes a given point in a circuit. An **electric circuit** is a closed path along which charged particles move. A **switch** is a device for making, breaking, or changing the connections in an electric circuit. Figure 4-3 shows the symbol for a switch.

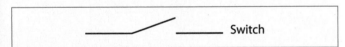

Figure 4-3. The symbol for a switch

UNIT OF CURRENT The SI unit of electric current, I, is the **ampere,** A. It is a fundamental unit. The coulomb, C, the unit of charge, is a derived unit defined to be the amount of charge that passes a point when a current of one ampere flows for one second. This relationship can be expressed as follows:

$$I = \frac{\Delta q}{t}$$

I is current in amperes, q is charge in coulombs, and t is time in seconds. An **ammeter** is a device used to measure current. The symbol for an ammeter is shown in Figure 4-4.

Figure 4-4. The symbol for an ammeter

CONDITIONS NECESSARY FOR AN ELECTRIC CURRENT In addition to a complete circuit, a difference in potential between two points in the circuit must exist for there to be an electric current. The potential difference may be supplied by a **cell,** a device that converts chemical energy to electrical energy, or a **battery,** a combination of two or more electrochemical cells. The potential difference can be measured with a device called a **voltmeter.** These devices are represented in an electric circuit diagram by the symbols shown in Figure 4-5.

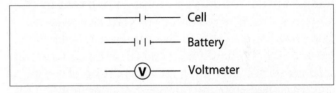

Figure 4-5. Symbols for sources of potential difference (voltage) and a voltmeter for measuring potential difference

Positive charges tend to move from points of higher potential to points of lower potential, or from positive potential to negative potential. Negative charges tend to move in the opposite direction. The direction of a current in an electric circuit can be defined as either of these directions. In some mathematical treatments it is convenient to treat the current as flowing from positive to negative, that is, as conventional current. However, it is more natural to choose the electron flow as the direction of current, because most currents consist of electrons in motion. This is the definition used in this book.

CONDUCTIVITY IN SOLIDS For a current to exist in an electric circuit, the circuit must consist of materials through which charge can move. The ability of a material to conduct electricity depends on the number of free charges per unit volume and on their mobility. **Conductivity** is a property of a material that depends on the availability of charges that are relatively free to move under the influence of an electric field. Pure metals have many electrons, and these electrons are not bound, or are only loosely bound, to any particular atom. Consequently, metals are good **conductors,**

because their electrons move readily. In nonmetallic elements or compounds, electrons are tightly bound and few are free to move. These types of materials are called <u>insulators</u>, because they are poor conductors.

RESISTANCE AND OHM'S LAW Electrical **resistance,** R, is the opposition that a device or conductor offers to the flow of electric current. The resistance of a conductor is the ratio of the potential difference applied to its ends and the current that flows through it. This relationship, called **Ohm's law,** is expressed as follows.

$$R = \frac{V}{I}$$

V is potential difference in volts, I is current in amperes, and R is resistance in volts per ampere. The **ohm,** Ω, is a derived SI unit equal to one volt per ampere. It should be noted that the equation is true for entire circuits or for any portion of a circuit, provided that the temperature does not change.

SAMPLE PROBLEM

A student measures a current of 0.10 ampere flowing through a lamp connected by short wires to a 12.0-volt source. What is the resistance of the lamp?

Solution: Identify the known and unknown values.

Known	Unknown
$V = 12.0\,V$	$R = ?\,\Omega$
$I = 0.10\,A$	

Substitute the known values into the equation for Ohm's law and solve.

$$R = \frac{V}{I} = \frac{12.0\,V}{0.10\,A} = 120\,\Omega$$

SAMPLE PROBLEM

A resistor was held at constant temperature in an operating electric circuit. A student measured the current through the resistor and the potential difference across it. The measurements are shown in the data table below.

Current (A)	Potential Difference (V)
0.010	2.3
0.020	5.2
0.030	7.4
0.040	9.9
0.050	12.7

(a) Using the information in the data table, construct a graph on the grid below.

• Mark an appropriate scale on the axis labeled Current (A).

• Plot the data points.

• Draw the best-fit line.

(b) Using your graph, find the slope of the best-fit line.

(c) What physical quantity does the slope represent?

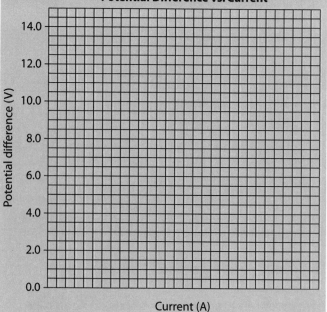

Potential Difference vs. Current

Solution:

(a)

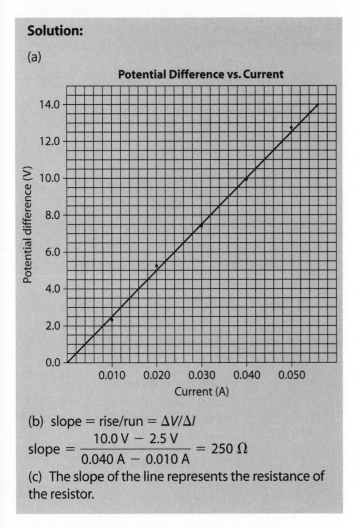

(b) slope = rise/run = $\Delta V / \Delta I$

$$\text{slope} = \frac{10.0\ \text{V} - 2.5\ \text{V}}{0.040\ \text{A} - 0.010\ \text{A}} = 250\ \Omega$$

(c) The slope of the line represents the resistance of the resistor.

FACTORS THAT AFFECT THE RESISTANCE OF A CONDUCTOR

The resistance of a conducting wire increases with the increasing length of a wire because the current (electrons) encounter and collide with an increasing number of atoms. That is, the resistance R of a wire varies directly with its length L, or $R \propto L$. As the thickness of a wire decreases, there are fewer spaces between atoms in the cross-section through which electrons can travel in a given period of time. For example, if two wires have the same composition and length but one has half the diameter of the other, the thinner wire will have one-quarter the cross-sectional area, and therefore four times the resistance. That is, the resistance R of a wire varies inversely with its cross-sectional area A, or $R \propto \frac{1}{A}$.

Resistivity, ρ, is a characteristic of a material that depends on its electronic structure and temperature. The resistance of a wire is directly proportional to its resistivity, that is, $R \propto \rho$. Good conductors have low resistivities and good insula-

tors have high resistivities. The SI unit for resistivity is the **ohm · meter**, or $\Omega \cdot$m. As the temperature of a conductor increases, its resistivity increases. The *Reference Tables for Physical Setting/Physics* contain a chart listing resistivities of several metals at 20°C.

Combining the factors yields the following equation for the resistance of a wire.

$$R = \frac{\rho L}{A}$$

ρ is the resistivity in ohm · meters, L is length in meters, A is cross-sectional area in square meters, and R is resistance in ohms.

SAMPLE PROBLEM

Determine the resistance of a 4.00-meter length of copper wire having a diameter of 2.00 millimeters. Assume a temperature of 20°C.

Solution: Identify the known and unknown values.

Known	Unknown
$\rho_{copper} = 1.72 \times 10^{-8}\ \Omega \cdot$m	$R = ?\ \Omega$
$L = 4.00$ m	
$d = 2.00 \times 10^{-3}$	

Substitute the known values into the resistance equations and solve.

$$R = \frac{\rho L}{A} = \frac{\rho L}{\pi (d/2)^2}$$

$$R = \frac{(1.72 \times 10^{-8}\Omega \cdot \text{m})(4.00\ \text{m})}{\pi (1.00 \times 10^{-3}\ \text{m})} \neq$$

$$R = 2.19 \times 10^{-2}\ \Omega$$

A **resistor** is a device designed to have a definite amount of resistance. It can be used in a circuit to limit current flow or provide a potential drop. A **variable resistor** is a coil of resistance wire whose effective resistance can be varied by sliding a contact point. As more of the coil is used in a circuit, the resistance of the circuit increases, and the current decreases. The symbols for a resistor and variable resistor are shown in Figure 4-6.

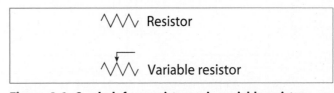

Figure 4-6. Symbols for a resistor and a variable resistor

Review Questions

29. A total of 20.0 coulombs of charge pass a given point in a conductor in 4.0 seconds. Determine the current in the conductor.

30. A wire carries a current of 2.0 amperes. How many electrons pass a given point in this wire in 1.0 second? (1) 1.3×10^{18} (2) 2.0×10^{18} (3) 1.3×10^{19} (4) 2.0×10^{19}

31. Which condition must exist between two points in a conductor in order to maintain a flow of charge? (1) a potential difference (2) a magnetic field (3) a low resistance (4) a high resistance

32. In the diagram below, which of the switches must be closed in order for the lamp to light?

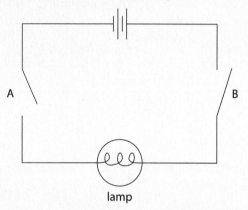

lamp

(1) A only (2) B only (3) both A and B

33. Which graph best represents the relationship between potential difference applied to a conductor and the resulting current through the conductor? (Assume constant temperature.)

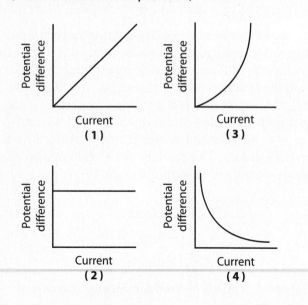

34. The graph below shows the relationship between potential difference and current in a simple circuit.

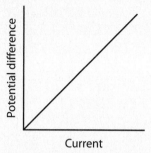

For any point on the line, what does the ratio of potential difference to current represent? (1) work in joules (2) power in watts (3) resistance in ohms (4) charge in coulombs

35. A 20.-ohm resistor has 40. coulombs of charge passing through it in 5.0 seconds. What is the potential difference across the resistor? (1) 8.0 V (2) 1.0×10^2 V (3) 1.6×10^2 V (4) 2.0×10^2 V

36. The graph below represents the relationship between the potential difference across a metal conductor and the current through the conductor at constant temperature.

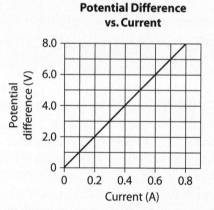

What is the resistance of the conductor? (1) 1 Ω (2) 0.01 Ω (3) 0.1 Ω (4) 10 Ω

37. A potential difference of 12 volts is applied across a circuit having a 4.0-ohm resistance. What is the current in the circuit?

38. In the diagrams below, ℓ represents a unit length of copper wire and A represents a unit cross-sectional area. Which copper wire has the smallest resistance at room temperature?

39. If the temperature of a metal conductor is reduced, its resistance will usually (1) decrease (2) increase (3) remain the same

40. The resistance of a wire at constant temperature depends on the wire's (1) length only (2) type of metal only (3) length and cross-sectional area only (4) length, type of metal, and cross-sectional area

41. On the axes below, sketch the general shape of the graph that shows the relationship between the resistance of a copper wire of uniform cross-sectional area and the wire's length at constant temperature.

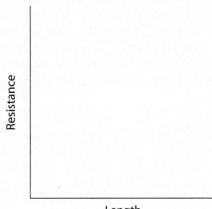

42. A piece of wire has a resistance of 8 ohms. What is the resistance of a second piece of wire of the same composition, same diameter, and at the same temperature, but with one half the length of the first wire?

43. An aluminum wire has a resistance of 48 ohms. A second aluminum wire of the same length and at the same temperature, but with twice the cross-sectional area, would have a resistance of (1) 12 Ω (2) 24 Ω (3) 48 Ω (4) 96 Ω

44. What is the resistance of a 10.0-meter long copper wire having a cross-sectional area of 1.50×10^{-6} m^2 at 20°C? (1) 1.15×10^{-1} Ω (2) 1.15×10^{-2} Ω (3) 1.15×10^{-13} Ω (4) 1.15×10^{-14} Ω

45. A 5.00-meter long tin wire has a cross-sectional area of 2.00×10^{-6} m^2 and a resistance of 0.35 ohm. Determine the resistivity of tin.

46. At 20°C carbon has a resistivity of 3.5×10^{-5} Ω·m. What is the ratio of the resistivity of carbon to the resistivity of copper? (1) 1:2 (2) 2:1 (3) 200:1 (4) 2000:1

47. Unlike most metals, the resistivity of carbon decreases with increasing temperature. As the temperature of carbon increases, its resistance (1) decreases (2) increases (3) remains the same

48. An aluminum wire and a tungsten wire have the same cross-sectional area and the same resistance at 20°C. If the aluminum wire is 4.0×10^{-2} meter long, what is the length of the tungsten wire? (1) 1.0×10^{-2} m (2) 2.0×10^{-2} m (3) 4.0×10^{-2} m (4) 8.0×10^{-2} m

Electric Circuits

The simplest electric circuit consists of a source of electrical energy, such as a battery; connecting wires; and a circuit element, such as a lamp or a resistor, that converts electrical energy to light or heat. The current in the circuit is dependent on the potential difference V provided by the battery at the ends of the circuit element, and the resistance R of the circuit element. These quantities are related to each other by

Ohm's Law, $I = \dfrac{V}{R}$. Figure 4-7 shows a simple electric circuit.

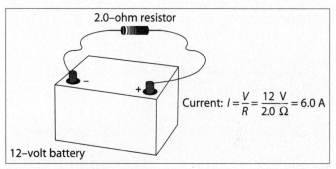

Current: $I = \dfrac{V}{R} = \dfrac{12 \text{ V}}{2.0 \text{ Ω}} = 6.0 \text{ A}$

Figure 4-7. A simple circuit

When two or more resistors are present in a circuit, there are two basic methods of connecting them—in series or in parallel.

SERIES CIRCUITS A **series circuit** is a circuit in which all parts are connected end to end to provide a single path for the current. Figure 4-8 shows three resistors connected in series with a battery. The resistors are differentiated by the use of subscripts R_1, R_2, and R_3.

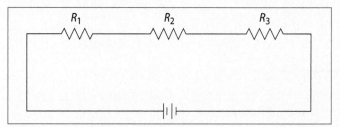

Figure 4-8. Resistors in a series circuit

Since there is only one current path in a series circuit, the current is the same through each resistor. For resistors in series, the current is given by $I = I_1 = I_2 = I_3 = \ldots$. The applied potential difference at the terminals equals the sum of the potential differences across the individual resistors. That is, $V = V_1 + V_2 + V_3 + \ldots$. However, by Ohm's law $V = IR_{eq}$ where R_{eq} is the equivalent resistance of the entire circuit. **Equivalent resistance** is the single resistance that could replace the several resistors in a circuit. Substituting yields $IR_{eq} = I_1R_1 + I_2R_2 + I_3R_3 + \ldots$. However, because $I = I_1 = I_2 = I_3 = \ldots$, it follows that $IR_{eq} = IR_1 + IR_2 + IR_3 + \ldots$. Dividing each term in the equation by the common factor I yields $R_{eq} = R_1 + R_2 + R_3 + \ldots$.

To summarize for series circuits:

$$I = I_1 = I_2 = I_3 = \ldots$$
$$V = V_1 + V_2 + V_3 + \ldots$$
$$R_{eq} = R_1 + R_2 + R_3 + \ldots$$

SAMPLE PROBLEM

Three resistors, with resistances of 4.0 ohms, 6.0 ohms, and 8.0 ohms respectively, are connected in series to an applied potential difference of 36 volts. Determine (a) the equivalent resistance, (b) the current through each resistor, and (c) the potential drop across each resistor.

Solution: Identify the known and unknown values.

Known	Unknown
$R_1 = 4.0\ \Omega$	$R_{eq} = ?\ \Omega$
$R_2 = 6.0\ \Omega$	$I_1, I_2, I_3, = ?\ A$
$R_3 = 8.0\ \Omega$	$V_1, V_2, V_3, = ?\ V$

(a) Substitute the known resistance values into the equation for equivalent resistance of a series circuit and solve for R_{eq}.

$$R_{eq} = R_1 + R_2 + R_3$$
$$R_{eq} = 4.0\ \Omega + 6.0\ \Omega + 8.0\ \Omega = 18.0\ \Omega$$

(b) Substitute the known values for V and R_{eq} into the equation for Ohm's law and solve for I.

$$I = \frac{V}{R_{eq}} = \frac{36\ V}{18.0\ \Omega} = 2.0\ A$$

The current is the same throughout a series circuit.

$$I = I_1 = I_2 = I_3 = 2.0\ A$$

(c) Ohm's law is used to calculate the voltage drop across each resistor.

$$V_1 = I_1R_1 = (2.0\ A)(4.0\ \Omega) = 8.0\ V$$
$$V_2 = I_2R_2 = (2.0\ A)(6.0\ \Omega) = 12\ V$$
$$V_3 = I_3R_3 = (2.0\ A)(8.0\ \Omega) = 16\ V$$

Note that when resistors in a circuit are connected in series, the sum of the potential differences across the individual resistors is equal to the applied potential difference.

$$V = V_1 + V_2 + V_3 = 8.0\ V + 12\ V + 16\ V = 36\ V$$

PARALLEL CIRCUITS A **parallel circuit** is a circuit in which the elements are connected between two points, with one of the two ends of each component connected to each point. Consequently, there are two or more paths for current flow. As shown in Figure 4-9, current is divided among the branches of the circuit.

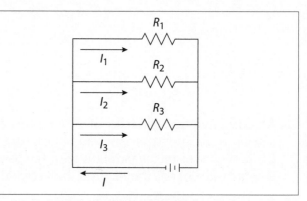

Figure 4-9. Currents in a parallel circuit: The total current I is divided among the three branches of the circuit.

In a parallel circuit, the sum of the currents in the branches is equal to the total current from the source. That is, $I = I_1 + I_2 + I_3 + \ldots$. The potential difference across each branch of the parallel circuit is the same as that of the potential difference supplied by the source, so $V = V_1 = V_2 = V_3 = \ldots$.

However, according to Ohm's law $I = \dfrac{V}{R}$ for each branch of the circuit. Substituting yields $I = \dfrac{V_1}{R_1} + \dfrac{V_2}{R_2} + \dfrac{V_3}{R_3} + \ldots$. You know by Ohm's law that $I = \dfrac{V}{R_{eq}}$ for the circuit. Therefore,

$$\frac{V}{R_{eq}} = \frac{V}{R_1} + \frac{V}{R_2} + \frac{V}{R_3} + \ldots$$ Dividing each term by

V yields $\dfrac{1}{R_{eq}} = \dfrac{1}{R_1} + \dfrac{1}{R_2} + \dfrac{1}{R_3} + \ldots$.

To summarize for parallel circuits:

$$I = I_1 + I_2 + I_3 + \ldots$$
$$V = V_1 = V_2 = V_3 = \ldots$$
$$\frac{1}{R_{eq}} = \frac{1}{R_1} + \frac{1}{R_2} + \frac{1}{R_3} + \ldots$$

Note that in a parallel circuit the equivalent resistance R_{eq} is always less than the resistance of any branch. In addition, since V is the same for each branch, the current in each branch is inversely proportional to its resistance. As additional resistors or electrical devices are connected in parallel in a given circuit, the total resistance of the circuit decreases. Consequently the total current in the circuit increases, perhaps to dangerous levels. A fuse or circuit breaker is inserted in the main line of each circuit in the home as a safety device. If the current becomes too large, the fuse or circuit breaker opens.

SAMPLE PROBLEM

Three resistors of 4.0 ohms, 6.0 ohms, and 12 ohms are connected in parallel to an applied potential difference of 12 volts. Calculate (a) the equivalent resistance, (b) the potential difference across each resistor, and (c) the current through each resistor.

Solution: Identify the known and unknown values.

Known	Unknown
$R_1 = 4.0\ \Omega$	$R_{eq} = ?\ \Omega$
$R_2 = 6.0\ \Omega$	$V = ?\ V$
$R_3 = 12.0\ \Omega$	$I_1 = ?\ A$
	$I_2 = ?\ A$
	$I_3 = ?\ A$

(a) Substitute the known resistance values into the equation for equivalent resistance of a parallel circuit and solve for R_{eq}.

$$\frac{1}{R_{eq}} = \frac{1}{R_1} + \frac{1}{R_2} + \frac{1}{R_3}$$
$$\frac{1}{R_{eq}} = \frac{1}{4.0\ \Omega} + \frac{1}{6.0\ \Omega} + \frac{1}{12\ \Omega}$$
$$\frac{1}{R_{eq}} = \frac{3.0}{12\ \Omega} + \frac{2.0}{12\ \Omega} + \frac{1.0}{12\ \Omega}$$
$$R_{eq} = 2.0\ \Omega$$

(b) The potential difference across each branch of the circuit is the same as the applied potential difference.

$$V = V_1 = V_2 = V_3 = 12\ V$$

(c) Ohm's law is used to calculate the current through each resistor.

$$I_1 = \frac{V_1}{R_1} = \frac{12\ V}{4.0\ \Omega} = 3.0\ A$$
$$I_2 = \frac{V_2}{R_2} = \frac{12\ V}{6.0\ \Omega} = 2.0\ A$$
$$I_3 = \frac{V_3}{R_3} = \frac{12\ V}{12\ \Omega} = 1.0\ A$$

Note that when resistors are connected in parallel in a circuit, the sum of the currents in the resistors is equal to the total current (the current leaving the source).

$$I = I_1 + I_2 + I_3$$
$$I = 3.0\ A + 2.0\ A + 1.0\ A = 6.0\ A$$
$$\text{Check: } I = \frac{V}{R_{eq}} = \frac{12\ V}{2.0\ \Omega} = 6.0\ A$$

METERS IN A CIRCUIT As noted earlier, an ammeter is used to measure current and a voltmeter is used to measure potential difference. An ammeter is always connected in series with the circuit element being measured, whereas a voltmeter is always connected in parallel. The diagrams in Figure 4-10 show an ammeter and a voltmeter connected to determine the current through and potential difference across resistor R_1.

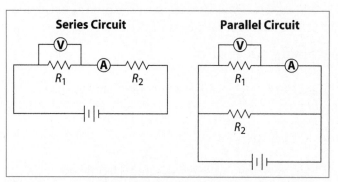

Figure 4-10. Connecting ammeters and voltmeters: The diagram shows how to use an ammeter and a voltmeter to measure the current through and the potential difference across the resistor R_1 in a series circuit and in a parallel circuit.

CONSERVATION OF CHARGE IN ELECTRIC CIRCUITS Charge in an electric circuit must be conserved. At any junction in a circuit, the sum of the currents entering the junction must equal the sum of the currents leaving it. Figure 4-11 on the next page illustrates the conservation of charge at a junction.

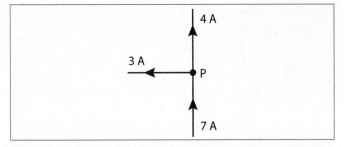

Figure 4-11. Current traveling near junction P in an electric circuit: Note that the sum of currents leaving the junction (3 A + 4 A) equals the current entering the junction (7 A).

ELECTRIC POWER Recall from Topic 3 that power is the time rate of doing work or expending energy. That is $P = \frac{W}{t}$ where work W is in joules, time t is in seconds, and power P is in watts. The derived SI unit for power is the **watt,** W. In fundamental units, one watt equals one $\frac{\text{kilogram} \cdot \text{meter}^2}{\text{second}^3}$. Power is a scalar quantity.

Electrical power is the product of potential difference and current. That is, $P = VI$ where power P is in watts, potential difference V is in volts, and current I is in amperes. It can be seen that this equation is valid by analyzing the units.

$$(1 \text{ volt})(1 \text{ ampere}) = \left(1\frac{\text{joule}}{\cancel{\text{coulomb}}}\right)\left(1\frac{\cancel{\text{coulomb}}}{\text{second}}\right)$$

$$= 1 \frac{\text{joule}}{\text{second}}$$

$$= 1 \text{ watt}$$

By Ohm's law $V = IR$, so IR can be substituted for V in the equation $P = VI$. This yields:

$$P = VI = (IR)I = I^2R$$

Because $I = \dfrac{V}{R}$, it follows by substitution that

$$P = VI = V\left(\frac{V}{R}\right) = \frac{V^2}{R}$$

These relationships are summarized below.

$$P = VI = I^2R = \frac{V^2}{R}$$

SAMPLE PROBLEM

A potential difference of 60.0 volts is applied across a 15-ohm resistor. What is the power dissipated in the resistor?

Solution: Identify the known and unknown values.

Known	Unknown
$V = 60.0$ V	$P = ?$ W
$R = 15\ \Omega$	

Substitute the known values into the equation for power and solve.

$$P = \frac{V^2}{R} = \frac{(60.0\ V)^2}{15\ \Omega} = 240\ W$$

ELECTRICAL ENERGY Recall from Topic 3 that energy is the capacity for doing work. In an electric circuit the total **electrical energy** W is equal to the product of the power consumed P and the time t of charge flow. That is,

$$W = Pt = VIt = I^2Rt = \frac{V^2t}{R}$$

The SI derived unit for electrical energy is the **joule,** J. In fundamental units, one joule equals one $\frac{\text{kilogram} \cdot \text{meter}^2}{\text{second}^2}$. Electrical energy is a scalar quantity.

SAMPLE PROBLEM

A current of 0.40 ampere is measured in a 150-ohm resistor. How much energy is expended by the resistor in 30. seconds?

Solution: Identify the known and unknown values.

Known	Unknown
$I = 0.40$ A	$W = ?$ J
$R = 150\ \Omega$	
$t = 30.$ s	

Substitute the known values into the equation for electrical energy and solve.

$$W = I^2Rt = (0.40\ A)^2(150\ \Omega)(30.\ s) = 720\ J$$

49. The circuit diagram below shows three voltmeters connected across resistors.

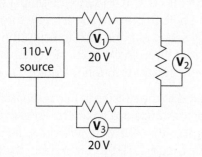

What is the reading of voltmeter V_2?

50. The diagram below shows two resistors connected to a 20.-volt battery.

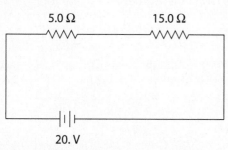

If the current through the 5.0-ohm resistor is 1.0 ampere, what is the current through the 15.0-ohm resistor?

51. The diagram below shows a circuit with three resistors.

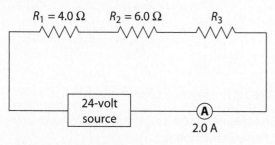

What is the resistance of resistor R_3? (1) 6.0 Ω (2) 2.0 Ω (3) 12 Ω (4) 4.0 Ω

52. An electric circuit contains an operating heating element and a lit lamp. Which statement best explains why the lamp remains lit when the heating element is removed from the circuit? (1) The lamp has less resistance than the heating element. (2) The lamp has more resistance than the heating element. (3) The lamp and heating element are connected in series. (4) The lamp and heating element are connected in parallel.

53. A 4-ohm resistor and an 8-ohm resistor are connected in series. If the current through the 4-ohm resistor is 2 amperes, the current through the 8-ohm resistor is (1) 1 A (2) 2 A (3) 0.5 A (4) 4 A

54. A 10.-ohm resistor and a 5.0-ohm resistor are connected as shown in the diagram below.

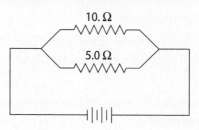

If the current through the 10.-ohm resistor is 1.0 ampere, then the current through the 5.0-ohm resistor is (1) 15 A (2) 2.0 A (3) 0.50 A (4) 0.30 A

55. In the circuit diagram below, ammeter A measures the current supplied by a 10.-volt battery.

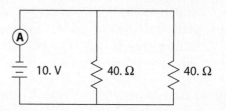

The current measured by ammeter A is (1) 0.13 A (2) 2.0 A (3) 0.50 A (4) 4.0 A

56. Which two of the resistor arrangements below have the same equivalent resistance?

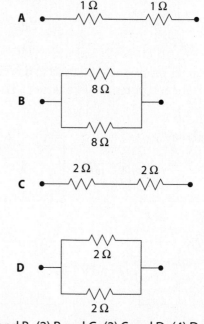

(1) A and B (2) B and C (3) C and D (4) D and A

57. A physics student is given three 12-ohm resistors with instructions to create the circuit that would have the lowest possible resistance. The correct circuit would be a (1) series circuit with an equivalent resistance of 36 Ω (2) series circuit with an equivalent resistance of 4 Ω (3) parallel circuit with an equivalent resistance of 36 Ω (4) parallel circuit with an equivalent resistance of 4 Ω

58. If a 15-ohm resistor is connected in parallel with a 30.-ohm resistor, the equivalent resistance is (1) 15 Ω (2) 2.0 Ω (3) 10. Ω (4) 45 Ω

59. Which circuit below would have the lowest voltmeter reading?

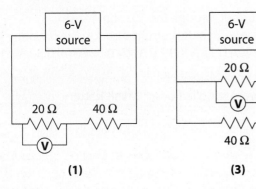

(1)

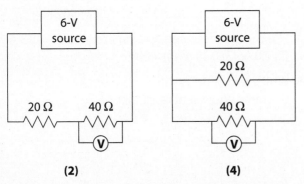

(3)

(2)

(4)

60. Which circuit below could be used to determine the total current and potential difference of a parallel circuit?

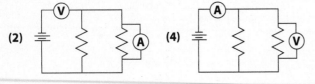

(1)   (3)

(2)   (4)

61. A simple electrical circuit contains a battery, a light bulb, and a properly connected ammeter. The ammeter has a very low internal resistance because it is connected in (1) parallel with the bulb to have little effect on the current through the bulb (2) parallel with the bulb to prevent current flow through the bulb (3) series with the bulb to have little effect on the current through the bulb (4) series with the bulb to prevent current through the bulb

62. Compared to the resistance being measured, the internal resistance of a voltmeter is designed to be very high so that the meter will draw (1) no current from the circuit (2) little current from the circuit (3) most of the current from the circuit (4) all the current from the circuit

63. Which diagram below shows correct current direction in a circuit segment?

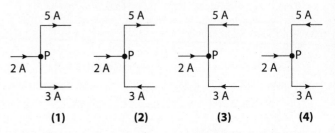

(1)   (2)   (3)   (4)

64. The diagram below shows currents in a segment of an electric circuit.

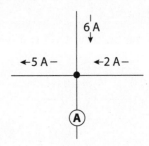

What is the reading of ammeter A?

65. The diagram below represents currents in branches of an electric circuit.

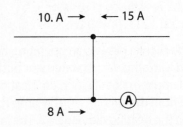

What is the reading on ammeter A? (1) 13 A (2) 17 A (3) 3 A (4) 33 A

66. Which combination of current and potential difference would use energy at the greatest rate?
(1) 7 A at 110 V (2) 6 A at 110 V (3) 3 A at 220 V
(4) 4 A at 220 V

67. How much time is required for an operating 100-watt light bulb to dissipate 10 joules of electrical energy? (1) 1 s (2) 0.1 s (3) 10 s (4) 1000 s

68. While operating at 120 volts, an electric toaster has a resistance of 15 ohms. The power used by the toaster is (1) 8.0 W (2) 120 W (3) 960 W (4) 1800 W

69. An electric dryer consumes 6.0×10^6 joules of energy when operating at 220 volts for 30. minutes. During operation, the dryer draws a current of approximately (1) 10. A (2) 15 A (3) 20. A (4) 25 A

70. What is the approximate amount of electrical energy needed to operate a 1600-watt toaster for 60. seconds? (1) 27 J (2) 1500 J (3) 1700 J (4) 96,000 J

71. To increase the brightness of a desk lamp, a student replaces a 60-watt light bulb with a 100-watt light bulb. Compared to the 60-watt light bulb, the 100-watt light bulb has (1) less resistance and draws more current (2) less resistance and draws less current (3) more resistance and draws more current (4) more resistance and draws less current

Base your answers to questions 72 through 75 on the diagram below, which represents a circuit containing a 120-volt power supply with switches S_1 and S_2 and two 60.-ohm resistors.

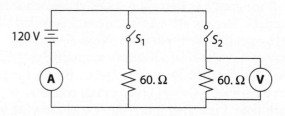

72. If switch S_1 is kept open and switch S_2 is closed, what is the circuit's resistance?

73. If switch S_2 is kept open and switch S_1 is closed, how much current will flow through the circuit?

74. When both switches are closed, what is the current in the ammeter?

75. When both switches are closed, what is the reading of the voltmeter?

Base your answers to questions 76 through 80 on the diagram below, which represents an electrical circuit.

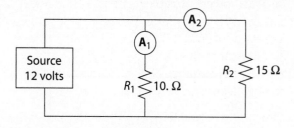

76. The equivalent resistance of the circuit is (1) 25 Ω (2) 6.0 Ω (3) 5.0 Ω (4) 0.17 Ω

77. Determine the potential difference across resistor R_2.

78. Determine the magnitude of the current flowing through ammeter A_1.

79. Compared to the current in ammeter A_1, the current in ammeter A_2 is (1) less (2) greater (3) the same

80. If another resistor is added to the circuit in parallel, the equivalent resistance of the circuit would (1) decrease (2) increase (3) remain the same

Base your answers to questions 81 through 85 on the following information and diagram. Two resistors, R_1 and R_2, and an ammeter are connected to a constant 30.-volt source. The equivalent resistance of the circuit is 6.0 ohms.

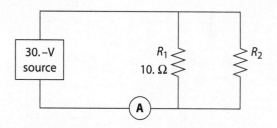

81. The resistance of R_2 is equal to (1) 6.0 Ω (2) 2.0 Ω (3) 15 Ω (4) 4.0 Ω

82. Determine the current read by ammeter A.

83. Determine the power developed in resistor R_1 alone.

84. Compared to the potential difference across the source, the potential difference across R_2 is (1) less (2) greater (3) the same

85. If the resistance of R_2 were increased, the current through R_2 would (1) decrease (2) increase (3) remain the same

Base your answers to questions 86 through 89 on the circuit diagram below.

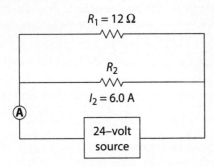

$R_1 = 12\ \Omega$

R_2

$I_2 = 6.0$ A

Ⓐ

24–volt source

86. The current in ammeter A is (1) 1.0 A (2) 2.0 A (3) 6.0 A (4) 8.0 A

87. How much energy is used by the 12-ohm resistor in 30. minutes? (1) 48 J (2) 3.6×10^3 J (3) 1.1×10^4 J (4) 8.6×10^4 J

88. If resistance R_2 were removed, the potential difference across R_1 would (1) decrease (2) increase (3) remain the same

89. If resistance R_2 were removed, the current in ammeter A would (1) decrease (2) increase (3) remain the same

Base your answers to questions 90 through 94 on the electric circuit below. Note that the switch is in the open position.

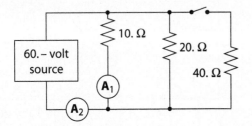

60. – volt source

10. Ω

20. Ω

40. Ω

A_1

A_2

90. What is the reading of ammeter A_1? (1) 0.16 A (2) 6.0 A (3) 60. A (4) 600 A

91. What is the reading of ammeter A_2? (1) 9.0 A (2) 2.0 A (3) 12 A (4) 18 A

92. Determine the power developed in the 10.-ohm resistor.

93. Compared to the potential drop across the 10.-ohm resistor, the potential drop across the 20.-ohm resistor is (1) less (2) greater (3) the same

94. Compared to the current through ammeter A_1 when the switch is open, the current passing through ammeter A_1 when the switch is closed is (1) less (2) greater (3) the same

Base your answers to questions 95 through 99 on the following information. An electric heater rated at 4800 watts is operated at 120 volts.

95. Determine the resistance of the heater.

96. Determine the amount of energy used by the heater in 10.0 seconds.

97. If the heater is replaced with one having a greater resistance, the amount of heat energy produced each second will (1) decrease (2) increase (3) remain the same

98. If another heater is connected in parallel with the first one and both operate at 120 volts, the current in the first heater will (1) decrease (2) increase (3) remain the same

99. If the original heater is operated at less than 120 volts, the amount of heat produced will (1) decrease (2) increase (3) remain the same

Magnetism

A **magnet** is a material in which the spinning electrons of its atoms are aligned with one another. This motion of charges relative to each other produces a **magnetic force.** Even if two magnets are at rest relative to each other, they exert magnetic force because the electrons within them are in motion. Many permanent magnets are made of an alloy of aluminum, nickel, and cobalt.

A magnet has two ends called poles, where the magnetic force is strongest. One end is called the north-seeking **magnetic pole** (N-pole), and the other end is the south-seeking magnetic pole (S-pole). No matter how many times a magnet is broken, each piece always has a north pole and a south pole. Like magnetic poles repel each other and unlike poles attract each other. **Magnetism** is the force of attraction or repulsion between magnetic poles. Unmagnetized pieces of iron and steel are readily magnetized by pulling them across a pole of a strong magnet or by having them interact with a direct current.

Earth is like a large magnet with a S-pole near the geographic North Pole (the northern end of its axis of rotation) and an N-pole near the geographic South Pole. The N-pole of a compass, a device having a magnetized needle that can spin freely, is attracted toward Earth's S-pole (geographic North Pole). Earth's magnetic field results from the motion of its molten iron and nickel core.

MAGNETIC FIELDS The region where magnetic force exists around a magnet or any moving charged object is called its **magnetic field.** Just as a gravitational or electric field allows objects to interact without coming into direct contact with each other, a magnetic field allows magnets to interact without touching. A magnetic field exerts a force on any moving charge and can be measured and detected by this effect.

MAGNETIC FLUX LINES Imaginary lines that map out the magnetic field around a magnet are known as **magnetic field lines** or **magnetic flux lines.** Iron filings sprinkled on a card and held above a magnet are often used to map a magnetic field. The filings show the effects of magnetic force in the region surrounding a magnet and produce a pattern similar to the magnetic field lines. Magnetic flux lines always form closed loops and never intersect. Concentrated lines of flux emerge from the N-pole of a magnet, curve around the magnet, and then enter the S-pole of the magnet. The direction of a magnetic field is defined as the direction in which the N-pole of a compass would point in the field. When the field lines are curved, the direction of the field is determined by the direction of the N-pole of a compass placed along the tangent to the field at that point. Figure 4-12 shows the locations of the lines of magnetic flux around some bar magnets and around a horseshoe magnet.

MAGNETIC FIELD STRENGTH The number of magnetic lines of flux per unit area passing through a plane perpendicular to the direction of the lines is called the **magnetic field strength,** B, or flux density. Magnetic field strength is a vector quantity, as are gravitational field strength and electric field strength. The **weber,** Wb, is a derived SI unit for measuring the number of lines of flux. The **tesla,** T, is the derived SI unit of flux density or magnetic field strength. One tesla is equal to one weber per square meter.

 # Review Questions

100. A magnetic field is produced by (1) moving electrons (2) moving neutrons (3) stationary protons (4) stationary ions

101. The presence of a uniform magnetic field may be detected by using a (1) stationary charge (2) small mass (3) beam of neutrons (4) magnetic compass

102. Which is the unit of magnetic flux in the SI system? (1) joule (2) weber (3) coulomb (4) ampere

103. The diagram below shows a compass placed near the north pole, N, of a bar magnet.

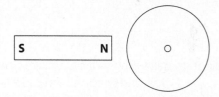

Which diagram best represents the position of the needle of a compass as it responds to the magnetic field of the bar magnet?

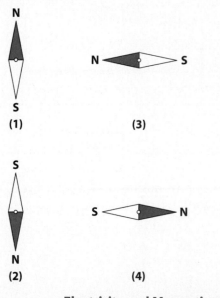

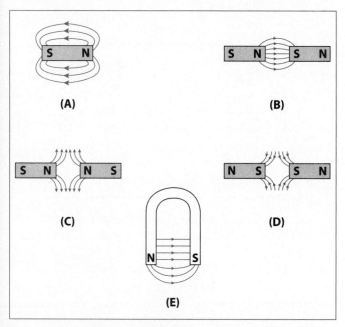

Figure 4-12. **Lines of magnetic flux around some bar magnets and a horseshoe magnet**

104. A coil of wire is wrapped around a piece of iron and connected to a battery. Due to the current through the coil, the iron develops a polarity as shown in the diagram below.

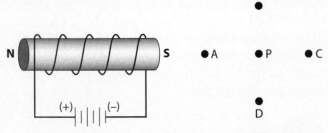

Toward which point would the north pole of a compass placed at point P point?

105. Which diagram correctly shows a magnetic field configuration?

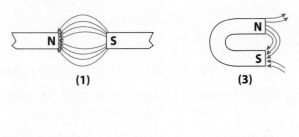

106. The diagram below shows a coil of wire connected to a power supply and wrapped around a U-shaped piece of iron. The arrows indicate the direction of the resulting magnetic field.

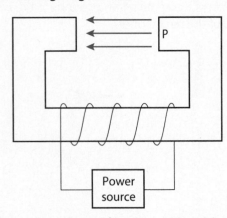

What is the polarity of P? (1) positive (2) negative (3) north (4) south

107. Which diagram best represents the lines of magnetic flux between the ends of two bar magnets?

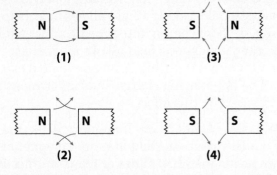

108. The diagram below represents the magnetic lines of force around a bar magnet.

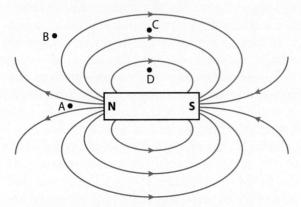

At which point is the magnitude of the magnetic field strength of the bar magnet greatest?

109. The diagram below represents magnetic lines of force within a region of space.

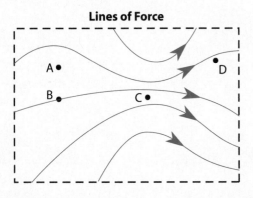

At which point is the magnetic field strongest?

Electromagnetic Induction

Electromagnetic induction is the process of generating a potential difference in a conductor due to relative motion between the conductor and a magnetic field. If the conductor "cuts" across the magnetic flux lines, a magnetic force acts on the electrons in the conductor, causing them to move from one end toward the other. This results in a difference in the amount of negative charge at each end of the conductor, in other words, a potential difference. The difference in potential created in a conductor due to its relative motion in a magnetic field is called an **induced potential difference.** Figure 4-13 shows a potential difference being induced in a conductor.

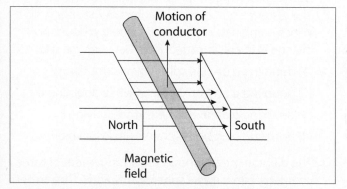

Figure 4-13. Electromagnetic induction: The diagram shows the direction of motion of a straight conductor relative to a magnetic field that produces a maximum induced potential difference in the conductor.

   If the conductor is part of a complete circuit, an electric current is induced. If the conductor is moved parallel to the lines of flux (that is, it does not "cut" them) no potential difference is induced and there is no current, even if the conductor is part of a complete circuit.

ELECTROMAGNETIC RADIATION Oscillating or accelerating electric charges produce changing electric and magnetic fields that radiate outward into the surrounding space in the form of waves. Such a combined electric and magnetic wave is called an **electromagnetic wave**. A discussion of electromagnetic waves is included in Topic 5.

Review Questions

110. For which two angles between the direction of motion of a wire and a magnetic field can a potential difference be induced across the wire?
(1) 0° and 45° (2) 0° and 90° (3) 45° and 90°
(4) 45° and 180°

111. The diagram below represents a straight conductor between the poles of a permanent magnet.

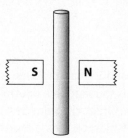

In which direction should the wire be moved to induce a potential difference? (1) toward N
(2) toward S (3) toward the top of the page
(4) into the page

112. A conductor is moved perpendicularly through magnetic field B as represented in the diagram below.

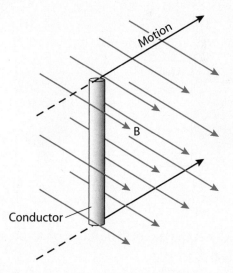

What is being induced in the conductor? (1) potential difference (2) resistance (3) power (4) current

Questions for Regents Practice

Part A

1. A sphere has a charge of -6.40×10^{-7} coulomb. Approximately how many electrons must be removed to make the sphere neutral?

   (1) 2.50×10^{-13}

   (2) 1.60×10^{12}

   (3) 4.00×10^{12}

   (4) 7.03×10^{24}

2. An inflated balloon that has been rubbed against a person's hair is touched to a neutral wall and remains attracted to it. Which diagram best represents the charge distribution on the balloon and wall?

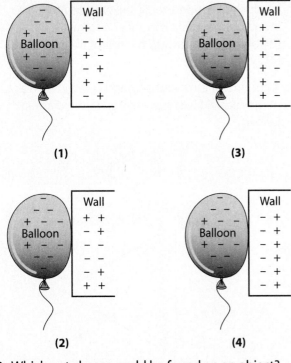

   (1)   (3)

   (2)   (4)

3. Which net charge could be found on an object?

   (1) 1.60×10^{-20} C

   (2) 2.40×10^{-19} C

   (3) 6.80×10^{-19} C

   (4) 8.00×10^{-18} C

4. After a neutral object loses 2 electrons, it will have a net charge of

   (1) $-2e$

   (2) $+2e$

   (3) $-3.20 \times 10^{-19}\, e$

   (4) $+3.20 \times 10^{-19}\, e$

5. The electrostatic force between two positive point charges is F when the charges are 48 centimeters apart. When these point charges are placed 24 centimeters apart, the electrostatic force between them is

   (1) $\dfrac{F}{4}$, and attracting

   (2) $4F$, and attracting

   (3) $\dfrac{F}{4}$, and repelling

   (4) $4F$, and repelling

6. A repulsive electrostatic force of magnitude F exists between two metal spheres of identical charge q. The distance between the centers of the spheres is r. Which combination of changes would produce no change in the electrostatic force between the spheres?

   (1) doubling q on one sphere while doubling r

   (2) doubling q on both spheres while doubling r

   (3) doubling q on one sphere while halving r

   (4) doubling q on both spheres while halving r

7. The diagram below shows the arrangement of three charged hollow metal spheres, A, B, and C. The arrows indicate the direction of the electric forces acting between the spheres. At least two of the spheres are positively charged.

   Which sphere if any could be negatively charged?

   (1) sphere A

   (2) sphere B

   (3) sphere C

   (4) no sphere

8. An electrostatic force of 20.0 newtons is exerted on a charge of 8.00×10^{-2} coulomb at point P in an electric field. The magnitude of the electric field strength at P is

   (1) 4.00×10^{-3} C/N

   (2) 1.60 N · C

   (3) 20.0 N/C

   (4) 2.50×10^2 N/C

9. If 6.40×10^{-19} joule of work is required to move a proton between two points A and B in an electric field, what is the potential difference between points A and B?

(1) 6.40×10^{-19} V

(2) 4.00×10^{-19} V

(3) 6.40 V

(4) 4.00 V

10. How much energy is required to move 3.20×10^{-19} coulomb of charge through a potential difference of 5.0 volts?

(1) 5.0 eV

(2) 2.0 eV

(3) 10. eV

(4) 10.0 eV

11. The diagram below shows a simple electric circuit.

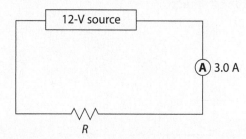

How much charge passes through resistor R in 2.0 seconds?

(1) 36 C

(2) 6.0 C

(3) 3.0 C

(4) 4.0 C

12. A wire carries a current of 6.0 amperes. How much charge passes a point in the wire in 2.0 minutes?

(1) 720 C

(2) 360 C

(3) 3.0 C

(4) 12 C

13. A simple circuit has a total resistance of 1.00×10^2 ohms and an applied potential difference of 2.00×10^2 volts. The amount of charge passing any point in the circuit in 2.00 seconds is

(1) 1.26×10^{19} C

(2) 2.00 C

(3) 2.52×10^{19} C

(4) 4.00 C

14. The ratio of the potential difference across a conductor to the current in the conductor is called

(1) voltage

(2) resistivity

(3) resistance

(4) power

15. A metal conductor is used in an electric circuit. The electrical resistance provided by the conductor could be increased by

(1) decreasing the length of the conductor

(2) decreasing the applied voltage in the circuit

(3) increasing the temperature of the conductor

(4) increasing the cross-sectional area of the conductor

16. A uniform aluminum wire has a resistance of 100 ohms. If the wire is cut into 10 equal lengths, the resistance of each piece will be

(1) 1 Ω   (2) 10 Ω   (3) 100 Ω   (4) 1000 Ω

17. A 6.50-meter long copper wire at 20°C has a cross-sectional area of 3.0 millimeters². What is the resistance of the wire?

(1) 3.7×10^{-8} Ω   (3) 3.7×10^{-2} Ω

(2) 3.73×10^{-8} Ω   (4) 3.73×10^{-2} Ω

18. A 4.00-meter long aluminum wire at 20°C has a radius of 2.5×10^{-3} meter. What is the resistance of the wire?

(1) 1.4×10^{-5} Ω   (3) 1.0×10^{-2} Ω

(2) 5.7×10^{-3} Ω   (4) 5.7×10^{-1} Ω

19. In the circuit shown below, voltmeter V_2 reads 80. volts.

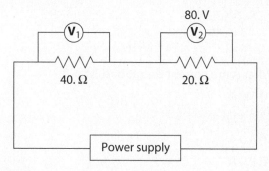

What is the reading of voltmeter V_1?

(1) 160 V

(2) 80. V

(3) 40. V

(4) 20. V

20. The diagram below shows three resistors connected to a 12-volt battery.

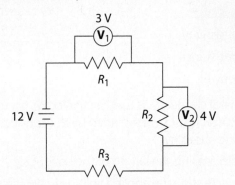

If voltmeter V₁ reads 3 volts and voltmeter V₂ reads 4 volts, what is the potential drop across resistor R_3?

(1) 12 V

(2) 5 V

(3) 0 V

(4) 4 V

21. As more resistors are added in series across a battery, the potential drop across each resistor

(1) decreases

(2) increases

(3) remains the same

22. The diagram below represents a series circuit containing three resistors.

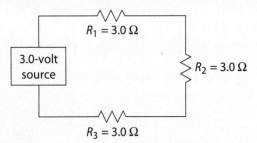

What is the current through resistor R_2?

(1) 1.0 A

(2) 0.33 A

(3) 3.0 A

(4) 9.0 A

23. Resistors R_1 and R_2 have an equivalent resistance of 6 ohms when connected in the circuit shown below.

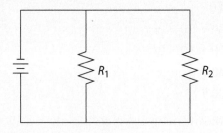

The resistance of R_1 could be

(1) 1 Ω

(2) 5 Ω

(3) 8 Ω

(4) 4 Ω

24. The diagram below shows three resistors connected to a 9-volt source.

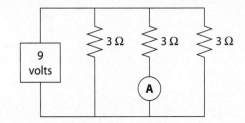

What is the current in ammeter A?

(1) 1 A

(2) 0.3 A

(3) 3 A

(4) 9 A

25. A 10-ohm and a 20-ohm resistor are connected in parallel to a constant voltage source. If the current through the 10-ohm resistor is 4 amperes, the current through the 20-ohm resistor is

(1) 1 A

(2) 2 A

(3) 8 A

(4) 4 A

26. Which circuit segment has an equivalent resistance of 6 ohms?

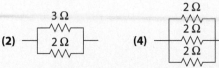

27. In which circuit shown below could the readings of voltmeters V_1 and V_2 and ammeter A be correct?

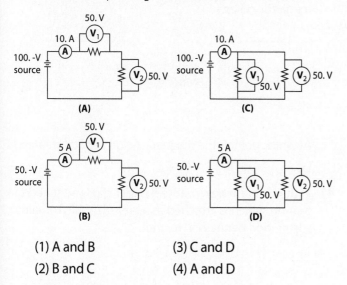

(1) A and B

(3) C and D

(2) B and C

(4) A and D

28. Ammeters A_1, A_2, and A_3 are placed in a circuit as shown below.

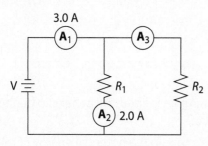

What is the reading of ammeter A_3?

(1) 1.0 A

(2) 2.0 A

(3) 3.0 A

(4) 5.0 A

29. The diagram below shows the current in a segment of a direct current circuit.

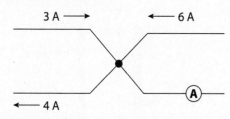

What is the reading of ammeter A?

(1) 1 A

(2) 5 A

(3) 7 A

(4) 8 A

30. A light bulb operating at 120 volts draws a current of 0.50 ampere for 240 seconds. The power rating of the light bulb is

(1) 30. W

(2) 60. W

(3) 75 W

(4) 120 W

31. The heating element on an electric stove dissipates 4.0×10^2 watts of power when connected to a 120-volt source. What is the electrical resistance of this heating element?

(1) 0.028 Ω

(2) 0.60 Ω

(3) 3.3 Ω

(4) 36 Ω

32. The same potential difference is applied to two lamps, A and B. The resistance of lamp A is twice the resistance of lamp B. Compared to the power developed by lamp B, the power developed by lamp A is

(1) less

(2) greater

(3) the same

33. A clothes dryer connected to a 240-volt line draws 30. amperes of current for 20. minutes. Approximately how much electrical energy is consumed by the dryer?

(1) 4.8×10^3 J

(2) 7.2×10^3 J

(3) 1.4×10^5 J

(4) 8.6×10^6 J

34. An electric iron draws a current of 5 amperes and has a resistance of 20 ohms. The amount of energy used by the iron in 40 seconds is

(1) 1×10^2 J

(2) 5×10^2 J

(3) 4×10^3 J

(4) 2×10^4 J

35. An operating 75-watt lamp is connected to a 120-volt outlet. How much electrical energy does the lamp use in 1.0 hour?

(1) 4.5×10^3 J

(2) 2.7×10^5 J

(3) 5.4×10^5 J

(4) 3.2×10^7 J

36. Magnetic flux density may be measured in

(1) N/m^2

(2) Wb/m^2

(3) C/m^2

(4) J/m^2

37. The diagram below shows a point located between two magnetic poles.

What is the direction of the magnetic field at point A?

(1) to the left

(2) to the right

(3) toward the top of the page

(4) toward the bottom of the page

38. Which diagram best represents the magnetic field near the poles of a horseshoe magnet?

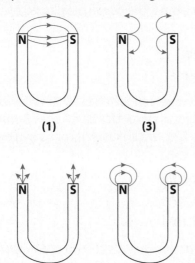

39. Which diagram best represents the magnetic field between two magnetic north poles?

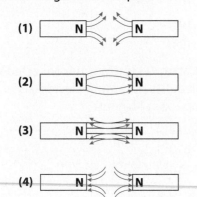

40. The diagram below shows the magnetic field that results when a piece of iron is placed between unlike magnetic poles.

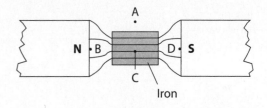

At which point is the magnetic field strength greatest?

(1) A   (2) B   (3) C   (4) D

41. In the diagram below, a steel paper clip is attached to a string, which is attached to a table. The clip remains suspended beneath a magnet.

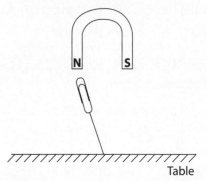

As the magnet is lifted, the paper clip begins to fall as a result of

(1) an increase in the potential energy of the clip

(2) an increase in the gravitational field strength near the magnet

(3) a decrease in the mass of the paper clip

(4) a decrease in the magnetic field strength near the clip

42. In the diagram below a straight wire is at rest in a uniform magnetic field directed into the page.

$$\begin{matrix} X & X & X \\ X & X & X \\ X & X & X \\ X & X & X \\ X & X & X \\ X & X & X \end{matrix}$$

Magnetic field

A potential difference will be induced in the wire if it is moved

(1) toward the top of the page   (3) into the page

(2) toward the right of the page   (4) out of the page

43. The diagram below shows the cross section of a wire that is perpendicular to the page in a uniform magnetic field directed to the right.

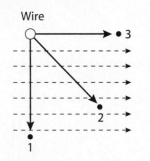

Wire

Toward which direction could the wire be moved to induce an electric potential?

(1) 1 only

(2) both 1 and 2

(3) 3 only

(4) both 1 and 3

44. A potential difference is induced in a wire moving through a magnetic field, if the angle between the magnetic field and the wire is

(1) 0°   (3) 180°

(2) 90°   (4) 360°

Part B

45. In the diagram below, the open circle represents an uncharged metal sphere located midway between two charged spheres, A and B. On the diagram, using + for positive and − for negative, mark at least six charges to represent the arrangement of charges in the uncharged sphere. [1]

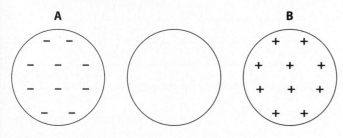

A   B

46. Determine the charge to mass ratio $(\frac{e}{m})$ for an electron. [2]

47. Three identical metal spheres are mounted on insulating stands. Initially, sphere A has a net charge of q and spheres B and C are uncharged. Sphere A is touched to sphere B and removed. Then sphere A is touched to sphere C and removed. What is the final charge on sphere A in terms of q? [1]

48. Charge A is +2.0 microcoulombs and charge B is +1.0 microcoulomb. If the force that A exerts on B is 1.0×10^{-2} newton, what is the force that B exerts on A? [1]

49. In the diagram below, two identical spheres A and B have equal net positive charges.

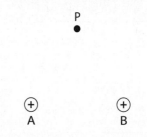

On the diagram, sketch an arrow that best represents the direction of the resultant electric field at point P. [1]

Base your answers to questions 50 through 53 on the following information and diagram. Two small spheres A and B are separated by a distance of 0.50 meter. The charge on sphere A is +2.4 microcoulombs and the charge on sphere B is −2.4 microcoulombs.

50. On the diagram sketch at least three electric field lines in the region between sphere A and sphere B. Draw an arrowhead on each field line to show the proper direction. [2]

51. Determine the magnitude of the force between the two charged spheres. [2]

52. On the graph below, draw the general shape of the graph representing electrostatic force versus the distance separating the two oppositely charged spheres. [1]

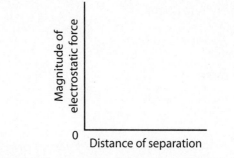

53. The two spheres are brought into contact and then separated. After separation, what is the charge on each sphere? [1]

Base your answers to questions 54 through 58 on the following information and diagram. Two parallel plates are charged to a potential difference of 10.0 volts. Points A, B, and C are located in the region between the plates.

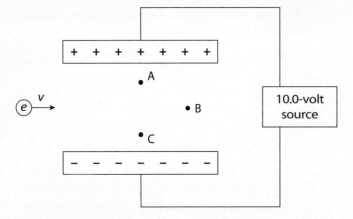

54. Sketch at least three electric field lines in the region between the oppositely charged parallel plates. Draw lines with arrowheads in the proper direction. [2]

55. If an electron were projected into the electric field with a velocity *v*, as shown, it would

(1) deflect into the page

(2) deflect out of the page

(3) deflect toward the top of the page

(4) deflect toward the bottom of the page

56. Compared to the magnitude of the electric field strength at point B, the magnitude of the electric field strength at point A is

(1) less

(2) greater

(3) the same

57. Compared to the work done in moving an electron from point A to point B to point C, the work done against the electric field in moving an electron directly from point A to point C is

(1) less

(2) greater

(3) the same

58. As a proton moves from A to B to C, the magnitude of the electric force on the proton

(1) decreases

(2) increases

(3) remains the same

59. Which graph below best represents how the resistance *R* of a series of tungsten wires of uniform length and temperature varies with cross-sectional area *A*?

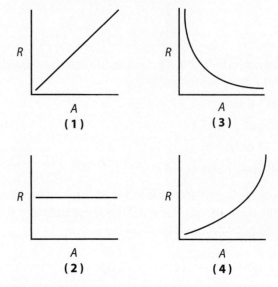

60. The table below shows the length and cross-sectional area of four pieces of copper wire at the same temperature.

Wire	Length (m)	Cross-sectional Area (m²)
A	10	2×10^{-6}
B	10	1×10^{-6}
C	1	2×10^{-6}
D	1	1×10^{-6}

Which wire has the highest resistance? [1]

Base your answers to questions 61 through 64 on the following information and graph. Four different conductors of equal length and equal cross-sectional area were held at constant temperature while the potential difference across each was varied. The resulting current through each conductor was measured. The data are represented in the graph below.

Current vs. Potential Difference

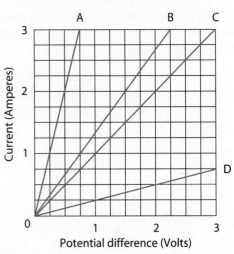

61. Which conductor has the greatest resistance? [1]

62. Which conductor has the smallest resistivity? [1]

63. Determine the resistance of conductor B. [2]

64. Determine the rate of energy use in conductor B at 1.4 volts. [2]

Base your answers to questions 65 through 67 on the circuit diagram below.

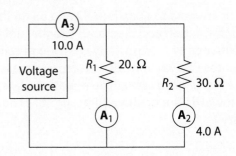

65. Determine the potential difference across the source. [2]

66. What is the current reading of ammeter A_1?
    (1) 10.0 A   (3) 3.0 A
    (2) 6.0 A   (4) 4.0 A

67. Determine the power dissipated by resistor R_2. [2]

Base your answers to questions 68 through 72 on the following information and diagram. A 5.0-ohm resistor, a 15.0-ohm resistor, and an unmarked resistor are connected as shown with a 15-volt source. The ammeter reads a current of 0.50 ampere.

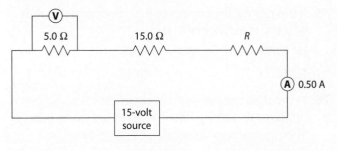

68. Determine the reading of the voltmeter across the 5.0-ohm resistor. [2]

69. Determine the total electrical energy used in the circuit in 10.0 minutes. [2]

70. The value of the unmarked resistor is
    (1) 0 Ω   (3) 20. Ω
    (2) 10. Ω   (4) 30. Ω

71. Compared to the power dissipated by the 5.0-ohm resistor, the power dissipated by the 15.0-ohm resistor is
    (1) less
    (2) greater
    (3) the same

72. If the 5.0-ohm resistor were removed from the circuit and the remaining circuit elements reattached to the source in the same manner as in the original diagram, the reading of the ammeter would be
    (1) less than 0.50 A
    (2) more than 0.50 A
    (3) equal to 0.50 A

Base your answers to questions 73 through 75 on the following information and diagram. Three resistors are connected in parallel across a 24-volt source. The ammeter reads 3.0 amperes.

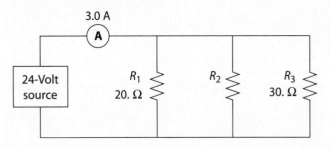

73. The equivalent resistance of the circuit is

(1) 0.13 Ω   (3) 58 Ω

(2) 8.0 Ω   (4) 72 Ω

74. Determine the current in resistor R_1. [2]

75. If the ratio of the current in R_3 to the current in R_2 is 4 : 5, the resistance of R_2 is

(1) 5.0 Ω   (3) 24 Ω

(2) 8.0 Ω   (4) 60. Ω

76. In the diagram below steel paper clips A and B are attached to a string, which is attached to the table. The clips remain suspended beneath a magnet.

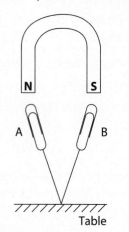

Label each of the paper clips in the diagram with its induced polarity. [1]

77. On the diagram of a bar magnet below, sketch at least four magnetic lines of flux with arrowheads to represent the magnetic field around the magnet. [2]

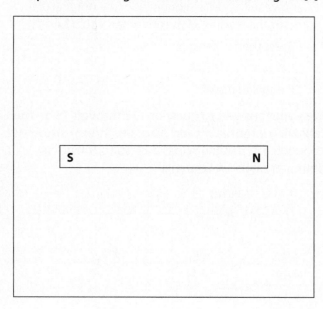

Base your answers to questions 78 through 80 on your knowledge of electricity.

78. Explain why it would be highly impractical to have household circuits wired in series. [1]

79. Explain why the tungsten filament of a 150-watt incandescent bulb is thicker and shorter than the filament of a 60-watt incandescent bulb. [1]

80. Explain why an electron appears to defy gravity as it accelerates upward between two oppositely charged parallel plates. [1]

81. The diagram below represents a particle of mass m and charge $+q$ located between two oppositely charged parallel plates. The electric field intensity between the plates is E.

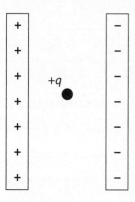

On the diagram draw and label all the force vectors acting on the particle. [2]

Part C

Base your answers to questions 82 and 83 on the following information and diagram. Potential difference V exists between two oppositely charged parallel metal plates in a vacuum. An electron of mass m_e and charge e starts from rest at the negative plate and travels towards the positive plate. (Ignore the effect of gravity.)

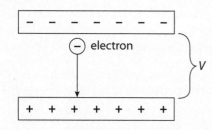

82. Determine the maximum speed v of the electron in terms of V, m_e, and e. [2]

83. The electron is replaced with a proton that starts from rest at the positive plate and travels toward the negative plate. Compare the maximum speed of the proton to the maximum speed of the electron in question 82 and give evidence to support your answer. [1]

84. According to Ohm's law an ohm is equivalent to a volt per ampere. The ohm can be expressed in terms of the fundamental units kilogram, meter, second, and ampere. Show how $1 \frac{V}{A} = 1 \frac{kg \cdot m^2}{A^2 \cdot s^3}$ [3]

85. Determine the radius r of a conductor in terms of its length ℓ, resistance R, and resistivity ρ. [2]

Base your answers to questions 86 through 90 on the following information. An electric broiler is rated 1440 watts and 120 volts. The broiler is connected to a 120-volt line.

86. Draw a diagram of the circuit, showing a voltmeter and an ammeter properly connected to determine the actual power (wattage) of the broiler. [2]

87. Determine the resistance of the heating coil, if the broiler is operating at the rated power. [2]

88. Assuming that all of the electrical energy used is converted to heat energy, determine the energy the broiler produces in 10.0 minutes. [2]

89. A 15-ampere fuse protects the electrical power supply line. Determine how much additional current can be drawn from the line before the fuse blows. [2]

90. A "short circuit" is a circuit containing a path of very low resistance in parallel with some other circuit element, such as a lamp. Explain the effect a short circuit would have on the power output of the broiler. [1]

Base your answers to questions 91 through 96 on the following information. A 3.0-ohm resistor and a 6.0-ohm resistor are connected in parallel to an applied potential difference of 12 volts.

91. Using appropriate symbols from the *Reference Tables for Physical Setting/Physics*, draw a labeled circuit diagram. [1]

92. Determine the current in the 6.0-ohm resistor. [2]

93. Determine the potential drop across the 3.0-ohm resistor. [1]

94. What is the power developed in the circuit? [3]

95. An additional 2.0-ohm resistor is connected in parallel in the circuit. Explain what effect, if any, this action would have on the amount of current drawn by the 6.0-ohm resistor. [1]

96. Compare the equivalent resistance of the 3.0-ohm resistor and the 6.0-ohm resistor when connected in parallel to their equivalent resistance when connected in series. [1]

Base your answers to questions 97 through 104 on the following information and data table.

A student performed an experiment with the intention of verifying Ohm's law for a household light bulb labeled 150 W. In addition to the light bulb, the student had available to him a socket appropriate for a lamp, a variable source of potential difference, an ammeter, a voltmeter, and connecting wires of negligible resistance. After correctly connecting the ammeter and voltmeter in a circuit with the bulb and source, the student increased the applied potential difference in increments of 1.0 volt and recorded the reading of the ammeter each time. The student took only one reading of the ammeter for each potential difference value. The student's data are shown in the table below.

Potential Difference (V)	Current (A)
0.0	0.00
1.0	0.08
2.0	0.16
3.0	0.20
4.0	0.22
5.0	0.24
6.0	0.26
7.0	0.27

97. Using appropriate symbols from the *Reference Tables for Physical Setting/Physics* and a box labeled "power source," draw and label a complete circuit showing:

- the lamp connected to the power source [1]

- the ammeter connected to measure the current through the lamp [1]

- the voltmeter connected to measure the potential difference across the lamp [1]

98. Using the information in the data table, construct a graph using the grid on the following page by:

- plotting the data points [1]

- drawing the curve of best fit [1]

- writing an appropriate title above the grid [1]

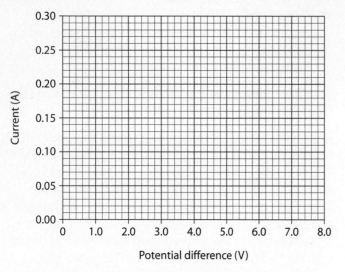

99. Determine the slope of the graph at the 3.0-volt reading. [2]

100. What is the physical significance of the slope of the line at any point? [1]

101. The student concluded that the lamp does not obey Ohm's law. Based on your knowledge of physics and the graph, state the most likely reason why. [1]

102. On the same graph used in question 98, sketch a line representing a device that obeys Ohm's law. [1]

103. Determine the maximum power developed by the lamp during the experiment. [2]

104. Explain why your answer to question 103 does not agree with the 150 W label on the bulb. [1]

Base your answers to questions 105 through 109 on the following information and data table. In an experiment, a potential difference of 2.0 volts was applied to various lengths of wire of the same cross-sectional area and metallic composition at a temperature of 20°C. The resulting current was measured and the data recorded in the table below. The student calculated the resistance for each length of wire and recorded that in the table as well.

Length (cm)	Potential Difference (V)	Current (mA)	Resistance
40.	2.0	500	4.0
80.	2.0	240	8.3
120.	2.0	170	12
160.	2.0	120	17
200.	2.0	100	20.

105. Using the information in the data table, construct a graph on the grid below by:

- plotting the data points [1]

- drawing the curve of best fit [1]

- writing an appropriate title above the grid [1]

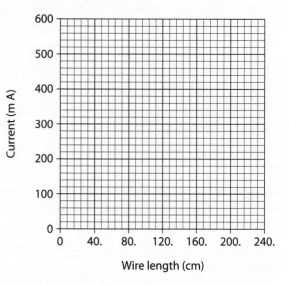

106. Based on your graph, state the relationship between current and wire length. [1]

107. What unit should be written on the data table for resistance? [1]

108. On the axes below sketch the general shape of the graph that shows the relationship between resistance and wire length based on information in the data table. [1]

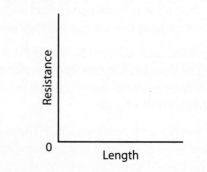

109. The diameter of the wire is 3.18×10^{-4} meter. Determine the resistivity of the 200.-centimeter-long wire. [3]

Waves

VOCABULARY

absolute index of refraction	hertz	ray
amplitude	incident ray	reflected ray
angle of incidence	interference	refracted ray
angle of reflection	law of reflection	reflection
angle of refraction	longitudinal wave	refraction
antinode	medium	resonance
constructive interference	natural frequency	Snell's law
destructive interference	node	speed
	normal	standing wave
diffraction	period	superposition
Doppler effect	periodic wave	transverse wave
electromagnetic spectrum	phase	vacuum
electromagnetic wave	principle of superposition	wave
		wave front
frequency	pulse	wavelength

Introduction to Waves

A **wave** is a vibratory disturbance that propagates through a **medium** (body of matter) or field. Every wave has, as its source, a particle vibrating or oscillating about an average position. For example, a sound wave can be produced by a vibrating tuning fork and a radio wave can be generated by accelerating electrons in a transmitter.

Waves and Energy Transfer

Waves transfer energy from one place to another by repeated small vibrations of particles of a medium or by repeated small changes in the strength of a field. The source provides the initial vibrations, but there is no actual transfer of mass from the source. Only energy is transferred from the source. The propagation of mechanical waves, such as sound and water waves, requires a material medium. Electromagnetic waves, such as visible light and radio waves, can travel through a **vacuum,** which is a region of empty space.

Pulses and Periodic Waves

A wave may be classified as either a pulse or a periodic wave. A **pulse** is a single short disturbance that moves from one position to another in a field or medium. For example, a pulse produced on a stretched rope moves horizontally along the rope, as shown in Figure 5-1.

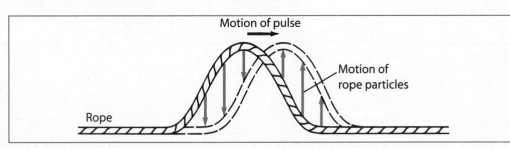

Figure 5-1. A pulse on a rope: A pulse is a single vertical disturbance transmitted horizontally at a definite speed.

The speed of a pulse depends upon the type and properties of the medium. Pulse speed is constant if the medium is a uniform material with the same properties throughout. If the pulse reaches an interface or boundary of a new medium, part of the pulse is transmitted through the new medium, part is absorbed, and part is reflected back to the source. **Reflection** is the rebounding of a pulse or wave as it strikes a barrier.

Ceiling tiles, draperies, and carpeting help minimize noise levels in a room. These irregularly shaped surfaces absorb some of the energy of sound waves that strike them. The reflected sound waves have less energy than the original waves.

If the right end of the rope in Figure 5-1 was attached to a fixed unyielding body, such as a wall, the pulse would be completely reflected. None of the wave energy would be absorbed or transmitted. The reflected pulse, however, would be inverted, as shown in Figure 5-2.

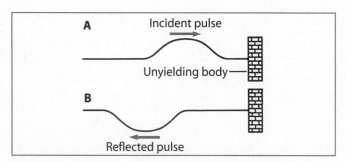

Figure 5-2. A pulse is reflected and inverted: (A) A wave pulse travels to the right along a rope attached to a brick wall. **(B)** When the pulse reaches the wall, it is reflected back toward the left in an inverted position.

This inversion can be explained by Newton's third law. When the pulse in Figure 5-2 arrives at the wall, the pulse exerts an upward force on the wall. Because the wall does not move, it exerts a force of equal magnitude on the rope in the opposite direction, which is downward. This reaction force inverts the pulse just before it is reflected back through the original medium.

If the initial disturbance that causes a pulse is repeated regularly, without interruption or change, a series of regular, evenly timed disturbances in the medium is produced. This series of regularly repeated disturbances of a field or medium is called a **periodic wave.**

Types of Wave Motion

A wave in which the motion of the vibratory disturbance is parallel to the direction of propagation or travel of the wave through the medium is called a **longitudinal wave.** Sound waves, compression waves in a spring, and earthquake P-waves are examples of longitudinal waves. A longitudinal wave is represented in Figure 5-3. Notice that the arrows indicating direction of motion of the wave and direction of particle motion are parallel to each other.

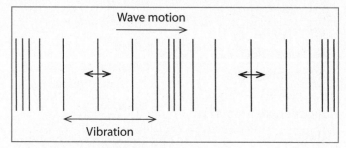

Figure 5-3. Longitudinal wave

Another type of wave, a **transverse wave,** is one in which the motion of the vibratory disturbance is perpendicular, or at right angles to the direction of travel of the wave. An easy way to remember this is that the symbol for perpendicular lines, ⊥, is the first letter in the word transverse, T, inverted. The transverse wave shown in Figure 5-4 is produced in a rope if the end is moved up and down or side to side. The direction of motion of the rope determines the plane of the wave's motion, which is always perpendicular to the rope's vibration. Electromagnetic waves and earthquake S-waves are examples of other transverse waves.

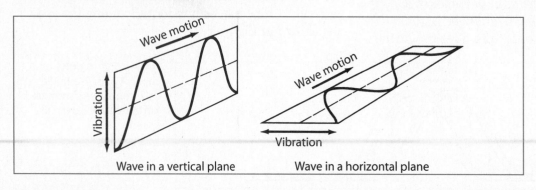

Figure 5-4. Transverse waves: These transverse waves have the same direction of travel but are in different planes.

Characteristics of Periodic Waves

Periodic waves are not described solely by their type, such as longitudinal or transverse. Other characteristics distinguish an individual wave from another similar wave. Some of these characteristics are described below.

FREQUENCY The complete series of changes at one point in a medium as a wave passes is called a cycle. The number of cycles, or complete vibrations, experienced at each point per unit time is called the **frequency,** f, of the wave. A frequency of 1 cycle per second is called 1 **hertz.** The hertz, Hz, is the derived SI unit of frequency. In fundamental units, 1 Hz equals 1/s, or s^{-1}, which can be read as *per second*.

The frequency of a sound wave determines its pitch, whereas the frequency of a light wave determines its color. The human ear can detect frequencies in the range of 20 to 20,000 hertz, and the human eye perceives frequencies of approximately 3.84×10^{14} to 7.69×10^{14} hertz.

PERIOD The time required for one complete vibration to pass a given point in the medium is called the **period** of the wave and is denoted by T. Note that this is a capital letter. The period of a periodic wave is inversely proportional to frequency and is given by this formula.

$$T = \frac{1}{f}$$

T is the period in seconds and f is the frequency in hertz or per second. The second, s, is the SI unit for period.

AMPLITUDE The graph of the displacement of a wave versus time is called the wave's waveform. The discussion that follows treats only the relatively simple sine wave, which has the shape of a sine curve. All complex waveforms may be analyzed in terms of the interactions of many different sine waves.

The **amplitude** of a mechanical wave is the maximum displacement of a particle of the medium from its rest or equilibrium position. The amplitude of a wave in a field is the maximum change in the field strength from its normal value.

In a transverse wave, the position of maximum displacement of a particle of the medium in the positive direction (for example, upward) is called a crest. The position of maximum displacement in the negative direction (downward) is called a trough. The greater the amplitude of the wave, the higher the crests and the lower the troughs. Transverse waves of various amplitudes are shown in Figure 5-5.

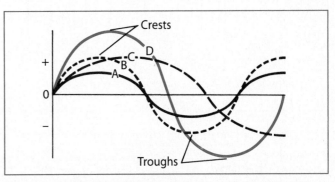

Figure 5-5. Wave amplitudes: Waves A and B have the same frequency but different amplitudes. Waves B and C have the same amplitudes but different frequencies. Wave D has the greatest amplitude of the four waves.

In a longitudinal wave, the periodic displacements of the particles of the medium produce regions of maximum compression called condensations that alternate with regions of maximum expansion called rarefactions. The greater the amplitude of the wave, the greater the compression of the particles in the condensations and the greater the separation of the particles in the rarefactions. Figure 5-6 on the following page shows compressions and rarefactions in a longitudinal wave.

The amplitude of a wave is related to the amount of energy it transmits. The greater the amplitude of a light wave, the greater the light intensity or brightness. The greater the amplitude of a sound wave, the louder the sound. The amplitude of a sound wave is not related to its frequency or pitch.

PHASE Points on successive wave cycles of a periodic wave that are displaced from their rest position by the same amount in the same direction and are moving in the same direction (away from or towards their rest positions) are said to have the same **phase,** or to be "in phase" with each other. For example, in a transverse wave, all the wave crests are in phase. In Figure 5-7 on the next page points A and E are in phase, B and F are in phase, and C and G are in phase.

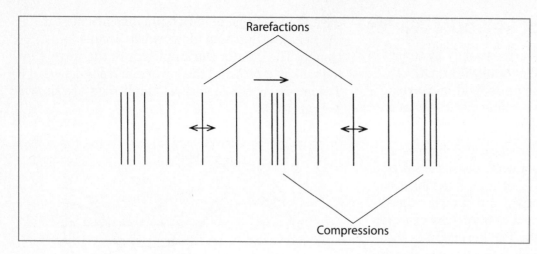

Rarefactions

Compressions

Figure 5-6. Compressions and rarefactions of a longitudinal wave

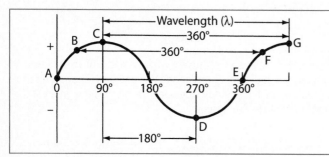

Figure 5-7. Phase relations in a wave

A simple way to determine if two points on a wave are in phase is to picture cutting out a template of the waveform between the points. If the template can be lifted, placed adjacent to one of the points and traced without interruption to make the original sine wave form, the points are in phase.

Because there are 360° in a complete circle, one complete cycle of a periodic wave is often represented as equal to 360°. One half-cycle is then 180°. Points on a wave that are 180° apart are said to be "out of phase." In Figure 5-7, points C and D are out of phase.

WAVELENGTH The distance between any two successive points in phase with one another in a periodic wave is called the **wavelength** of the wave. In Figure 5-7, the distance between points C and G, B and F, and A and E is one wavelength. Wavelength is represented by the symbol λ and is measured in units of length, such as meters and nanometers. If two points on a transverse wave are 180° out of phase, the distance between them is one-half wavelength or $\frac{1}{2}$ λ.

The wavelength of a transverse wave is often measured between successive crests or troughs. The wavelength of a longitudinal wave is measured between successive compressions or rarefactions.

SPEED OF WAVES The **speed** of a wave is equal

to the product of its wavelength and frequency.

$$v = f\lambda$$

Frequency, f, is in hertz, wavelength, λ, is in meters, and speed, v, is in meters per second. This relation is valid for all waves in all media.

The speed of a wave depends upon its type and the medium through which it travels. Often at baseball games the bat is *seen* hitting the ball before the crack of the bat is *heard*. Why? Light travels at 3.00×10^8 meters per second in air, whereas sound travels only 346 meters per second in air at 25°C. The light from the bat hitting the ball reaches your eyes before the sound reaches your ears.

SAMPLE PROBLEM

The following diagram shows a segment of a periodic wave in a spring traveling to the right to point I.
(a) What type of wave is represented in the diagram?
(b) What is the amplitude of the wave?
(c) What is the wavelength of the wave?
(d) If the frequency of the wave is 2.0 hertz, what is the period of the wave?
(e) Determine the speed of the wave.
(f) Name two points on the wave that are in phase.
(g) Immediately after the wave moves through point I, will point H move up, down, left, or right?

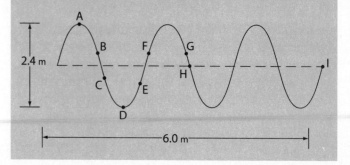

Solution:

(a) The particles of the medium vibrate perpendicular to the direction of wave motion. Thus, the wave is transverse.

(b) The at-rest position is represented by the horizontal dashed line. Displacement is the vertical distance from the at-rest position to the curve. Therefore, the maximum displacement is $\frac{1}{2}$ the vertical height of the diagram or 1.2 m.

(c) Three complete wavelengths are shown. Divide the given length by 3.

$$\lambda = \frac{6.0 \text{ m}}{3} = 2.0 \text{ m}$$

(d) Use the relationship $T = \frac{1}{f}$. Substitute the known values and solve.

$$T = \frac{1}{f} = \frac{1}{2.0 \text{ Hz}} = 0.50 \text{ s}$$

(e) Use the relationship $v = f\lambda$. Substitute the known values and and solve.

$$v = (2.0 \text{ Hz})(2.0 \text{ m}) = 4.0 \text{ m/s}$$

(f) Notice that points B and C are moving in the same direction and are the same distance from the at-rest position of the medium, but they do not have the same displacement and thus are out of phase. Points B and F have the same displacement from the at-rest position, but are moving in opposite directions, up and down, respectively, and therefore are out of phase. B and G are in phase because they have the same displacement and are moving in the same direction.

(g) The dashed line in the following diagram shows how the entire waveform would appear in the next instant of time. Point H moves up.

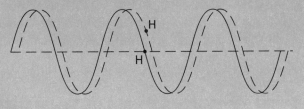

Review Questions

1. A single vibratory disturbance that moves from point to point in a medium is called a (1) period (2) periodic wave (3) wavelength (4) pulse

2. What generally occurs when a pulse reaches a boundary between two different media? (1) All of the pulse is reflected. (2) All of the pulse is absorbed. (3) All of the pulse is transmitted. (4) Part of the pulse is reflected, part is absorbed, and part is transmitted.

3. Diagram A shows a glass tube containing undisturbed air molecules. Diagram B shows the same glass tube as a wave passes through it. What type of wave produced the disturbance shown in Diagram B?

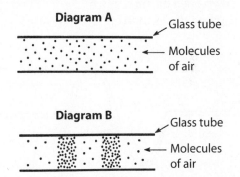

4. When a transverse wave moves through a medium, what is the action of the particles of the medium?
   (1) They travel through the medium with the wave.
   (2) They vibrate in a direction parallel to the direction in which the wave is moving.
   (3) They vibrate in a direction perpendicular to the direction in which the wave is moving.
   (4) They remain at rest.

5. Compression waves in a spring are an example of
   (1) longitudinal waves (2) transverse waves
   (3) elliptical waves (4) torsional waves

6. Wave motion in a medium transfers (1) energy only
   (2) mass only (3) both energy and mass
   (4) neither energy nor mass

7. Periodic waves are produced by a wave generator at the rate of one wave every 0.50 second. What is the period of the wave to the correct number of significant figures?

8. Which phrase best describes a periodic wave?
   (1) a single pulse traveling at constant speed
   (2) a single pulse traveling at varying speed in the same medium
   (3) a series of pulses at irregular intervals
   (4) a series of pulses at regular intervals

9. In the following diagram, the solid line represents a wave generated in a rope. As the wave moves to the right, point P on the rope is moving towards which position? (1) A (2) B (3) C (4) D

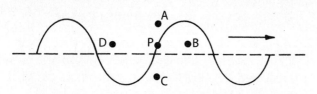

10. In the following diagram, a transverse wave is moving on a rope. In which direction will segment x move as the wave passes through it?

(1) down only
(2) up only
(3) down, then up, then down
(4) up, then down, then up

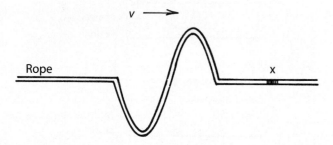

11. Which wave characteristic is defined as the number of cycles of a periodic wave occurring per unit time?

12. If the frequency of a sound wave is 440. cycles per second, its period is closest to

(1) 2.27×10^{-3} second/cycle
(2) 0.752 second/cycle
(3) 1.33 seconds/cycle
(4) 3.31×10^2 seconds/cycle

13. If the frequency of a sound wave is doubled, the period of the sound wave is (1) halved (2) doubled (3) unchanged (4) quadrupled

14. The following diagram represents a transverse wave. The amplitude of the wave is represented by the distance between points (1) A and B (2) A and C (3) A and D (4) D and E

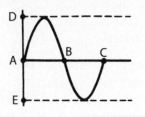

15. If the frequency of a sound wave in air at STP remains constant, the wave's energy can be varied by changing its (1) amplitude (2) speed (3) wavelength (4) period

16. The following diagram shows a transverse wave. Which two points on the wave are in phase? (1) A and E (2) B and F (3) C and E (4) D and F

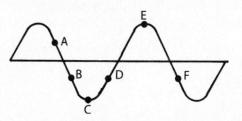

17. The following diagram shows a transverse wave. Which point on the wave is 180° out of phase with point P?

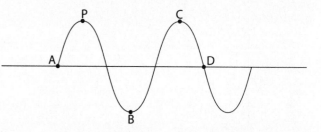

18. The diagram that follows shows a train of waves moving along a string. What is the wavelength?

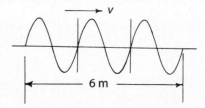

19. The wavelength of the periodic wave shown in the following diagram is 4.0 meters. What is the distance from point B to point C to the correct number of significant figures?

20. An 8.0-meter long ocean wave passes the end of a dock every 5.0 seconds. What is the speed of the wave?

21. A sound wave travels at 340 meters per second. After 0.50 second, how far from the source of the wave has the wave traveled?

22. The following diagram represents a wave traveling in a uniform medium. Which characteristic of the wave is constant? (1) amplitude (2) frequency (3) period (4) wavelength

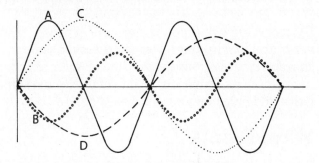

Base your answers to questions 23 through 25 on the following diagram, which represents four transverse waves in the same medium.

23. Which two waves have the same amplitude?

24. Which two waves have the same wavelength?

25. Which two waves have the same frequency?

26. A wave has a frequency of 2.0 hertz and a speed of 3.0 meters per second. The distance covered by the wave in 5.0 seconds is (1) 30. m (2) 15 m (3) 7.5 m (4) 6.0 m

27. A wave traveling at 5.00×10^4 meters per second has a wavelength of 2.50×10^1 meters. What is the frequency of the wave? (1) 1.25×10^6 Hz (2) 2.00×10^3 Hz (3) 5.00×10^{-4} Hz (4) 5.00×10^3 Hz $f =$

28. Sound waves with constant frequency of 250 hertz are traveling through air at STP. Determine the wavelength of the sound waves.

29. What total distance will a sound wave travel in air in 3.00 seconds at STP?

Base your answers to questions 30 through 33 on the information and diagram that follow.

A periodic wave, having a frequency of 40. hertz, travels to the right in a uniform medium as shown.

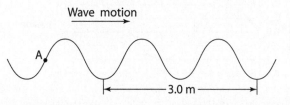

30. On the diagram, draw one or more arrows to indicate the direction of motion of point A in the next instant of time.

31. On the diagram, label a point P that is in phase with point A.

32. Determine the speed of the wave.

33. Determine the period of the wave.

34. What type of wave is sound traveling in water?

Base your answers to questions 35 and 36 on the following information.

The elapsed time between successive crests of a transverse wave passing a given point is 0.080 second.

35. Determine the period of the wave.

36. Determine the frequency of the wave.

Base your answers to questions 37 through 39 on the following information.

The distance from one crest of a water wave to the next crest is 4.0 meters. One crest passes an observation point every 2.5 seconds.

37. Determine the speed of the wave.

38. How much time is required for the wave to travel 50. meters?

39. How far will the wave travel in 4.0 seconds?

40. The diagram below shows a periodic wave W traveling to the right in a uniform medium.

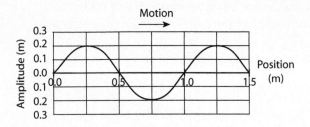

On the grid below sketch at least one cycle of a periodic wave having twice the amplitude and half the wavelength of wave W.

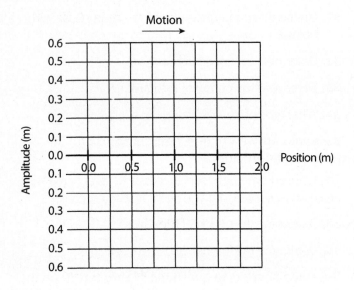

41. A sound wave is produced by a musical instrument for 0.40 second. If the frequency of the wave is 370 hertz, how many complete waves are produced in that time period?

42. Write an equation that correctly relates the speed v, wavelength λ, and period T of a periodic wave.

43. A wave x meters long passes through a medium at y meters per second. The frequency of the wave could be expressed as (1) $\frac{y}{x}$ Hz (2) $\frac{x}{y}$ Hz (3) xy Hz (4) $(x + y)$ Hz

44. Which is a unit for the amplitude of a transverse wave? (1) m/s (2) s (3) Hz (4) m

45. If the frequency of a sound wave increases, the wavelength of the wave in air will (1) decrease (2) increase (3) remain the same

46. Which phrase best describes the wavelength of a sound wave in air at STP? (1) inversely proportional to its amplitude and inversely proportional to its frequency (2) inversely proportional to its amplitude and directly proportional to its frequency (3) independent of its amplitude and inversely proportional to its frequency (4) independent of its amplitude and directly proportional to its frequency

47. A water wave travels a distance of 10.0 meters in 5.0 seconds. What can be determined from this information? (1) the speed of the wave only (2) the period of the wave only (3) the speed and frequency of the wave (4) the period and frequency of the wave

Periodic Wave Phenomena

By observing two types of mechanical waves, transverse and longitudinal, you can discover some characteristics of waves and the behavior of waves under various conditions. Some of these characteristics and behaviors are discussed below.

Wave Fronts

When water drips from a leaky faucet into a water-filled sink, waves spread, or radiate, in concentric circles along the surface of the water from the point where the drips strike the surface. In a three-dimensional medium such as air, waves radiate in concentric spheres from a vibrating point. All points on a wave that are in phase comprise a wave front. A **wave front** is the locus of all adjacent points on a wave that are in phase. For example, in the waves in the sink, all of the points on one of the crests constitute a wave front. Two successive crests are separated by a distance of one wavelength and, therefore, are in phase.

Doppler Effect

When a source and an observer (receiver) of waves are moving relative to each other, the observed frequency is different from the frequency of the vibrating source. This change in observed or apparent frequency due to relative motion of source and observer is called the **Doppler effect.**

If the source is approaching the observer, or if the observer is approaching the source, the frequency appears to increase. If the source is receding from the observer or the observer is receding from the source, the frequency appears to decrease. Because the speed of the waves in the medium is not affected by the Doppler effect, it can be seen from the equation $v = f\lambda$ that the change in apparent wavelength is inversely proportional to the change in apparent frequency.

The wave front diagrams in Figure 5-8 illustrate the changes in apparent frequency and wavelength caused by the Doppler effect. In Figure 5-8A, the source is stationary, and the four successive wave fronts (1, 2, 3, and 4) are equally spaced circles in all directions. The observed wavelength and frequency are the same for all stationary observers. In Figure 5-8B, the source is moving from right to left. Each successive wave front has a different center. To a stationary observer at the left, the wavelengths appear shorter and the frequency higher; to a stationary observer at the right, the effect is the opposite.

The Doppler effect can cause changes in the apparent pitch of a sound wave because the ear perceives a sound wave of higher frequency as a sound of higher pitch. Thus the pitch of an approaching sound source is higher than its pitch when the source is stationary, and the pitch drops lower as the source passes the observer and begins to recede.

Visible light waves are subject to a similar effect. The human eye perceives light waves of different frequencies as differences in color. Light waves of the lowest frequency (longest wavelength) that the eye can detect are seen as red, while those of highest frequency (shortest wavelength) are seen as blue-violet. Other colors are distributed between these extremes in the visible spectrum. Because of the Doppler effect, the apparent color of an approaching light source is shifted toward the blue-violet end of the spectrum, while that of a receding source is shifted toward the red end. If the light source is a mixture of many frequencies, such as the light from a star, its light appears slightly bluer if it is approaching an observer, or slightly redder if it is receding, than it would appear if it were not moving relative to the observer.

APPLICATIONS OF THE DOPPLER EFFECT

The Doppler effect has practical applications in weather forecasting and police work. For example, the speed of a car can be determined by a computerized radar system. If a car is at rest and a beam of radio waves is directed at the car from a stationary source, the incident and reflected waves have the same frequency. If the car is moving toward the source of the radar, however, the reflected waves have a higher frequency than the waves emitted by the source. The greater the car's speed toward the radar source, the greater the Doppler shift in frequency. In a similar way, if the car is moving away from the source of radar, the frequency of the reflected waves decreases by an amount that depends upon the speed of the car. Thus, equipped with a "radar gun," a law-enforcement officer can detect speed-limit violators "coming or going."

Interference

Superposition occurs when two or more waves travel through the same medium simultaneously. The **principle of superposition** states that the resultant displacement at any point is the algebraic sum of the displacements of the individual waves. The effect of the superposition is called **interference,** which may be constructive or destructive. Although any number of waves may superpose, the discussion that follows is restricted to two waves.

Constructive interference occurs when the wave displacements of two in-phase waves in the same medium are in the same direction. The algebraic sum of the displacements is an amplitude greater than that of either of the original waves. Maximum constructive interference occurs when the waves

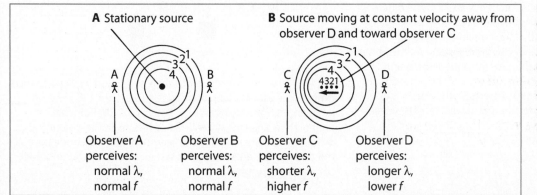

Figure 5-8. The Doppler effect: (A) When the source is stationary, the wave fronts are equally spaced in all directions. **(B)** When the source is moving, the wave fronts are closer together in the direction in which the source is moving.

A Stationary source

B Source moving at constant velocity away from observer D and toward observer C

Observer A perceives: normal λ, normal f

Observer B perceives: normal λ, normal f

Observer C perceives: shorter λ, higher f

Observer D perceives: longer λ, lower f

are in phase and crest superposes on crest. Thus, maximum constructive interference occurs when the phase difference is equal to 0°, as shown in Figure 5-9A. The point of maximum displacement of a medium when two waves are interacting is called an **antinode.**

When two waves of equal frequency and amplitude whose phase difference is 180° or $\frac{1}{2}\lambda$ meet at a point (for example, crest to trough), there is maximum **destructive interference,** as shown in Figure 5-9B. Maximum destructive interference results in the formation of **nodes** (points or lines), which are regions of zero displacement of the medium. Intermediate degrees of interference occur between the regions of maximum constructive interference and maximum destructive interference.

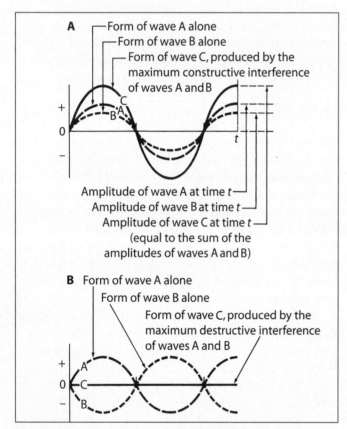

Figure 5-9. Constructive and Destructive Interference:
(A) Waves A and B have the same frequency and a phase difference of 0°. As a result, they show maximum constructive interference, producing wave C. Note that the amplitudes of A and B always add up to the amplitude of C at every instant of time. This is demonstrated for the time t at the extreme right of the graph.
(B) Waves A and B have the same frequency and the same amplitude, but a phase difference of 180°. As a result, they show maximum destructive interference. Notice that waves A and B cancel each other.

Beats are produced by the interference of two notes of slightly different frequencies that are heard simultaneously.

TWO SOURCES IN PHASE IN THE SAME MEDIUM When two in-phase point sources generate waves in the same medium, a symmetrical interference pattern results because of maximum constructive and destructive interference. Figure 5-10A shows two identical point sources, S_1 and S_2, producing wave crests (solid lines) and wave troughs (dashed lines) that interfere. The path difference from any point of constructive interference to the sources, S_1 and S_2, is an even number of half-wavelengths. For example, along antinodal line P_1P_4, the difference in path length from any point on the line to S_1 and S_2 is 0λ. In Figure 5-10B, point A is on an antinodal line because distance AS_1 differs from distance AS_2 by two half-wavelengths. On the other hand, point B is on a nodal line because distance BS_1 differs from distance BS_2 by an odd number of half-wavelengths. Nodal lines occur midway between antinodal lines.

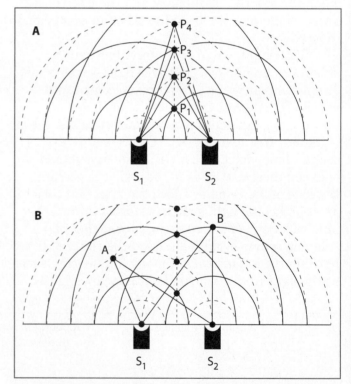

Figure 5-10. Interference of waves produced by two identical point sources: (A) Along antinodal line P_1P_4, the difference in path length from any point to S_1 and S_2 is 0λ. **(B)** Point A is an antinode because the distance AS_1 differs from the distance AS_2 by an even number of half-wavelengths. Point B is a node because the distance BS_1 differs from the distance BS_2 by an odd number of half-wavelengths.

Standing Waves

When two waves having the same amplitude and frequency travel in opposite directions through a medium, a standing wave is formed. A **standing wave** is a pattern of wave crests and troughs that remains stationary in a medium. The nodes and antinodes are stationary and the wave appears to stand still. Standing waves are easily produced in a stretched string that is fixed at both ends. Wave trains traveling along the string are reflected at the ends and travel back with the same frequency and amplitude. Figure 5-11 illustrates several possible standing waves in a string. Note that a node appears at each end of the string. The distance between two successive nodes is equal to $\frac{1}{2}\lambda$.

Resonance

Every elastic body has a particular frequency called its **natural frequency** at which it will vibrate if disturbed. When a periodic force is applied to an elastic body, it absorbs energy and the amplitude of its vibration increases. The vibration of a body at its natural frequency because of the action of a vibrating source of the same frequency is called **resonance.** For example, a nonvibrating tuning fork, having a natural frequency of 512 hertz, will resonate when a vibrating tuning fork with a natural frequency of 512 hertz is brought near it. Furthermore, it is possible for an opera singer to shatter a glass by maintaining a note with a frequency equal to the natural frequency of the glass. The transfer of energy by resonance increases the amplitude of vibrations in the glass until its structural strength is exceeded. Probably the most dramatic example of resonance was the collapse of the Tacoma Narrows Bridge in the state of Washington in 1940. High winds set up standing waves in the bridge in addition to vibrations in a torsional (twisting) mode. Resonance increased the amplitude of vibrations until the bridge collapsed.

Diffraction

The spreading of waves into the region behind a barrier in the wave's path is called **diffraction.** Parallel water wave fronts incident on a small opening are diffracted to form concentric semicircular fronts. These semicircular fronts have the same wavelength as the incident wave if the medium is uniform throughout, as shown in Figure 5-12A. If the opening through which the wave is diffracted is much larger than one wavelength of the incident wave, diffraction effects are small, as shown in Figure 5-12B.

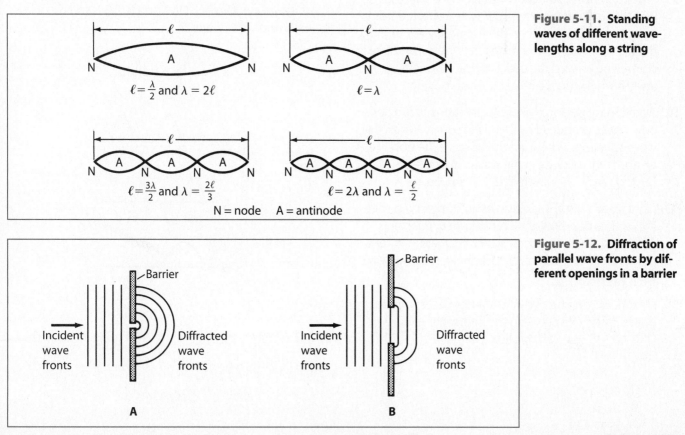

Figure 5-11. Standing waves of different wavelengths along a string

$\ell = \frac{\lambda}{2}$ and $\lambda = 2\ell$

$\ell = \lambda$

$\ell = \frac{3\lambda}{2}$ and $\lambda = \frac{2\ell}{3}$

$\ell = 2\lambda$ and $\lambda = \frac{\ell}{2}$

N = node   A = antinode

Figure 5-12. Diffraction of parallel wave fronts by different openings in a barrier

Barrier

Incident wave fronts

Diffracted wave fronts

Barrier

Incident wave fronts

Diffracted wave fronts

A

B

Review Questions

48. What term describes the variations in the observed frequency of a sound wave when there is relative motion between the source and the receiver?

49. The vibrating tuning fork shown in the diagram that follows produces a constant frequency. The tuning fork is being moved to the right at constant speed, and observers are located at points A, B, C, and D. Which observer hears the lowest frequency?

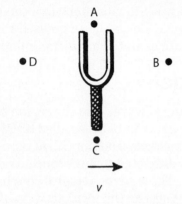

50. The driver of a car hears the siren of an ambulance that is moving away from her. If the actual frequency of the siren is 2000. hertz, the frequency heard by the driver may be (1) 1900. Hz (2) 2000. Hz (3) 2100. Hz (4) 4000. Hz

51. A police officer's stationary radar device indicates that the frequency of the radar wave reflected from an automobile is less than the frequency emitted by the radar device. This indicates that the automobile is (1) moving toward the police officer (2) moving away from the police officer (3) not moving

52. A stationary person makes observations of the periodic waves produced by a moving source. When the wave source recedes from the observer, he observes an apparent increase in the wave's (1) speed (2) frequency (3) wavelength (4) amplitude

53. Light from a distant star displays a Doppler red shift. This shift is best explained by assuming the star is (1) decreasing in temperature (2) increasing in temperature (3) moving toward Earth (4) moving away from Earth

54. Maximum constructive interference occurs when the phase difference between the intersecting wave is (1) 0° (2) 45° (3) 90° (4) 180°

55. By how many degrees should two waves be out of phase to produce maximum destructive interference?

56. The diagram below shows a rope with two pulses moving along it in the directions shown.

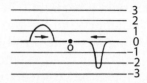

What is the resultant wave pattern at the instant when the maximum displacement of both pulses is at point O on the rope?

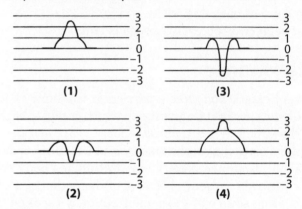

57. The following diagram shows four waves that pass simultaneously through a region. Which two waves will produce maximum constructive interference if they are combined? (1) A and B (2) A and C (3) B and C (4) C and D

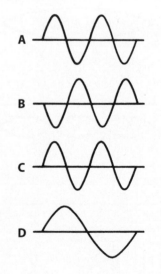

58. Which pair of waves will produce a resultant wave with the smallest amplitude?

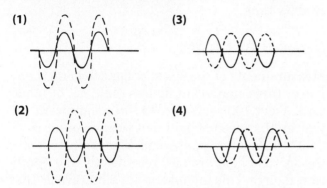

59. The following diagram represents two waves traveling simultaneously in the same medium. At which of the given points will maximum constructive interference occur?

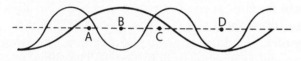

60. Standing waves are produced by two waves traveling in opposite directions in the same medium. The two waves must have (1) the same amplitude and the same frequency (2) the same amplitude and different frequencies (3) different amplitudes and the same frequency (4) different amplitudes and different frequencies

61. In order for standing waves to form in a medium, two waves must (1) have the same frequency (2) have different amplitudes (3) have different wavelengths (4) travel in the same direction

62. When the stretched string of the apparatus represented in the following diagram is made to vibrate, point P does not move. Point P is most probably the location of (1) a node (2) an antinode (3) maximum amplitude (4) maximum pulse

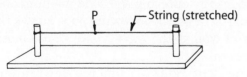

Base your answers to questions 63 and 64 on the following diagram, which shows a standing wave in a rope.

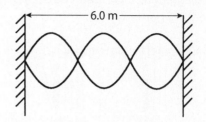

63. How many nodes are represented?

64. If the rope is 6.0 meters long, what is the wavelength of the standing wave?

65. Two waves traveling in the same medium interfere to produce a standing wave. What is the phase difference in degrees between the two waves at a node?

66. Two wave sources operating in phase in the same medium produce the circular wave patterns shown in the diagram that follows. The solid lines represent wave crests and the dashed lines represent wave troughs. Which point is at a position of maximum destructive interference?

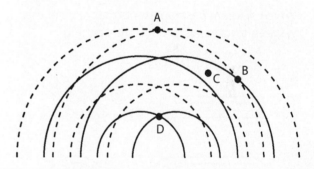

67. An opera singer's voice is able to break a thin crystal glass if a note sung and the glass have the same natural (1) speed (2) frequency (3) amplitude (4) wavelength

68. When an opera singer hits a high-pitch note, a glass on the opposite side of the opera hall shatters. Which statement best explains this phenomenon? (1) The amplitude of the note increases before it reaches the glass. (2) The singer and the glass are separated by an integral number of wavelengths. (3) The frequency of the note and the natural frequency of the glass are equal. (4) The sound produced by the singer slows down as it travels from the air into the glass.

69. A wave spreads into the region behind a barrier. What is this phenomenon called?

70. Which diagram best illustrates diffraction of waves incident on a barrier?

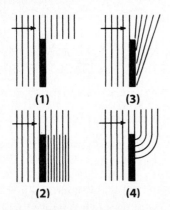

(1)   **(3)**

(2)   **(4)**

71. The diagram that follows represents straight wave fronts approaching a narrow opening in a barrier.

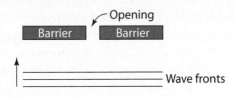

Which diagram best represents the shape of the waves after passing through the opening?

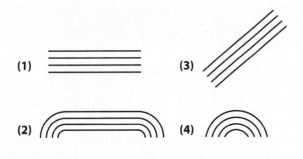

(1)   **(3)**

(2)   **(4)**

Light

The human eye can perceive only an extremely small fraction of the electromagnetic spectrum. That portion of the spectrum, which allows us to see, is called light and covers the range of wavelengths from approximately 3.90×10^{-7} to 7.81×10^{-7} meter. (The electromagnetic spectrum will be discussed in detail later in this topic.) Obviously, these wavelengths are too small to measure with a ruler as you might measure the wavelength of a transverse wave on a rope or a water wave in a shallow tank.

Speed of Light

Measurements of the speed of light to more than two or three significant figures could not be made until about 100 years ago. To three significant figures, the speed of light in a vacuum or air is 3.00×10^8 meters per second. Measurements of the speed of light are now recorded to nine significant figures. This more accurate data reveals that the speed of light in air is slightly less than it is in a vacuum. The speed of light in a vacuum is represented by the symbol c, an important physical constant.

The speed of light in a vacuum is the upper limit for the speed of any material body. No object can travel faster than c. The speed of light in a material medium is always less than c. The equation $v = f\lambda$ applies to light waves. Therefore, $c = f\lambda$, where f is the frequency of a light wave and λ is its wavelength in a vacuum.

Ray Diagrams

Because it is not possible to see individual wave fronts in a light wave, a ray is used to indicate the direction of wave travel. A **ray** is a straight line that is drawn at right angles to a wave front and points in the direction of wave travel. Ray diagrams show only the direction of wave travel, not the actual waves. An **incident ray** is a ray that originates in a medium and is incident on a boundary or an interface of that medium with another medium. A **reflected ray** is a ray that has rebounded from a boundary or interface. A **refracted ray** is a ray that results from an incident ray entering a second medium obliquely. Figure 5-13 on the following page shows these rays as well as the wave fronts whose motion they represent.

Incident, reflected, and refracted rays form corresponding angles measured from a line called the normal. The **normal** is a line drawn perpendicular to the barrier or to the interface between two media at the point where the incident ray strikes. In ray diagrams, all the rays and the normal lie in a single plane.

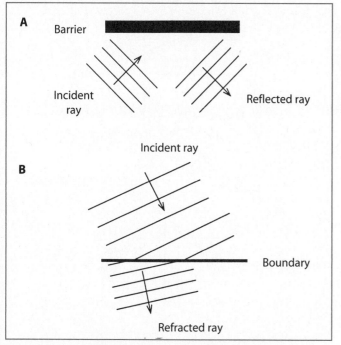

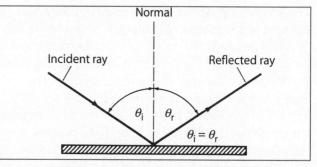

Figure 5-14. The law of reflection: The angle of incidence equals the angle of reflection.

Figure 5-13. Reflected and refracted rays: (A) shows the direction of a reflected wave front at a barrier. **(B)** shows how a wave front changes at a boundary between two media.

Reflection of Light

The **angle of incidence,** θ_i, is the angle between the incident ray and the normal to the surface at the point where the ray strikes the surface. The ray rebounds from the surface at the **angle of reflection,** θ_r, which is the angle between the reflected ray and the normal to the surface at the point of reflection. The **law of reflection** states that the angle of incidence is equal to the angle of reflection.

$$\theta_i = \theta_r$$

Figure 5-14 illustrates the law of reflection. This law is valid for all types of waves including light, water, and sound waves. The reflection of sound waves is called an echo.

Parallel light rays incident on a smooth plane surface are reflected parallel to each other because all the normals to the surface are parallel. See Figure 15-5A. However, when a beam of parallel

light rays strikes an irregular surface, the reflected rays are scattered in all directions. The surface irregularities produce nonparallel normals. Each individual ray obeys the laws of reflection and produces the effect shown in Figure 5-15B.

IMAGES FORMED BY REFLECTIONS FROM A PLANE MIRROR The law of reflection is the basis for the formation of an image by a plane mirror. If several light rays originating from the same point are reflected from a plane mirror, the reflected rays appear to come from a single point on the other side of the mirror forming a virtual image. A <u>virtual image</u> is a point from which light rays appear to diverge without actually doing so. In Figure 5-16A on the next page, point P_i is the virtual image of point P_o. The virtual image is formed where light rays originating from P_o appear to intersect for the observer. The rays of light reaching the observer's eye actually come from the object P_o and are reflected by the mirror so as to appear to come from the image P_i. The virtual image cannot be projected on a screen. A geometric proof shows that the distance of the virtual image P_i from the mirror is equal to the distance of the object P_o from the mirror.

The image of an object in front of a plane mirror can be constructed as shown in Figure 5-16B. The image point corresponding to any given point on the object can be located by tracing the path of any two rays originating from the given point on the object. One ray can be the ray perpendicular to the mirror.

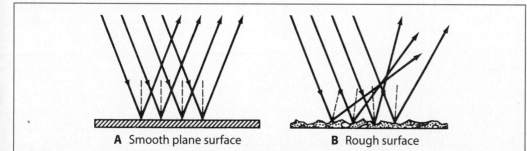

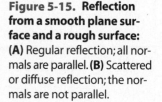

A Smooth plane surface   **B** Rough surface

Figure 5-15. Reflection from a smooth plane surface and a rough surface: (A) Regular reflection; all normals are parallel. **(B)** Scattered or diffuse reflection; the normals are not parallel.

The second ray can be drawn at any other angle to the mirror. By means of geometry, it can be shown that the image is the same distance behind the mirror as the object is in front of it, and the image and the object are also the same size. Although the image formed by a vertical mirror is erect with respect to the object, it is reversed from left to right. For example, the top of the image of a printed page is the top of the page, but the print reads backward.

The minimum size of a vertical, plane mirror for viewing the entire body is one-half the viewer's height, as illustrated in Figure 5-17. By the law of reflection, the angle of incidence of a light ray is equal to the angle of reflection. Looking straight ahead into a plane mirror positioned in front of you and perpendicular to the floor, you see your eyes. If you look halfway down the mirror, you see your toes. If you raise your eyes and look at the mirror at a distance halfway between your eyes and the top of your head, you see the top of your head. Thus, the minimum size of a plane mirror for viewing the entire body is one-half the viewer's height.

Refraction of Light

Waves travel at different speeds in different media, so when a wave travels from one medium to another, the speed of the wave changes. If the wave is incident on the interface between two media at an angle other than 90°, the direction of wave travel changes in the new medium. That means that both the speed and the direction of a wave usually change as the wave enters a new medium obliquely. The change in direction of a wave due to a change in speed at the boundary between two different media is called **refraction.** If the wave fronts of an incident wave are parallel to the interface, the angle of incidence is 0° and the wave may change speed upon entering the new medium, but the direction of the wave does not change.

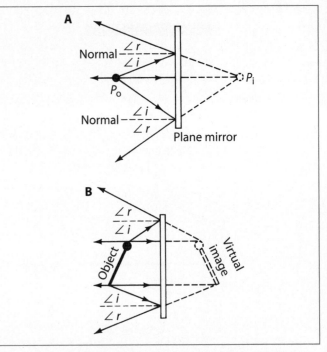

Figure 5-16. Image formation by a plane mirror: (A) All rays from a point source are reflected as though coming from an image point P_i, as far behind the mirror as P_o is in front of it. **(B)** Any two reflected rays that originate from a point on an object are sufficient to locate the virtual image of that point by extending the reflected rays until they intersect behind the mirror.

The amount of refraction of a ray depends upon the properties of the two media at the interface and is measured by the angle of refraction. The **angle of refraction** is the angle between a ray emerging from the interface of two media and the normal to that interface at the point where the ray emerges.

Speed of Light and Refraction

When a light ray in air is incident on an interface with water at an angle of incidence of 0°, the ray of light slows down upon entering the more optically dense water, but does not change its direction of

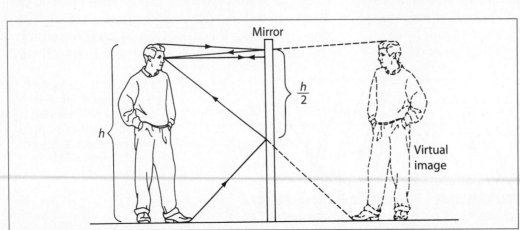

Figure 5-17. Your image in a vertical mirror: The symbol h represents your height. The portions of the mirror above and below the length marked $\frac{h}{2}$ are unnecessary for seeing your full image.

travel. Figure 5-18A shows an incident ray approaching the interface between air and water along the normal. The ray is not refracted as it travels from air into water. The ray travels more slowly in water than in air but its frequency remains the same. The speed of a wave is proportional to its wavelength when frequency is constant, so its wavelength in water is shorter than its wavelength in air.

The situation is different when a light ray passes obliquely from a less dense medium such as air into a more dense medium such as water. In this case, the ray is refracted towards the normal, as shown in Figure 5-18B. Upon entering the denser medium, the ray's frequency does not change, but its wavelength decreases as its speed decreases. If the path of the ray is from a more dense medium, such as water, into a less dense medium, such as air, the ray is refracted away from the normal, as shown in Figure 5-18C. Upon entering the less dense medium, the ray's frequency does not change, but its wavelength increases as its speed increases.

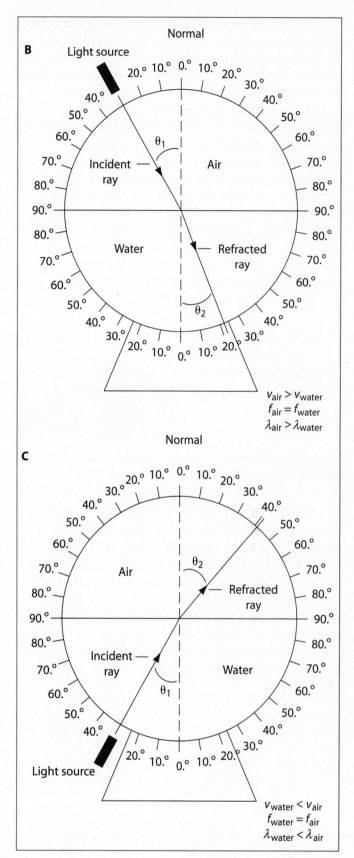

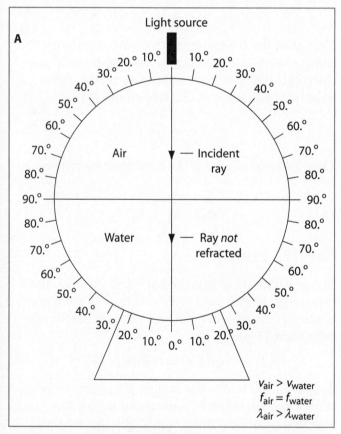

Figure 5-18. Refraction of light: (A) A light ray passes from a less dense medium, air, into a more dense medium, water, at an angle of incidence of 0°. **(B)** A light ray passes obliquely from a less dense medium, air, into a more dense medium, water, at an angle of incidence of 30°. The ray is refracted toward the normal. **(C)** A light ray passes obliquely from a more dense medium, water, into a less dense medium, air, at an angle of incidence of 30°. The ray is refracted away from the normal.

The refraction of light explains many everyday phenomena such as mirages and the visibility of the sun after it has actually disappeared below the horizon, as illustrated in Figure 5-19. Because the density of Earth's atmosphere increases gradually as Earth's surface is approached from space, sunlight entering the atmosphere obliquely, as it does at sunset, is gradually refracted to produce a curved path. Your brain has learned to assume that light entering your eyes has been traveling in straight lines. Thus, at sunset you "see" the sun higher in the sky than it actually is. When you "see" the sun on the horizon, it has already set.

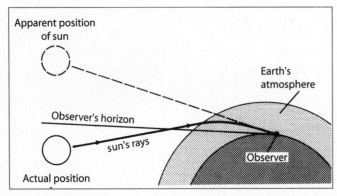

Figure 5-19. Curvature of the sun's rays by refraction in Earth's atmosphere

Another example of refraction is the apparent bending of a straw placed in a glass of water. The submerged portion of the straw appears to be closer to the surface than it actually is. Light from the submerged tip of the straw is bent away from the normal upon entering the less-dense air, as shown in Figure 5-20. To an observer, who interprets what is seen as light traveling in a straight line, the submerged tip of the straw seems closer to the surface than it actually is.

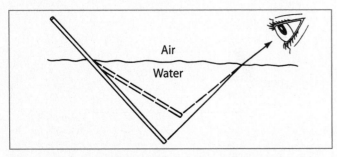

Figure 5-20. Refraction of light: Light rays from the tip of the straw are bent away from the normal as they emerge from the water. The effect is to make the straw appear to bend at the surface of the water.

Absolute Index of Refraction

The **absolute index of refraction, n,** is the ratio of the speed of light in a vacuum, c, to the speed of light in a material medium, v.

$$n = \frac{c}{v}$$

The absolute index of refraction has no units because both c and v are measured in the same units. The greater the value of n, the more optically dense the medium and the slower light travels in the medium. The absolute indices of refraction for a variety of materials are listed in the *Reference Tables for Physical Setting/Physics*.

Solving the equation for c yields $c = nv$. Thus, the following equations apply for two different media.

$$n_1 v_1 = n_2 v_2 \quad \text{or} \quad \frac{n_2}{n_1} = \frac{v_1}{v_2}$$

Also, the following equations apply for any two media.

$$v_1 = f\lambda_1 \text{ and } v_2 = f\lambda_2$$

Note that the frequency of the wave does not change as the wave enters a new medium. Thus, the relationship between the speeds and wavelengths of the wave in the two media is this.

$$\frac{v_1}{v_2} = \frac{\lambda_1}{\lambda_2}$$

These relationships can be combined as follows.

$$\frac{n_2}{n_1} = \frac{v_1}{v_2} = \frac{\lambda_1}{\lambda_2}$$

Snell's Law

The mathematical relationship that governs the refraction of light as it passes obliquely from one medium to another of different optical density is called **Snell's law.**

$$n_1 \sin \theta_1 = n_2 \sin \theta_2$$

Angles θ_1 and θ_2 are the angles of incidence and refraction respectively, and n_1 and n_2 are the absolute indices of refraction of the incident and refractive media, respectively.

Snell's law can be rearranged in this way.

$$\frac{\sin \theta_1}{\sin \theta_2} = \frac{n_2}{n_1}$$

The ratio n_2/n_1 is called the relative index of refraction for the two media.

SAMPLE PROBLEM

The diagram represents a ray of monochromatic light, having a frequency of 5.09×10^{14} hertz, as it is about to emerge from liquid glycerol into air. The index of refraction of glycerol, n_1, is 1.47. The index of refraction of air, n_2, is 1.00.

(a) On the diagram, label the angle of incidence θ_1. Determine its measure to the nearest degree.
(b) Determine the corresponding angle of refraction to the nearest degree.
(c) On the diagram, draw the refracted light ray, label the angle of refraction θ_2, and indicate its measure to the nearest degree.
(d) At a boundary between two media, some of the incident light is always reflected. On the diagram, draw the reflected ray, label the angle of reflection θ_r, and indicate its measure to the nearest degree.
(e) Determine the speed of light in glycerol.
(f) Determine the wavelength of the light in air in nanometers to the proper number of significant digits.
(g) What is the ratio of the speed of light in glycerol to the speed of light in air?

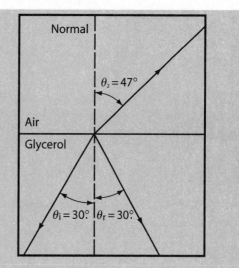

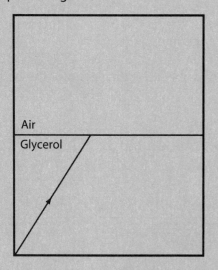

Solution: Identify the known and unknown values.

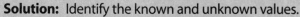

Known	Unknown
$f = 5.09 \times 10^{14}$ Hz	$\theta_1 = ?$ degrees
$n_1 = 1.47$	$\theta_2 = ?$ degrees
$n_2 = 1.00$	$\theta_r = ?$ degrees
	$v = ?$ m/s
	$\lambda = ?$ nm
	ratio $v_1/v_2 = ?$

(a) On the diagram, draw a normal to the surface at the point of incidence. The angle of incidence is measured from the normal.
See the diagram that follows. The angle of incidence is 30°.

(b) Use the equation $n_1 \sin \theta_1 = n_2 \sin \theta_2$. Note that the subscript 1 refers to the incident medium and the subscript 2 refers to the refractive medium. Solve the equation for $\sin \theta_2$.

$$\sin \theta_2 = \frac{n_1 \sin \theta_1}{n_2}$$

Substitute the known values and solve for θ_2.

$$\sin \theta_2 = \frac{(1.47)(\sin 30.°)}{1.00} = 0.735$$

$$\theta_2 = 47°$$

(c) The angle of refraction is in air and is measured from the normal using a protractor.

(d) The angle of incidence equal the angle of reflection. Thus, the angle of reflection is 30.°, and is measured from the normal.

(e) Solve the equation $n = c/v$ for v.

$$v = \frac{c}{n}$$

Substitute known values and solve for v.

$$v = \frac{3.00 \times 10^8 \text{ m/s}}{1.47} = 2.04 \times 10^8 \text{ m/s}$$

(f) Solve the equation $c = f\lambda$ for the wavelength, λ.

$$\lambda = \frac{c}{f}$$

Substitute the known values and solve.

$$\lambda = \frac{3.00 \times 10^8 \text{ m/s}}{5.09 \times 10^{14} \text{ Hz}}$$

$$\lambda = 5.89 \times 10^{-7} \text{ m}$$

$$\lambda = 589 \text{ nm}$$

(g) To find the ratio of the speed of light in air to the speed of light in glycerol, use the following relationship.

$$\frac{v_1}{v_2} = \frac{n_2}{n_1}$$

Substitute the known values and solve for $\frac{v_1}{v_2}$.

$$\frac{v_1}{v_2} = \frac{n_2}{n_1} = \frac{1.00}{1.47}$$

The Electromagnetic Spectrum

Light waves are **electromagnetic waves** which consist of periodically changing electric and magnetic fields and move through a vacuum at speed $c = 3.00 \times 10^8$ meters per second. All electromagnetic waves, regardless of their frequency and wavelength, are produced by accelerating charged particles. The **electromagnetic spectrum,** which is the complete range of frequencies and wavelengths of electromagnetic waves, is shown in Figure 5-21. Notice that visible light is only a small portion of the spectrum.

There are no sharp divisions between the various kinds of electromagnetic waves. They are classified according to the methods by which they are generated or received. For example, radio waves, used for communication systems, are produced by charges accelerating in a wire.

Microwaves are used in radar systems in air-traffic control, for transmitting long-distance telephone communications in outer space, and to cook food. The frequency of microwaves used in a microwave oven is the same as the natural rotational frequency of water molecules. Resonance is produced in water molecules contained in food and the resulting internal energy due to vibration heats the food.

Infrared waves appear as heat when absorbed by objects. Practical applications of the infrared portion of the electromagnetic spectrum include heat lamps used in physical therapy and infrared photography.

Visible light is approximately one percent of the electromagnetic spectrum. It is produced by the rearrangement of electrons in atoms and molecules. The wavelengths that the human eye can detect are in the range of approximately 400 to 700 nanometers.

Ultraviolet light is the part of sunlight that causes sunburns. The ozone layer of the atmos-

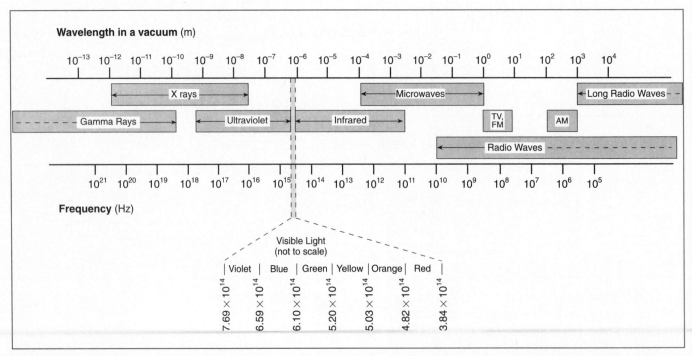

Figure 5-21. The electromagnetic spectrum

phere filters practically all of the high frequency components of ultraviolet radiation from the sun, but the inner atmosphere readily transmits the remaining lower frequency ultraviolet radiation. Some commercial skin lotions are designed to absorb ultraviolet rays to prevent them from affecting the skin.

X rays are used as diagnostic tools by physicians. Living tissues and organisms can be destroyed by X rays, so precautions should be taken to avoid overexposure.

Gamma rays are emitted by radioactive nuclei. This electromagnetic radiation is harmful to living tissues.

Review Questions

72. How long does it take light to travel a distance of 100. meters? (1) 3.00×10^{10} s (2) 3.00×10^{8} s (3) 3.33×10^{-7} s (4) 3.33×10^{7} s

73. Determine the wavelength in a vacuum of a light wave having a frequency of 5.3×10^{14} hertz. Express your answer in nanometers to the proper number of significant digits.

74. What is the frequency of a light wave having a wavelength of 5.00×10^{-7} meter in a vacuum? (1) 6.00×10^{-14} Hz (2) 6.00×10^{14} Hz (3) 6.00×10^{15} Hz (4) 6.00×10^{16} Hz

75. The following diagram shows parallel rays of light interacting with a barrier. Which phenomenon of light is illustrated?

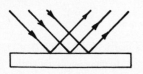

76. Which diagram best represents the reflection of object O in plane mirror M?

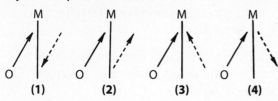

77. A ray is reflected from a surface, as shown in the diagram that follows. Which letter represents the angle of incidence?

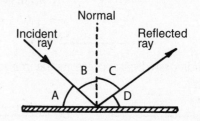

78. A tall person stands in front of a vertical plane mirror 2.0 meters high, as shown in the following diagram. A ray of light reflects off the mirror, allowing him to see his foot. Approximately how far up the mirror from the floor does this ray strike the mirror?

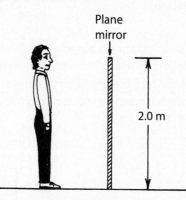

(1) 1.0 m (2) 2.0 m (3) 0.25 m (4) 0 m

79. The image of an object is viewed in a plane mirror. What is the ratio of the object size to the image size? (1) 1:1 (2) 2:1 (3) 1:2 (4) 1:4

80. The following diagram represents a light ray being reflected from a plane mirror. The angle between the incident and reflected ray is 70.° What is the angle of incidence for this ray?

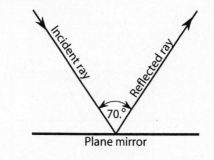

(1) 20.° (2) 35° (3) 55° (4) 70.°

81. An object is placed in front of a plane mirror as shown in the following diagram.

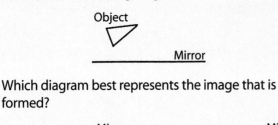

Which diagram best represents the image that is formed?

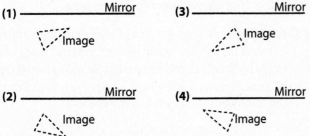

82. In the following diagram, a person is standing 5 meters from a plane mirror. The chair in front of the person is located 2 meters from the mirror. What is the distance between the person and the image he observes of the chair?

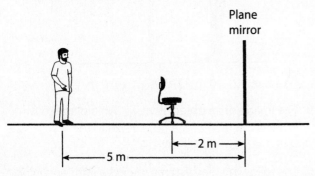

83. In the diagram that follows, ray R of monochromatic yellow light is incident upon a glass surface at an angle θ. Which resulting ray is *not* possible?

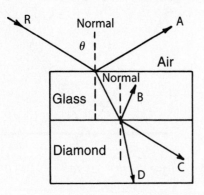

84. Which diagram best represents wave reflection?

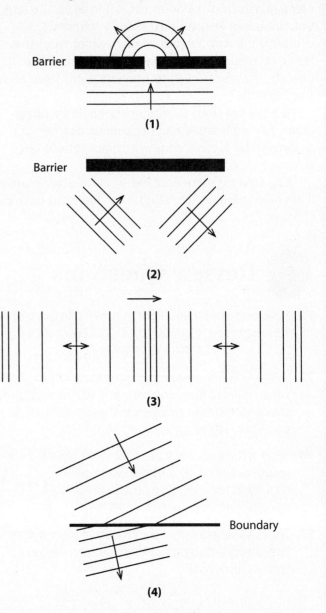

85. When a ray of light strikes a mirror perpendicular to its surface, what is the angle of reflection?

86. The change in the direction of a wave when it passes obliquely from one medium to another is called (1) diffraction (2) interference (3) refraction (4) superposition

87. As a wave enters a new medium, there may be a change in the wave's (1) frequency (2) speed (3) period (4) phase

88. Which arrow best represents the path that a monochromatic ray of light travels as it passes through air, corn oil, glycerol and back into air?

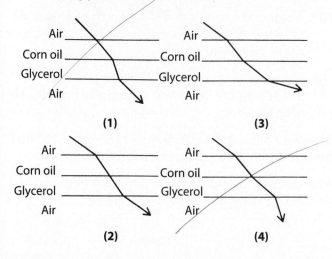

(1)   **(3)**

(2)   **(4)**

89. What occurs when light passes from water into flint glass? (1) Its speed decreases, its wavelength becomes shorter, and its frequency remains the same. (2) Its speed decreases, its wavelength becomes shorter, and its frequency increases. (3) Its speed increases, its wavelength becomes longer, and its frequency remains the same. (4) Its speed increases, its wavelength becomes longer, and its frequency decreases.

90. Which ray diagram best illustrates refraction?

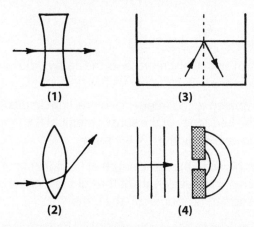

(1)   **(3)**

(2)   **(4)**

91. In the following diagram, ray AB is incident on surface XY at point B. If medium 2 has a lower index of refraction than medium 1, through which point will the ray most likely pass?

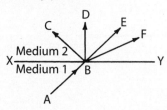

92. A beam of monochromatic red light passes obliquely from air into water. Which characteristic of the light does *not* change? (1) direction (2) velocity (3) frequency (4) wavelength

93. The speed of light in corn oil is the same as the speed of light in (1) diamond (2) flint glass (3) air (4) glycerol

94. If the speed of light in a medium is 2.00×10^8 meters per second, what is the absolute index of refraction for the medium?

95. In which medium is the wavelength of red light the shortest? (1) flint glass (2) crown glass (3) diamond (4) zircon

96. The frequency of a ray of light is 5.09×10^{14} hertz. What is the ratio of the speed of this ray in diamond to its speed in zircon?

97. In the diagram that follows, monochromatic light having a frequency of 5.09×10^{14} hertz in air is about to travel through crown glass, water, and diamond. In which substance does the light travel at the slowest speed?

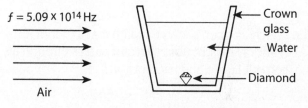

(not drawn to scale)

98. For a given angle of incidence, the greatest change in the direction of a light ray is produced when the light ray passes obliquely from air into (1) Lucite (2) glycerol (3) fused quartz (4) crown glass

99. The following diagram represents a wave traveling from medium 1 to medium 2.

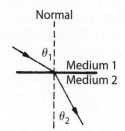

The relative index of refraction may be determined by calculating the ratio of (1) $\frac{\theta_1}{\theta_2}$ (2) $\frac{\sin \theta_2}{\sin \theta_1}$ (3) $\frac{\sin \theta_1}{\sin \theta_2}$ (4) $\frac{n_1}{n_2}$

100. A ray of light in air is incident on a block of Lucite at an angle of 60.° from the normal. The angle of refraction of this ray in Lucite is closest to (1) 35° (2) 45° (3) 60.° (4) 75°

101. A beam of monochromatic yellow light passes from air into a tank of salt water. As more salt is dissolved in the water, the index of refraction of the liquid increases and the speed of the light in the liquid (1) decreases (2) increases (3) remains the same

102. In the following diagram, a person observes an object resting on the bottom of a tank of water. To the observer, the object appears to be at which point?

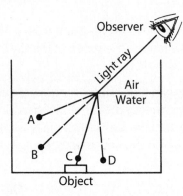

103. Which diagram shows the path that a monochromatic ray of light will travel as it passes through air, corn oil, Lucite, and back into air?

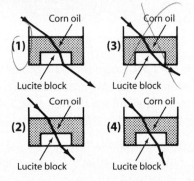

104. Which electromagnetic radiation has the shortest wavelength? (1) infrared (2) radio (3) gamma (4) ultraviolet

105. Which are *not* in the electromagnetic spectrum? (1) light waves (2) radio waves (3) sound waves (4) X rays

106. In a vacuum, all electromagnetic waves have the same (1) frequency (2) wavelength (3) speed (4) energy

107. A monochromatic beam of light with a frequency of 5.45×10^{14} hertz travels in a vacuum. What is the color of the light?

108. The wavelength of a typical AM radio wave is 3×10^3 meters. Determine the order of magnitude of its frequency.

Base your answers to questions 109 through 112 on the information and diagram that follow.

When a ray of monochromatic light passes from medium A to medium B, its speed decreases.

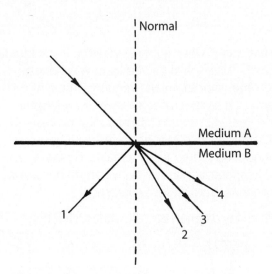

109. Which arrow best represents the path of the ray in medium B?

110. Compared to the frequency of the light in medium A, the frequency of the light in medium B is (1) lower (2) higher (3) the same

111. Compared to the wavelength of the light in medium A, the wavelength of the light in medium B is (1) shorter (2) longer (3) the same

112. According to information listed in the *Reference Tables for Physical Setting/Physics,* what could be the identity of substance B if medium A is corn oil?

Base your answers to questions 113 through 116 on the information and diagram that follow.

A ray of light having a frequency of 5.09×10^{14} hertz moves from air through substance B, through substance C, and back into air. The surfaces of substances B and C are parallel.

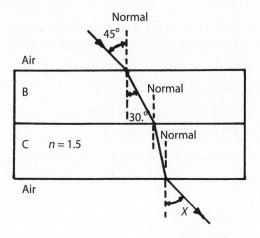

113. Determine the index of refraction of substance B.

114. Determine the speed of light in substance C.

115. If the angle of incidence of the light ray in air is increased, the angle of refraction in substance B will (1) decrease (2) increase (3) remain the same

116. The measure of angle X is (1) less than 45° (2) greater than 45° (3) equal to 45°

Base your answers to questions 117 through 120 on the information and diagram that follow.

A ray of monochromatic light traveling in air and having a frequency of 5.09×10^{14} hertz is incident upon the surface of plate X. The values of n in the diagram represent absolute indices of refraction.

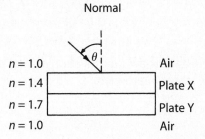

117. What is the relative index of refraction of the light going from plate X to plate Y? (1) $\frac{1.0}{1.7}$ (2) $\frac{1.0}{1.4}$ (3) $\frac{1.7}{1.4}$ (4) $\frac{1.4}{1.7}$

118. Determine the speed of the light ray in plate X.

119. Compared to angle θ, the angle of refraction of the light ray in plate X is (1) smaller (2) greater (3) the same

120. Compared to angle θ, the angle of refraction of the ray emerging from plate Y into air is (1) smaller (2) greater (3) the same

Questions for Regents Practice

Part A

1. A periodic wave travels through a rope, as shown in the following diagram. As the wave travels, what is transferred between points A and B?

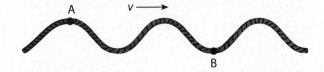

(1) mass only
(2) energy only
(3) both mass and energy
(4) neither mass nor energy

2. In which wave type is the disturbance parallel to the direction of wave travel?
(1) torsional
(2) longitudinal
(3) transverse
(4) circular

3. Which is an example of a longitudinal wave?
(1) gamma ray   (3) sound wave
(2) X ray   (4) water wave

4. A single pulse in a uniform medium transfers
(1) standing waves   (3) mass
(2) energy   (4) wavelength

5. The following diagram shows a transverse water wave moving in the direction shown by velocity vector *v*.

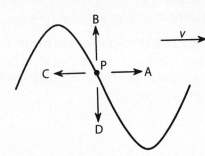

At the instant shown, a cork at point P on the water's surface is moving toward

(1) A   (3) C

(2) B   (4) D

6. The number of water waves passing a given point each second is the wave's

(1) frequency   (3) wavelength

(2) amplitude   (4) velocity

7. As a periodic wave travels from one medium to another, which pair of the wave's characteristics cannot change?

(1) period and frequency

(2) period and amplitude

(3) frequency and velocity

(4) amplitude and wavelength

8. The observed color of light depends on the light's

(1) speed   (3) intensity

(2) amplitude   (4) frequency

9. The reciprocal of the frequency of a periodic wave is the wave's

(1) period   (3) intensity

(2) amplitude   (4) speed

10. Which distance identifies the amplitude of the transverse wave in the following diagram?

(1) AE   (3) AC

(2) AB   (4) AD

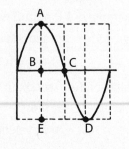

11. As a wave is refracted, which characteristic of the wave remains unchanged?

(1) velocity

(2) wavelength

(3) frequency

(4) direction

12. The ratio of the sine of the angle of incidence to the sine of the angle of refraction is equal to the

(1) angle of reflection

(2) speed of light

(3) change in the observed frequency

(4) relative index of refraction

13. In which medium does light travel at the slowest speed?

(1) water

(2) corn oil

(3) ethyl alcohol

(4) zircon

14. Which graph best represents the relationship between the frequency and period of a wave?

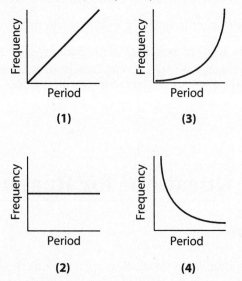

15. Which phenomenon is produced by two or more waves passing simultaneously through the same region?

(1) refraction

(2) diffraction

(3) interference

(4) reflection

16. Maximum constructive interference between two waves of the same frequency could occur when their phase difference is

(1) 1λ

(2) $\frac{\lambda}{2}$

(3) $\frac{3\lambda}{2}$

(4) $\frac{\lambda}{4}$

17. A car radio is tuned to the frequency being emitted from two transmitting towers. As the car moves at constant speed past the towers, as shown in the following diagram, the sound from the radio repeatedly fades in and out.

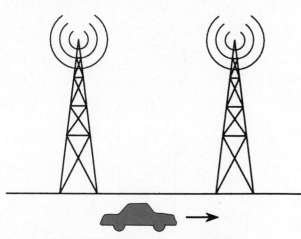

This phenomenon is best explained by

(1) refraction

(2) interference

(3) the Doppler effect

(4) resonance

18. Which wave phenomenon could *not* be demonstrated with a single wave pulse?

(1) a standing wave

(2) diffraction

(3) reflection

(4) refraction

19. If two identical sound waves arriving at the same point are in phase, the resulting wave has

(1) an increase in speed

(2) an increase in frequency

(3) a larger amplitude

(4) a longer period

20. Standing waves are produced by the interference of two waves of the same

(1) frequency and amplitude, but opposite directions

(2) frequency and direction, but different amplitudes

(3) amplitude and direction, but different frequencies

(4) frequency, amplitude, and direction

21. Two waves of the same wavelength λ interfere to form a standing wave pattern as shown in the following diagram.

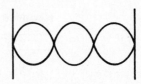

What is the straight-line distance between consecutive nodes?

(1) 1λ

(2) 2λ

(3) $\frac{1}{2}\lambda$

(4) $\frac{1}{4}\lambda$

22. An Earth satellite in orbit emits a radio signal of constant frequency. Compared to the emitted frequency, the frequency of the signal received by a stationary observer appears to be

(1) higher as the satellite approaches

(2) higher as the satellite moves away

(3) lower as the satellite approaches

(4) unaffected by the satellite's motion

23. The following diagram shows a light ray interacting with a barrier.

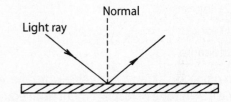

Which light phenomenon is illustrated?

(1) diffraction

(2) interference

(3) refraction

(4) reflection

24. The following diagram represents wave fronts traveling from medium X into medium Y.

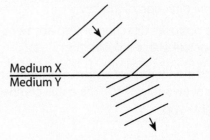

All points on any one wave front shown must be

(1) traveling with the same speed

(2) traveling in the same medium

(3) in phase

(4) superposed

25. Which diagram best illustrates the diffraction of waves?

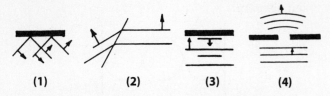

(1)   (2)   (3)   (4)

26. The following diagram represents shallow water waves of wavelength λ passing through two small openings A and B in a barrier.

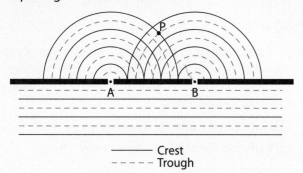

——— Crest
– – – Trough

Compared to the length of path BP, the length of path AP is

(1) 1λ longer

(2) 2λ longer

(3) $\frac{1}{2}$λ longer

(4) the same

27. Two points on a transverse wave which have the same magnitude of displacement from equilibrium are in phase if the points also have

(1) the same direction of displacement and the same direction of motion

(2) the same direction of displacement and the opposite direction of motion

(3) the opposite direction of displacement and the same direction of motion

(4) the opposite direction of displacement and the opposite direction of motion

28. A ray of monochromatic light is incident on a plane mirror at an angle of 30.° The angle of reflection for the light ray is

(1) 15°

(2) 30.°

(3) 60.°

(4) 90.°

29. Which waves are *not* electromagnetic?

(1) radio

(2) ultraviolet

(3) light

(4) sound

30. Which diagram best represents the reflection of light from an irregular surface?

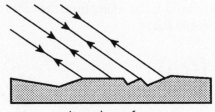

Irregular surface

(1)

Irregular surface

(2)

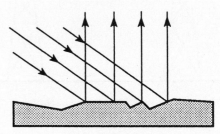

Irregular surface

(3)

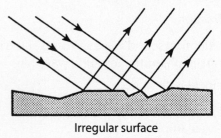

Irregular surface

(4)

31. Which graph best represents the relationship between frequency and wavelength for microwaves in a vacuum?

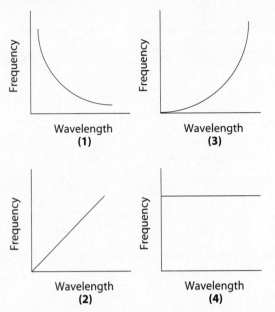

32. Two identical guitar strings are tuned to the same pitch. If one string is plucked, the other nearby string vibrates with the same frequency. This phenomenon is called

(1) resonance   (3) refraction

(2) reflection   (4) destructive interference

33. What is the color of light with a frequency of 5.65×10^{14} hertz?

(1) green

(2) red

(3) violet

(4) yellow

34. All electromagnetic waves have the same speed in

(1) water

(2) flint glass

(3) alcohol

(4) a vacuum

35. Electromagnetic radiation is produced by

(1) an accelerating electron

(2) an accelerating neutron

(3) an electron at constant velocity

(4) a neutron at constant velocity

36. Which of the following forms of electromagnetic radiation has the shortest wavelength?

(1) ultraviolet

(2) visible

(3) infrared

(4) radio

37. Which of the following colors of light has the lowest frequency?

(1) violet

(2) green

(3) yellow

(4) red

Part B

38. What is the period of a wave with a frequency of 250 hertz?

(1) 1.2×10^{-3} s

(2) 2.5×10^{-3} s

(3) 9.0×10^{-3} s

(4) 4.0×10^{-3} s

39. If the period of a wave is doubled, its wavelength is

(1) halved

(2) doubled

(3) unchanged

(4) quartered

40. What is the approximate speed of light in alcohol?

(1) 1.4×10^8 m/s

(2) 2.2×10^8 m/s

(3) 3.0×10^8 m/s

(4) 4.4×10^8 m/s

41. Periodic waves with a wavelength of 0.50 meter move with a speed of 0.30 meter per second in medium A. When the waves enter medium B, they travel at 0.15 meter per second. What is the wavelength of the waves in medium B?

(1) 20. m

(2) 1.8 m

(3) 0.50 m

(4) 0.25 m

42. In the following diagram, a ray of light enters a transparent medium from air.

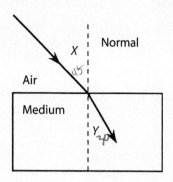

If angle X is 45° and angle Y is 30.°, what is the absolute index of refraction of the medium?

(1) 0.667

(2) 0.707

(3) 1.41

(4) 1.50

43. Which pair of moving pulses in a rope will produce destructive interference?

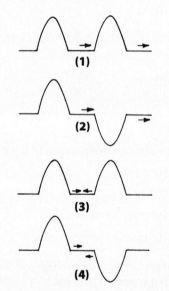

44. A ray of monochromatic light AB in air strikes a piece of glass at an incident angle θ, as shown in the following diagram.

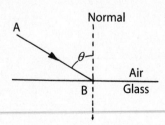

Which diagram best illustrates the ray's interaction with the glass?

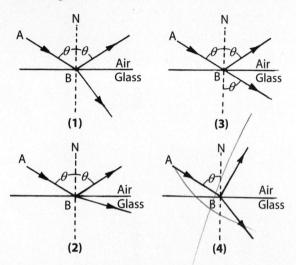

45. Which formula represents a constant for light waves of different frequencies in a vacuum?

(1) $f\lambda$ (3) λ/f

(2) f/λ (4) $f + \lambda$

46. What is the wavelength of X rays with a frequency of 1.5×10^{18} hertz traveling in a vacuum?

(1) 4.5×10^{26} m   (3) 5.0×10^{-10} m

(2) 2.0×10^{-10} m   (4) 5.0×10^{9} m

47. The following diagram shows the letter "L" in front of a plane mirror MM^1.

Which diagram best represents the image of the letter?

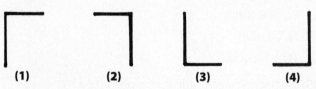

48. The time required for light to travel a distance of 1.50×10^{11} meters is closest to

(1) 5.00×10^{2} s

(2) 2.00×10^{-3} s

(3) 5.00×10^{-1} s

(4) 4.50×10^{19} s

Base your answers to questions 49 through 51 on the following information and diagram.

The diagram represents two light rays emerging from a candle flame and being reflected by a plane mirror.

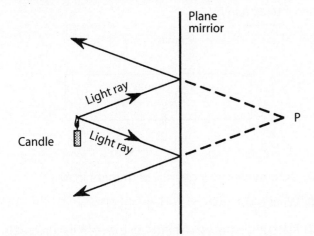

49. What does point P represent? [1]

50. If the candle was moved further away from the mirror, point P would

    (1) move closer to the mirror

    (2) move further away from the mirror

    (3) remain in the same location

51. On the axes below, sketch a graph to represent the relationship between the size of the object in front of a plane mirror and the size of its image. [1]

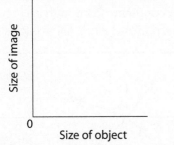

Base your answers to questions 52 through 55 on the following diagram, which represents the wave pattern produced by a vibrating source moving linearly in a shallow tank of water. The pattern is viewed from above and the lines represent crests.

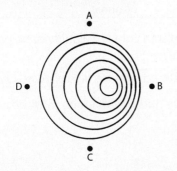

52. Towards which point is the source moving? [1]

53. What wave phenomenon is illustrated by the wave pattern? [1]

54. Compared to the frequency of the waves observed at point B, the frequency of waves observed at point D is

    (1) lower

    (2) higher

    (3) the same

55. The velocity of the source is increased. The wavelength of the waves observed at point D will

    (1) decrease

    (2) increase

    (3) remain the same

Base your answers to questions 56 through 62 on the following diagram, which represents a segment of a periodic wave traveling to the right in a steel spring.

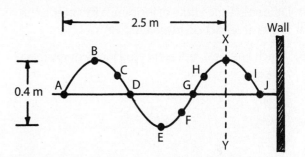

56. What is the amplitude of the wave? [1]

57. What is the wavelength of the wave? [1]

58. How many cycles of the wave are shown? [1]

59. If a crest passes line XY every 0.40 second, what is the frequency of the wave? [1]

60. Determine the speed of the wave. [2]

61. Name two points on the wave that are in phase. [1]

62. In the next instant of time, point G will move towards the

    (1) left of the page

    (2) right of the page

    (3) top of the page

    (4) bottom of the page

Base your answers to questions 63 through 68 on the following diagram, which represents two media with parallel surfaces in air and a ray of light ($f = 5.09 \times 10^{14}$ hertz) passing through them.

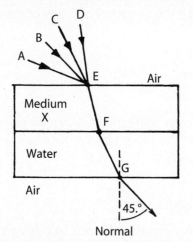

63. Determine the approximate speed of the light in water. [2]

64. Determine the angle of incidence in water, if the angle of refraction in air is 45°. [2]

65. Which line best represents the incident ray in air?

(1) AE

(2) BE

(3) CE

(4) DE

66. Compared to the speed of light in water, the speed of light in medium X is

(1) lower

(2) higher

(3) the same

67. Ray EFG would be a straight line if the index of refraction for medium X was

(1) less than 1.33

(2) greater than 1.33

(3) equal to 1.33

68. Compared to the wavelength of the light in air, the wavelength of the light in water is

(1) shorter

(2) longer

(3) the same

Base your answers to questions 69 through 73 on the following diagram and information.

A ray of monochromatic light having a wavelength of 4.00×10^{-7} meter passes from air through Lucite and then into air again.

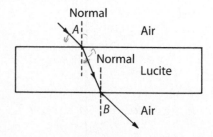

69. Determine the frequency of the light in air. [2]

70. What is the color of the light ray? [1]

71. Determine the wavelength of the light in Lucite. [2]

72. Compared to angle A, angle B is

(1) smaller   (3) the same

(2) larger

73. If angle A was increased, the angle of refraction in the Lucite would

(1) decrease   (3) remain the same

(2) increase

Base your answers to questions 74 through 77 on the following information and diagram.

Two light rays originate from source S in medium y. The dashed line represents a normal to each surface.

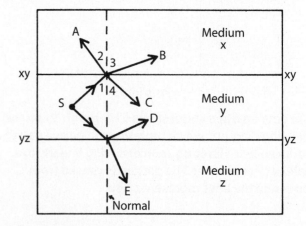

74. Which lettered light ray would *not* be produced in this situation? [1]

75. Which lettered light ray is a reflected ray? [1]

76. Which two numbered angles must be equal? [1]

77. Compared to the speed of light in medium x, the speed of light in medium z is

(1) less

(2) greater

(3) the same

Base your answers to questions 78 through 80 on the following information and diagram.

The sonar of a stationary ship sends a signal with a frequency of 5.0×10^3 hertz down through water. The speed of the signal is 1.5×10^3 meters per second. The echo from the bottom is detected 4.0 seconds later.

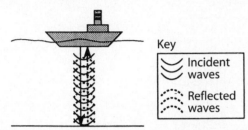

Key
≈ Incident waves
⋯ Reflected waves

78. Determine the wavelength of the sonar wave. [2]

79. Determine the depth of the water under the ship. [2]

80. The echo is an example of which wave phenomenon?

(1) diffraction

(2) reflection

(3) refraction

(4) interference

Base your answers to questions 81 through 84 on the following information and diagram.

A vibrating 1000-hertz tuning fork produces sound waves that travel at 340 meters per second in air. Points A and B are some distance from the tuning fork. Point P is 20. meters from the tuning fork.

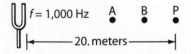

$f = 1,000$ Hz   A   B   P

|← 20. meters →|

81. Determine the time required for a sound wave to travel from the tuning fork to point P. [2]

82. Determine the wavelength of the sound waves produced by the tuning fork. [2]

83. If the waves are in phase at point A and B, then the minimum distance separating points A and B is

(1) 1λ

(2) 2λ

(3) $\frac{1}{4}\lambda$

(4) $\frac{1}{2}\lambda$

84. If the vibrating tuning fork is accelerated toward point P, the frequency of the sound observed at P is

(1) lower

(2) higher

(3) the same

Base your answers to questions 85 through 88 on your knowledge of wave phenomena.

85. When a person peers down into a swimming pool filled with water, the bottom appears closer to the person than it actually is because light is

(1) reflected

(2) refracted

(3) absorbed

(4) diffracted

86. As wind blows across the top of a chimney flue when the damper is open, the chimney "sings." This is an example of

(1) diffraction

(2) the Doppler effect

(3) refraction

(4) resonance

87. Explain why, when a rapidly moving fire engine is coming toward you, the pitch of its siren sounds higher than it does when the fire engine is at rest. [1]

88. Explain why a picture is seen less distinctly when it is covered with clear glass. [1]

Part C

Base your answers to questions 89 through 96 on the following information, diagram, and data table.

Seven pairs of students performed an experiment to determine the speed of sound in air in the classroom. The apparatus consisted of a tall cylinder nearly filled with water, a hollow glass tube, a 30-centimeter ruler, a Celsius thermometer, a tuning fork marked 512 hertz, and a rubber mallet. The glass tube was held vertically in the cylinder of water. After striking the tuning fork with the mallet, it was held over the open end of the tube as shown.

Keeping the vibrating fork just above the edge of the tube, the glass tube was slowly moved up and down in the water until the position was located where the sound was loudest. The length of the air column in the glass tube at this point was measured and recorded. The inside diameter of the tube and the temperature of the air inside the tube were also measured and recorded in the incomplete data table that follows. Each pair of students used the same tuning fork and all the data was collected within a 15-minute time interval.

Students were instructed to use the formula $\lambda = 4\ell + 1.6d$ to calculate the wavelength λ

of the sound wave that was produced in the air column by the tuning fork. They were also told to use the formula

$$v = 331\sqrt{1 + \frac{T_C}{273}}$$ to determine the accepted value

for v, the speed of sound in air in meters per second at a particular Celsius temperature T_C.

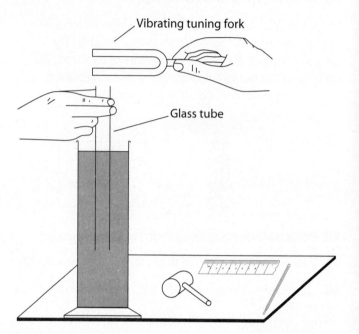
Vibrating tuning fork

Glass tube

	Length ℓ of air column (m)	Inside diameter d of tube (m)	Wavelength (m)	Frequency (Hz)	Temperature (°C)	Experimental speed of sound (m/s)	Accepted speed of sound, v (m/s)	Relative error (%)
Trial								
1	0.163	0.032		512	21.5			
2	0.149	0.039		512	21.5			
3	0.150	0.037	0.659	512	20.5	337	343	
4	0.149	0.037		512	21.5			
5	0.152	0.040		512	21.8			
6	0.159	0.038	0.697	512	21.5			
7	0.152	0.040		512	21.8			

Data Table

89. What type of wave was produced by the vibrating tuning fork? [1]

90. The loudest sound was produced when the natural frequency of the air in the column was the same as that of the vibrating tuning fork. What is the name of this wave phenomenon? [1]

91. What is the range of data collected for the length of the air column? [1]

92. What is the mean of the data collected for the inside diameter of the tube? [1]

93. How many significant digits were reported for the inside diameter of the tube in trial 5? [1]

94. Determine the wavelength for trial 1. [2]

95. Determine the accepted value for the speed of sound in air for trial 6. [2]

96. Determine the relative error for trial 3. [2]

Base your answers to questions 97 through 100 on the paragraph that follows and your knowledge of physics.

During a thunderstorm, a single bolt of lightning may develop 3.75 terawatts of power, but the lightning only lasts for 1.5×10^{-3} second. About 75% of the energy is dissipated as heat, which dramatically raises the temperature of the air in the lightning channel, causing the air to expand quickly. The movement creates sound waves that can be heard as thunder for distances up to 30. kilometers. An observer sees the flash of lightning before hearing the clap of thunder.

97. Express in scientific notation the power developed by the lightning bolt in watts to the proper number of significant figures. [1]

98. Determine approximately how much energy in joules the lightning bolt dissipates as heat. [2]

99. The observer is 30. kilometers from the lightning strike. Assuming the air is at STP, how much time elapses for the observer between the flash of lightning and when she hears the clap of thunder? [3]

100. What is the order of magnitude of the ratio of the speed of light in air to the speed of sound in air at STP? [1]

Base your answers to questions 101 through 105 on the following information and diagram.

A ray of monochromatic light, having a frequency of 5.09×10^{14} hertz, is traveling in air. The ray is incident on the surface of a block of flint glass at an angle of 40.°, as shown. Part of the light is reflected at the air-glass interface and part is refracted in the glass.

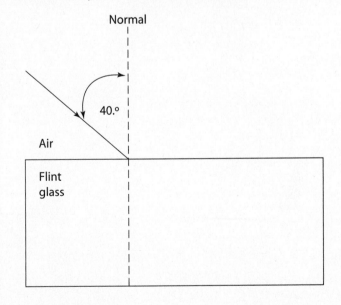

101. On the diagram, draw the reflected ray and label the angle of reflection θ, with its measure to the nearest degree. [2]

102. Determine the angle of refraction in the flint glass to the nearest degree. [2]

103. On the diagram, draw the refracted ray. Label it "refracted ray." [2]

104. Measure the angle between the reflected and refracted rays and indicate the value in the appropriate place on the diagram. [1]

105. Determine the wavelength of the light ray in flint glass. [2]

Base your answer to question 106 on the following information and diagram.

A ray of monochromatic light, having a frequency of 5.09×10^{14} hertz, is incident upon an interface of water and an unknown medium, X. The ray is refracted in medium X as shown.

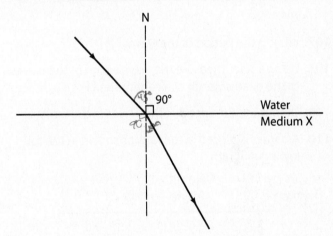

106. Find the speed of light in medium X. [4]

Base your answers to questions 107 through 110 on the following information and diagram. The diagram represents a wave generator having a constant frequency of 12 hertz and producing parallel wave fronts in a shallow tank of water. The velocity of the wave is *v*.

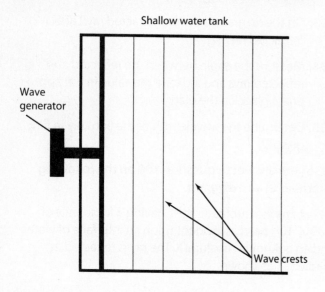

107. What is the period of the waves? [1]

108. Using a ruler, measure the wavelength of the waves to the nearest tenth of a centimeter. [1]

109. Determine the speed of the waves in the tank. [2]

110. A barrier is placed in the tank as shown in the following diagram.

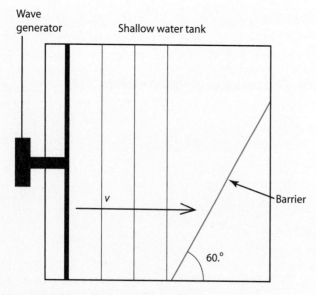

Use a protractor and a straight edge to construct an arrow to represent the direction of the velocity of the reflected waves. [1]

Base your answers to questions 111 through 113 on the following information and diagram.

Two waves, A and B, travel in the same direction in the same medium at the same time.

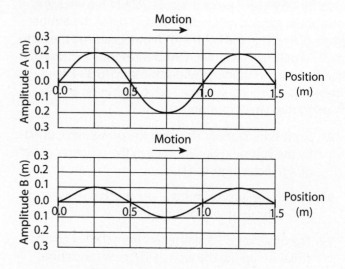

111. On the grid below draw the resultant wave produced by the superposition of waves A and B. [1]

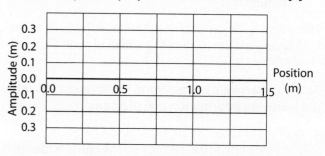

112. What is the amplitude of the resultant wave? [1]

113. What is the wavelength of the resultant wave? [1]

Modern Physics

VOCABULARY

absorption spectrum	excited state	positron
antimatter	ground state	quantized
antiparticle	hadron	quantum
antiquark	ionization potential	quantum theory
atom	lepton	quark
atomic spectrum	meson	spectral line
baryon	neutrino	Standard Model of Particle Physics
bright-line spectrum	nuclear force	stationary state
emission spectrum	nucleus	universal mass unit
energy level	photon	
energy-level diagram	Planck's constant	

Wave-Particle Duality of Energy and Matter

Earlier in this text, light, a form of electromagnetic radiation, was represented as a wave propagated by an interchange of energy between periodically varying electric and magnetic fields. Waves of electromagnetic energy are identified by their frequency, wavelength, amplitude, and velocity. In addition, electromagnetic radiation exhibits the phenomena of diffraction, interference, and the Doppler effect, which are readily explained by a wave model of light.

Waves Have a Particle Nature

The wave model of light, however, can not explain other phenomena such as interactions of light with matter. In these interactions, light—or other electromagnetic radiation—acts as if it is composed of particles possessing kinetic energy and momentum. For example, when light strikes matter, some of the light's momentum is transferred to the matter. Early in the last century it was discovered that light having a frequency above some minimum value and incident on certain metals caused electrons to be emitted from the metal. This phenomenon, called the photoelectric effect, could not be explained by a wave model of light. Albert Einstein explained the phenomenon using quantum theory developed by Max Planck.

Quantum Theory

Quantum theory assumes that electromagnetic energy is emitted from and absorbed by matter in discrete amounts or packets. Each packet of electromagnetic energy emitted or absorbed is called a **quantum** (plural, quanta) of energy. The amount of energy E of each quantum is directly proportional to the frequency f of the electromagnetic radiation. The proportionality constant between the energy of a quantum and its frequency is called **Planck's constant,** h. Thus, the energy of a quantum is given by this equation.

$$E = hf$$

E is in joules, f is in hertz, and h is a universal constant equal to 6.63×10^{-34} joule·second (J·s). The small energy values of quanta are often expressed in electronvolts, eV (1 eV $= 1.60 \times 10^{-19}$ J).

The quantum, or basic unit, of electromagnetic energy is called a **photon.** Although a photon is a massless particle of light, it carries both energy and momentum. The energy of a photon can be found using the previous equation. For light in a vacuum, $f = c/\lambda$ (Topic 5), so the energy of a photon can also be described in this way.

$$E_{photon} = hf = \frac{hc}{\lambda}$$

The equation states that the energy of a photon is directly proportional to its frequency and inversely proportional to its wavelength.

SAMPLE PROBLEM

The energy of a photon is 2.11 electronvolts.
(a) Determine the energy of the photon in joules.
(b) Determine the frequency of the photon.
(c) Determine the color of light associated with the photon.

Solution: Identify the known and unknown values.

Known	Unknown
$E = 2.11$ eV	$E = ?$ J
$h = 6.63 \times 10^{-34}$ J·s	$f = ?$ Hz
	color = ?

(a) Convert electronvolts to joules using the relationship 1 eV $= 1.60 \times 10^{-19}$ J

$$2.11 \text{ eV} \left(\frac{1.60 \times 10^{-19} \text{ J}}{1 \text{ eV}} \right) = 3.38 \times 10^{-19} \text{ J}$$

(b) To find the frequency, solve the equation $E = hf$ for frequency f.

$$f = \frac{E}{h}$$

Substitute the known values and solve.

$$f = \frac{3.38 \times 10^{-19} \text{J}}{6.63 \times 10^{-34} \text{ J·s}} = 5.10 \times 10^{14} \text{ Hz}$$

(c) According to the electromagnetic spectrum chart found in the *Reference Tables for Physical Setting/Physics*, a frequency of 5.10×10^{14} Hz corresponds to yellow light.

Photon-Particle Collisions

The photoelectric effect demonstrates that when a photon in the visible light range is incident on a metal surface, the photon's energy is completely absorbed and transferred to the emitted electron. However, when X-ray photons, which have much higher frequencies and energies than photons of visible light, strike a metal surface, not only are electrons ejected but electromagnetic radiation of lower frequency is also given off.

When an X-ray photon and an electron collide, some of the energy of the photon is transferred to the electron and the photon recoils with less energy. Less energy means that the photon has lower frequency. Figure 6-1 illustrates this phenomenon.

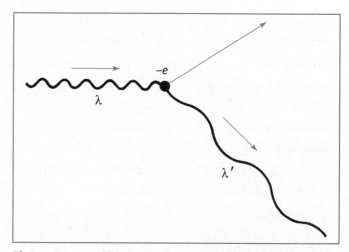

Figure 6-1. A collision of an X-ray photon and an electron in an atom: Besides the electron ejected from the atom, a photon of lower energy (longer wavelength) is also emitted (scattered) by the atom. The energy transferred to the electron equals the difference in energy between the incident photon and the scattered photon. The vector sum of the momentum of the electron and the scattered photon also equals the momentum of the incident photon.

Both energy, a scalar quantity, and momentum, a vector quantity, are conserved in this interaction, just as they are in collisions between particles. The incident photon loses energy and momentum, while the electron gains energy and momentum. Photons always travel at the speed of light. Thus, the momentum of a photon depends only on its wavelength or frequency.

Particles Have a Wave Nature

Just as radiation has both wave and particle characteristics, matter in motion has wave as well as particle characteristics. The wavelengths of the waves associated with the motion of ordinary objects, such as a thrown baseball, are too small to be detected. But the waves associated with the motion of particles of atomic or subatomic size, such as electrons, can produce diffraction and interference patterns that can be observed. Diffraction and interference phenomena provide evidence for the wave nature of particles.

Review Questions

1. In which part of the electromagnetic spectrum does a photon have the least energy? (1) gamma rays (2) microwaves (3) visible light (4) ultraviolet

2. The energy of a photon varies inversely with its (1) frequency (2) momentum (3) speed (4) wavelength

3. Compared to a photon of red light, a photon of blue light has a (1) lower frequency and shorter wavelength (2) lower frequency and longer wavelength (3) higher frequency and shorter wavelength (4) higher frequency and longer wavelength

4. On the axes that follow, sketch a line that represents the relationship between the energy of a photon and its frequency.

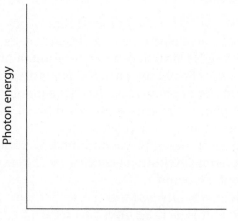

5. A photon of green light has a frequency of approximately 6.0×10^{14} hertz. The energy associated with this photon is approximately (1) 1.1×10^{-48} J (2) 6.0×10^{-34} J (3) 5.0×10^{-7} J (4) 4.0×10^{-19} J

6. Determine the energy of a photon having a wavelength of 4.00×10^{-7} meter.

7. A photon has an energy of 8.0×10^{-19} joule. What is this energy expressed in electronvolts? (1) 5.0×10^{-38} eV (2) 1.6×10^{-19} eV (3) 8.0×10^{-19} eV (4) 5.0 eV

8. A gamma photon collides with an electron at rest. During the interaction, the momentum of the photon (1) decreases (2) increases (3) remains the same

9. An X-ray photon collides with an electron in an atom, ejecting the electron and emitting another photon. During the collision there is a conservation of (1) momentum only (2) energy only (3) both momentum and energy (4) neither momentum nor energy

10. Experiments performed with light indicate that light exhibits (1) particle properties only (2) wave properties only (3) both particle and wave properties (4) neither wave nor particle properties

11. According to the quantum theory of light, light energy is carried in discrete units called (1) protons (2) photons (3) photoelectrons (4) quarks

Early Models of the Atom

An **atom** is the smallest particle of an element that retains the characteristics of the element. Models for the structure of the atom have evolved over centuries as scientists have developed more sophisticated methods and equipment for studying particles that are too small to be detected by the unaided eye.

Thomson's Model

Just over 100 years ago, J. J. Thomson discovered that electrons are relatively low-mass, negatively charged particles present in atoms. Because he knew that atoms are electrically neutral, Thomson concluded that part of the atom must possess a positive charge equal to the total charge of the atom's electrons. Thomson proposed a model in which the atom consists of a uniform distribution of positive charge in which electrons are embedded, like raisins in plum pudding.

Rutherford's Model

Less than two decades later, Ernest Rutherford proposed a different model of the atom. He performed experiments in which he directed a beam of massive, positively charged particles, traveling at approximately one-tenth the speed of light, at extremely thin gold foil. Rutherford postulated that if an atom was like those described in Thomson's model, there would be only small net Coulomb forces on a positively charged particle as it passed through or near a gold atom in the foil, and the particle would pass through the foil relatively unaffected. However, he found that, although nearly all the positively charged particles were not deflected from a straight-line path through the gold foil, a small number of particles were scattered at large angles.

To explain the large angles of deflection of those few particles, Rutherford theorized that the massive, energetic, positively charged particles must have collided with other even more massive positively charged particles. Assuming that atoms are symmetrical, he concluded that this concentration of mass and positive charge in the atom, which he called the nucleus, is located at the atom's center. From the relative number of deflected particles, he calculated that the nucleus is only about $\frac{1}{10,000}$ the diameter of the average atom.

Based on the results of these scattering experiments, Rutherford described an atom as being similar to a miniature solar system. The tiny nucleus at the center of the atom contains all the positive charge of the atom and virtually all of its mass. The nucleus is surrounded by enough electrons to balance the positive charge of the nucleus and make the atom electrically neutral. The electrons move in orbits around the nucleus and are held in orbit by Coulomb forces of attraction between their negative charges and the positive charge of the nucleus.

In Rutherford's model, the electrons orbiting the nucleus accelerate due to a change in direction of motion. Rutherford knew that these accelerated charges should radiate electromagnetic energy, lose kinetic energy and momentum in the process, and spiral rapidly to the nucleus. The radiated electromagnetic energy would increase in frequency and produce a continuous spectrum. This expected behavior is contradicted by the observed bright-line spectrum that is characteristic of each element. (Bright-line spectra will be discussed later in this topic.)

The Bohr Model of the Hydrogen Atom

About two years later, Niels Bohr attempted to explain why electrons in atoms can maintain their positions outside the nucleus rather than spiral into the nucleus and cause the atom to collapse. Bohr developed a model of the hydrogen atom based on these assumptions:

- All forms of energy are **quantized,** that is, an electron can gain or lose kinetic energy only in fixed amounts, or quanta.
- The electron in the hydrogen atom can occupy only certain specific orbits of fixed radius and no others.
- The electron can jump from one orbit to a higher one by absorbing a quantum of energy in the form of a photon.

- Each allowed orbit in the atom corresponds to a specific amount of energy. The orbit nearest the nucleus represents the smallest amount of energy that the electron can have. The electron can remain in this orbit without losing energy even though it is being constantly accelerated toward the nucleus by the Coulomb force of attraction.

When the electron is in any particular orbit, it is said to be in a **stationary state.** Each stationary state represents a specific amount of energy and is called an **energy level.** The successive energy levels of an atom are assigned integral numbers, denoted by $n = 1, n = 2$, etc. When the electron is in the lowest energy level ($n = 1$), it is said to be in the **ground state.** For a hydrogen atom, an electron in any level above the ground state is said to be in an **excited state.**

ENERGY LEVELS Any process that raises the energy level of electrons in an atom is called excitation. Excitation can be the result of absorbing the energy of colliding particles of matter, such as electrons, or of photons of electromagnetic radiation. A photon's energy is absorbed by an electron in an atom only if the photon's energy corresponds exactly to an energy-level difference possible for the electron. Excitation energies are different for different elements.

Atoms rapidly lose the energy of their various excited states as their electrons return to the ground state. This lost energy is in the form of photons (radiation) of specific frequencies, which appear as spectral lines in the characteristic spectrum of each element. A **spectral line** is a particular frequency of absorbed or emitted energy characteristic of an atom.

IONIZATION POTENTIAL An atom can absorb sufficient energy to raise an electron to an energy level such that the electron is essentially removed from the atom and an ion is formed. The energy required to remove an electron from an atom to form an ion is called the atom's **ionization potential.** An atom in an excited state requires a smaller amount of energy to become an ion than does an atom in the ground state.

Figure 6-2 shows the energy-level diagram for the hydrogen atom. An **energy-level diagram** is one in which the energy levels of a quantized system are indicated by distances of horizontal lines from a zero energy level. The energy level of an electron that has been completely removed from the atom ($n = \infty$) is defined to be 0.00 eV. Thus, all other energy levels have negative values. As an electron moves closer to the nucleus, the energy associated with the electron becomes smaller. Because an electron in the ground state has the lowest energy, its energy has the largest negative value. The *Physics Reference Tables for Physical Setting/Physics* contain energy level diagrams for hydrogen and mercury.

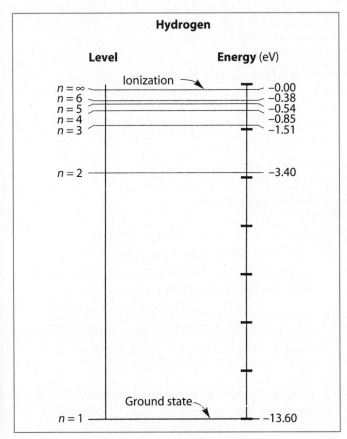

Figure 6-2. Energy levels for the hydrogen atom

LIMITATIONS OF BOHR'S MODEL Although Bohr's model explained the spectral lines of hydrogen, it could not predict the spectra or explain the electron orbits of elements having many electrons. Nevertheless, Bohr's model with its quantized energy levels set the stage for future atomic models.

The Cloud Model

Bohr's model of the atom has been replaced by the cloud model. In this model, electrons are not confined to specific orbits. Instead, they are spread out in space in a form called an electron cloud. The electron cloud is densest in regions where the probability of finding the electron is highest.

Complicated equations describe the shape, location, and density of each electron cloud in an atom. Each cloud corresponds to a particular location for an electron. By incorporating the cloud model into the Rutherford-Bohr model, scientists have been able to construct accurate models of the electron arrangements for all the elements.

Atomic Spectra

When the electrons in excited atoms of an element in the gaseous state return to lower energy states, they produce a specific series of frequencies of electromagnetic radiation called the **atomic spectrum** of the element. Each element has a characteristic spectrum that differs from that of every other element. Thus, the spectrum can be used to identify the element, even when the element is mixed with other elements.

The element helium was found on the sun before it was isolated on Earth. Spectral lines of the sun's corona were studied during a solar eclipse. The lines were not previously reported for any known element, so the new element was named helium from the Greek word for sun, *helios*.

Emission (Bright-Line) Spectra

Energy levels in an atom, introduced by Bohr, provided an explanation for atomic spectra. When an electron in an atom in an excited state falls to a lower energy level, the energy of the emitted photon is equal to the difference between the energies of the initial and final states.

$$E_{photon} = E_i - E_f$$

E_i is the initial energy of the electron in its excited state and E_f is the final energy of the electron in the lower energy level. Each energy difference between two energy levels corresponds to a photon having a specific frequency. A specific series of frequencies, characteristic of the element, is produced when the electrons of its atoms in excited states fall back to lower states or to the ground state. When these emitted frequencies are viewed in a spectroscope, the frequencies appear as a series of bright lines against a dark background and, therefore, are called a **bright-line spectrum** or an **emission spectrum.** In Figure 6-3 on the next page the energy emissions producing various series of lines in the ultraviolet, visible light, and infrared regions are indicated in the energy-level diagram for hydrogen.

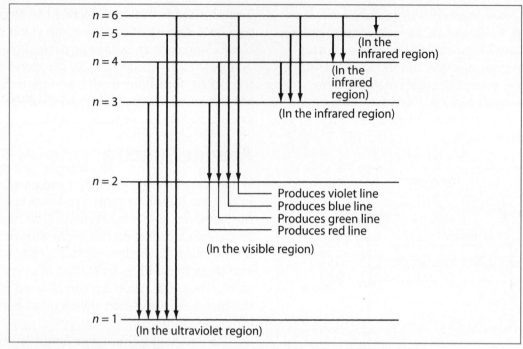

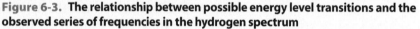

Figure 6-3. The relationship between possible energy level transitions and the observed series of frequencies in the hydrogen spectrum

Absorption Spectra

As explained earlier, an atom can absorb only photons having energies equal to specific differences in its energy levels. The frequencies and wavelengths of these absorbed photons are exactly the same as those of the photons emitted when electrons lose energy and fall between the same energy levels. If the atoms of an element are subjected to white light, which consists of all the visible frequencies, the atoms will selectively absorb the same frequencies that they emit when excited. The absorbed frequencies appear as dark lines in the otherwise continuous white-light spectrum. This series of dark lines, resulting from the selective absorption of particular frequencies in the white-light spectrum of an atom, is called an **absorption spectrum.** An atom will absorb a photon only if the photon possesses the exact amount of energy required to raise the atom to one of its possible excited states.

 **Review Questions**

Note to student: The answers to some of the following questions are based on information from the energy-level diagrams for hydrogen and mercury found in the *Reference Tables for Physical Setting/Physics.*

12. The lowest energy state of an atom is called its (1) ground state (2) ionized state (3) initial energy state (4) final energy state

13. Which electron transition in the hydrogen atom results in the emission of a photon with the greatest energy? (1) $n = 2$ to $n = 1$ (2) $n = 3$ to $n = 2$ (3) $n = 4$ to $n = 2$ (4) $n = 5$ to $n = 3$

14. What is the minimum energy required to ionize a hydrogen atom in the $n = 3$ state? (1) 13.60 eV (2) 12.09 eV (3) 5.52 eV (4) 1.51 eV

15. Which photon energy could be absorbed by a hydrogen atom that is in the $n = 2$ state? (1) 0.66 eV (2) 1.51 eV (3) 1.89 eV (4) 2.40 eV

16. Hydrogen atoms undergo a transition from the $n = 3$ energy level to the ground state. What is the total number of different photon energies that may be emitted by these atoms?

17. An electron in a mercury atom jumps from level a to level g by absorbing a single photon. What is the energy of the photon in electronvolts?

18. Which phenomenon provides evidence that the hydrogen atom has discrete energy levels?

19. As an atom absorbs a photon of energy, one of its electrons will (1) exchange energy levels with another of its electrons (2) undergo a transition to a higher energy level (3) undergo a transition to a lower energy level (4) increase its charge

20. Which transition between the energy levels of mercury causes the emission of a photon of highest frequency? (1) *e* to *d* (2) *e* to *c* (3) *c* to *b* (4) *b* to *a*

21. As an atom goes from the ground state to an excited state, the energy of the atom (1) decreases (2) increases (3) remains the same

22. It is possible for an excited hydrogen atom to return to the ground state by the emission of a single photon. Regardless of the initial excited state, this electron transition produces a spectral line in which region of the electromagnetic spectrum? (1) ultraviolet (2) infrared (3) visible light (4) radio waves

23. Determine the frequency of the photon emitted when an excited hydrogen atom changes from energy level $n = 3$ to $n = 2$.

24. An electron in a mercury atom changes from energy level *b* to level *e*. This energy-level change occurs as the atom (1) absorbs a 2.03-eV photon (2) absorbs a 5.74-eV photon (3) emits a 2.03-eV photon (4) emits a 5.74-eV photon

Base your answers to questions 25 through 27 on the information that follows.

A hydrogen atom emits a 2.55-electronvolt photon as its electron changes from one energy level to another.

25. Determine the energy level change for the electron.

26. Express the energy of the emitted photon in joules.

27. Determine the frequency of the emitted photon.

Base your answers to questions 28 through 30 on the following diagram, which represents three visible lines in the hydrogen spectrum. Either the energy or the frequency for each of these lines is given below the diagram.

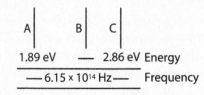

28. Which energy level transition produced line A? (1) $n = 2$ to $n = 1$ (2) $n = 3$ to $n = 2$ (3) $n = 4$ to $n = 3$ (4) $n = 5$ to $n = 2$

29. Determine the energy of the photons that produced line B.

30. Express the energy of line C in joules.

A photon with 14.60 electronvolts of energy collides with a mercury atom in its ground state.

31. Express the energy of the incident photon in joules.

32. Determine the frequency of the incident photon.

33. In what region of the electromagnetic spectrum is the frequency of the incident photon? (1) gamma rays (2) infrared (3) visible (4) ultraviolet

34. If the photon collision ionizes the atom, what is the maximum energy that the electron removed from the atom can have? (1) 0.00 eV (2) 4.22 eV (3) 10.38 eV (4) 14.60 eV

The Nucleus

Rutherford's experiments showed that all of the atom's positive charge and nearly all of its mass is contained in the nucleus. The **nucleus** is the core of an atom made up of one or more protons and (except for one of the isotopes of hydrogen) one or more neutrons. The protons and neutrons that make up the nucleus of an atom are called <u>nucleons</u>.

Nuclear Force

The positively charged protons in any nucleus containing more than one proton are separated by a distance of 10^{-15} meter. Consequently, a large repulsive Coulomb force exists between them. The gravitational force of attraction between protons is far too weak to counterbalance this electrostatic force of repulsion. Thus, there must exist a very strong attractive nuclear force to keep the protons concentrated in the nucleus of an atom. It is this **nuclear force,** which is an attractive force between protons and neutrons in an atomic nucleus, that is responsible for the stability of the nucleus.

The nuclear force of attraction between two protons in a nucleus is about 100 times stronger than the electrostatic force of repulsion. At distances greater than a few nucleon diameters, however, the nuclear force diminishes rapidly and becomes much less than the gravitational or electrostatic forces. Although nuclear forces are the strongest forces known to exist, they are effective only over a short distance.

Universal Mass Unit

The mass of an individual atom is a very small fraction of a kilogram. Consequently, for convenience, scientists use another unit called the universal mass unit, u, to express such masses. The **universal mass unit,** or atomic mass unit, is defined as $\frac{1}{12}$ the mass of an atom of carbon-12, which is a carbon atom having 6 protons, 6 neutrons, and 6 electrons. In universal mass units, the mass of the proton is 1.0073 u, the mass of the neutron is 1.0087 u, and the mass of an electron is 0.0005 u. In SI units, a mass of one universal mass unit, or 1 u, equals 1.66×10^{-27} kilogram.

Mass-Energy Relationship

Einstein showed that mass and energy are different forms of the same thing and are equivalent. The energy equivalent of mass is directly proportional to both the mass and the speed of light in a vacuum squared. The following equation expresses this relationship.

$$E = mc^2$$

E is energy in joules, m is mass in kilograms, and c is the speed of light in a vacuum, 3.00×10^8 meters per second. For example, if one kilogram of mass is converted to energy, the amount of energy produced is 9.00×10^{16} joules. Thus, the masses of subatomic particles can be expressed in joules, but more often they are expressed in an equivalent number of electronvolts.

SAMPLE PROBLEM

One universal mass unit equals 1.66×10^{-27} kg. Find the energy equivalent of 1 u in megaelectronvolts.

Solution: Identify the known and unknown values.

Known	*Unknown*
$m = 1.66 \times 10^{-27}$ kg	$E = ?$ MeV

From the *Reference Tables:*
$c = 3.00 \times 10^8$ m/s
$1 \text{ eV} = 1.60 \times 10^{-19}$ J
10^6 eV = 1 MeV

Write the equation that relates energy and mass.

$E = mc^2$

Substitute the known values and solve.

$E = (1.66 \times 10^{-27} \text{ kg})(3.00 \times 10^8 \text{ m/s})^2$
$E = 1.49 \times 10^{-10}$ J

Use the relationship between electronvolts and joules to convert the energy in joules to electronvolts.

$$E = (1.49 \times 10^{-10} \text{ J})\left(\frac{1 \text{ eV}}{1.60 \times 10^{-19} \text{ J}}\right)$$

$E = 9.31 \times 10^8$ eV

Use the relationship between eV and Mev to convert eV to MeV.

$$E = (9.31 \times 10^8 \text{ eV})\left(\frac{1 \text{ MeV}}{10^6 \text{ eV}}\right)$$

$E = 931$ MeV

Nuclear Mass and Energy

According to Einstein's mass-energy equation, any change in energy results in an equivalent change in mass. Mass-energy is conserved at all levels from cosmic to subatomic. For example, in a chemical reaction in which one kilogram of carbon combines with oxygen to form carbon dioxide, the amount of energy released is 3.3×10^7 joules. Even though this is a significant amount of energy, it is equivalent to only 4×10^{-10} kilogram of mass. The mass of the carbon dioxide formed in the reaction is slightly less than the mass of the carbon and oxygen before they reacted. This change in mass is too small to detect or measure. The same is true for all chemical reactions and other ordinary energy changes. However, in reactions involving the nuclei of atoms, the changes in energy relative to the masses involved are much larger, and the corresponding changes in mass can be measured.

The mass of a proton is 1.0073 u and the mass of a neutron is 1.0087 u. Thus, the total mass of two protons and two neutrons is 2(1.0073 u + 1.0087 u), or 4.0320 u. However, the mass of a helium-4 nucleus, which consists of two protons and two neutrons, is only 4.0016 u. Thus, the mass of the atomic nucleus is less than the sum of the masses of its individual nucleons when measured separately. This is true of every nucleus, with the exception of hydrogen-1, which has only one nucleon.

When nucleons come together to form a nucleus, energy is released and an equivalent amount of matter is lost. To break up the nucleus and separate the nucleons, work must to be done against the strong nuclear force of attraction. The energy needed to separate the nucleons appears as an equivalent increase in their total mass.

SAMPLE PROBLEM

A helium nucleus consisting of two protons and two neutrons has a mass of 4.0016 universal mass units. The mass of a proton is 1.0073 universal mass units and the mass of a neutron is 1.0087 universal mass units.
(a) Find the difference between the mass of the helium nucleus and the total mass of its constituents.
(b) Find the energy equivalent of this mass difference in electronvolts.

Solution: Identify the known and unknown values.

Known	Unknown
mass of helium nucleus = 4.0016 u	mass difference = ? u
	E = ? eV
mass of proton = 1.0073 u	
mass of neutron = 1.0087 u	

From the *Reference Tables*:
1 u = 931 MeV

(a) Determine the mass of the two protons and two neutrons.
mass of 2 protons = 2(1.0073 u) = 2.0146 u
mass of 2 neutrons = 2(1.0087 u) = 2.0174 u

Find the total mass of the four individual nucleons.
total mass = 2.0146 u + 2.0174 u = 4.0320 u

Find the difference between the masses of the individual nucleons and a helium nucleus.
mass difference = 4.0320 u − 4.0016 u = 0.0304 u

(b) Use the relationship between the universal mass unit and MeV, 1 u = 931 MeV.
E = (0.0304 u)(931 MeV/u) = 28.3 MeV

Studying Atomic Nuclei

The structure of the atomic nucleus and the nature of matter have been investigated using particle accelerators. These devices use electric and magnetic fields to increase the kinetic energies of charged particles, such as electrons and protons, and project them at speeds near the speed of light in a vacuum into samples of matter. Collisions between the high speed particles and atomic nuclei may disrupt the nuclei and release new particles. The study of these ejected particles can give useful information about the structure and forces within the nucleus. Scientists continue to study the atomic nucleus because the nucleus, and thus the atomic structure of an atom of an element determines the particular physical and chemical properties of the element. Each type of atom is different and distinct. A growing understanding of nuclear forces and structure will increase understanding of matter and its interactions.

Review Questions

35. Which particles are most likely to be found in an atomic nucleus? (1) neutrons only (2) protons only (3) both protons and neutrons (4) both neutrons and electrons

36. Which statement most accurately describes the interaction which binds a nucleus together? (1) long-range and weak (2) long-range and strong (3) short-range and weak (4) short-range and strong

37. What is the force that holds the nucleus of an atom together? (1) nuclear force (2) magnetic force (3) gravitational force (4) electrostatic force

38. It is difficult for a proton to approach the nucleus of an atom because of the (1) gravitational field (2) electrostatic field (3) magnetic field (4) nuclear force

39. One universal mass unit is defined as (1) the mass of an electron (2) the mass of a proton (3) the mass of a carbon-12 atom (4) $\frac{1}{12}$ the mass of a carbon-12 atom

40. In the equation $E = mc^2$, E may be expressed in (1) newtons/coulomb (2) joules/second (3) electronvolts (4) coulombs

41. As a star gives off energy in a thermonuclear reaction, the mass of the star (1) decreases (2) increases (3) remains the same

42. Determine how many joules of energy would be produced if 2.50×10^{-3} kilogram of matter was entirely converted to energy.

43. If the mass of one proton was totally converted into energy, the yield would be (1) 2.79×10^{-38} J (2) 5.01×10^{-19} J (3) 1.50×10^{-10} J (4) 9.00×10^{16} J

44. In a nuclear reaction, 9.90×10^{-13} joule of energy was released. Determine the mass equivalent of this energy.

45. Which graph best represents the relationship between energy and mass in the equation $E = mc^2$?

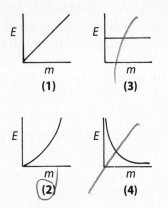

(1)   (3)

(2)   (4)

46. The following chart shows the masses of selected particles.

Particle	Mass
$^{235}_{92}U$	235.0 u
$^{138}_{56}Ba$	137.9 u
$^{95}_{36}Kr$	94.9 u
$^{1}_{0}n$	1.0 u

Consider the following equation.

$$^{235}_{92}U + {}^{1}_{0}n \rightarrow {}^{138}_{56}Ba + {}^{95}_{36}Kr + 3{}^{1}_{0}n + E$$

The energy E is equivalent to a mass of (1) 0.2 u (2) 2.0 u (3) 2.2 u (4) 0.0 u

The Standard Model of Particle Physics

Today, particle physicists are in the process of building a model of the structure of the nucleus. The current model, called the **Standard Model of Particle Physics,** is a theory, not a law, that is used to explain the existence of all the particles that have been observed and the forces that hold atoms together or lead to their decay.

The Fundamental Forces in Nature

In Topic 1, force was defined as a push or pull on a mass. In Topic 2, force was explained as a vector quantity causing an object to accelerate. In modern physics, scientist refer to particles as force carriers, because forces are brought about as a result of an exchange of particles.

There are four fundamental forces in nature: strong (nuclear), electromagnetic, weak, and gravitational. Table 6-1 gives an overview of the important characteristics of these four forces. The weak force, which has not yet been discussed in this text, is another short-range nuclear force that is responsible for the decay of some nuclear particles.

Table 6-1. The Fundamental Forces of Nature					
Force	**Relative Strength**	**Range of Force**	**Force Carrier**	**Mass**	**Charge**
strong (nuclear)	1	$\approx 10^{-15}$ m	gluon	0	0
electromagnetic	10^{-2}	proportional to $\frac{1}{r^2}$	photon	0	0
weak	10^{-13}	$<10^{-18}$ m	W boson W boson Z boson	80.6 GeV 80.6 GeV 91.2 GeV	$+e$ $-e$ 0
gravitational	10^{-38}	proportional to $\frac{1}{r^2}$	graviton	0	0

Electric and magnetic forces were treated independently earlier in this text, but they are actually combined as electromagnetic force. The weak force has successfully been combined with the electromagnetic force to produce a single electroweak force. Grand unification theories (GUTs) attempt to add the strong force to this combination. Theories of everything (TOEs), which would combine gravity with all the other forces, are not developed at this time. Scientists continue to try to resolve questions and inconsistencies in the standard model in much the same manner as Thomson, Rutherford, and Bohr made changes and amendments to the model for the structure of the atom.

Classification of Subatomic Particles

Particles can be classified according to the types of interactions they have with other particles. If the force carrier particles are excluded, all particles can be classified into two groups according to the types of interactions they have with other particles. A particle that interacts through the strong nuclear force, as well as the electromagnetic, weak, and gravitational forces, is called a **hadron.** Protons and neutrons are hadrons. A particle that interacts through the electromagnetic, weak, and gravitational forces, but *not* the strong nuclear force, is called a **lepton.** A lepton has a mass less than that of a proton. Electrons, positrons, and neutrinos are classified as leptons. A **positron** is a particle whose mass is equal to the mass of the electron, and whose positive electric charge is equal in magnitude to the negative charge of the electron. A **neutrino** is a neutral particle that has little, if any, mass but does possess both energy and momentum. The *Reference Tables for Physical Setting/Physics* give the names, symbols, and charges of the six members of the lepton family.

The hadron group can be subdivided into baryons and mesons. A **baryon** is an elementary particle that can be transformed into a proton or neutron and some number of mesons and lighter particles. A baryon is also known as a heavy particle. A **meson** is a particle of intermediate mass.

An antiparticle is associated with each particle. An **antiparticle** is a particle having mass, lifetime, and spin identical to the associated particle, but with charge of opposite sign (if charged) and magnetic moment reversed in sign. An antiparticle is denoted by a bar over the symbol for the particle.

For example, an antiproton, the antiparticle of a proton p, is denoted by the symbol $\bar{p}$. Thus, the antiproton would be described as a stable baryon carrying a unit negative charge, but having the same mass as a proton. The positron, noted earlier, is thus the antiparticle of the electron. The antineutron, the antiparticle of the neutron, has the same mass as the neutron and is also electrically neutral. However the magnetic moment and spin of the antineutron are in the same direction, whereas, the magnetic moment and spin of the neutron are in opposite directions. An antiparticle exists for the neutrino; the two are identical except for their direction of spin. **Antimatter** is material consisting of atoms that are composed of antiprotons, antineutrons, and positrons.

THE QUARK Baryons and mesons are composed of more fundamental particles called quarks. A **quark** is one of the basic particles, having charges of $\pm\frac{1}{3}e$ or $\pm\frac{2}{3}e$, from which many of the elementary particles may be built up. This implies that the charge on the electron is no longer considered to be the smallest nonzero charge that a particle may possess. The quarks are named *up, down, charm, strange, top,* and *bottom.* Every baryon is a combination of three quarks and every meson is a combination of a quark and an antiquark. An **antiquark** is the antiparticle of a quark, having electric charge, baryon number, and strangeness opposite in sign to that of the corresponding quark. The *Reference Tables for Physical Setting/Physics* give the names, symbols, and charges of the six members of the quark family. The quark content of a proton is *uud* (up, up, down) and the quark content of a neutron is *ddu* (down, down, up). When quarks combine to form baryons, their charges add algebraically to a total of 0, +1, or −1.

Review Questions

Base your answers to questions 47 through 52 on information given in Table 6-1.

47. Express the range of the strong force in picometers.

48. Express the range of the weak force in nanometers.

49. How many times stronger than the gravitational force is the electromagnetic force?

50. On the axes that follow, draw a line to represent the relationship between electromagnetic force F and the distance r separating two particles.

51. Express the mass of a weak boson having a charge of $+e$ in megaelectronvolts (MeV).

52. Express, in universal mass units, the mass of a boson having no charge.

53. A baryon may have a charge of (1) $-\frac{1}{3}e$ (2) $0\,e$ (3) $+\frac{2}{3}e$ (4) $+\frac{4}{3}e$

54. An antibaryon is composed of (1) three quarks (2) one quark and two antiquarks (3) three antiquarks (4) two quarks and one antiquark

55. What is the electric charge on a pion having quark composition $u\bar{d}$?

56. What is the electric charge on a particle having quark composition $d\bar{b}$?

57. A particle has a quark composition of dds. What is the charge on and classification of the particle? (1) $-1e$, baryon (2) $+1e$, baryon (3) $-1e$, meson (4) $+1e$, meson

58. A particle has a quark composition of $s\bar{u}$. What is the charge on and classification of the particle? (1) $-1e$, baryon (2) $+1e$, baryon (3) $-1e$, meson (4) $+1e$, meson

59. What is the mass of an antineutron in kilograms?

Questions for Regents Practice

Part A

1. In which part of the electromagnetic spectrum does a photon have the greatest energy?

(1) red

(2) infrared

(3) violet

(4) ultraviolet

2. The energy of a photon varies directly with its

(1) frequency

(2) wavelength

(3) speed

(4) rest mass

3. The wavelength of photon A is greater than the wavelength of photon B. Compared to the energy of photon A, the energy of photon B is

(1) less

(2) greater

(3) the same

4. Which is conserved when a photon and a free electron collide?

(1) velocity only

(2) both velocity and energy

(3) momentum only

(4) both momentum and energy

5. The concept that electrons exhibit wave properties can best be demonstrated by the

(1) collisions between photons and electrons

(2) existence of an electron antiparticle

(3) production of electron interference patterns

(4) classification of the electron as a lepton

6. Compared to the amount of energy required to excite an atom, the amount of energy released by the atom when it returns to the ground state is

(1) less

(2) greater

(3) the same

7. A hydrogen atom is excited to the $n = 3$ state. In returning to the ground state, the atom could *not* emit a photon with an energy of

   (1) 1.89 eV

   (2) 10.20 eV

   (3) 12.09 eV

   (4) 12.75 eV

8. During which energy level change of the hydrogen atom does the emitted photon have the shortest wavelength?

   (1) $n = 5$ directly to $n = 2$

   (2) $n = 4$ directly to $n = 2$

   (3) $n = 2$ directly to $n = 4$

   (4) $n = 2$ directly to $n = 5$

9. Which type of force overcomes the repulsive electrostatic force between protons in the nucleus of an atom?

   (1) magnetic

   (2) nuclear

   (3) gravitational

   (4) centripetal

10. How much energy would be generated if a 1.00×10^{-3}-kilogram mass was completely converted to energy?

    (1) 9.31×10^{-1} MeV

    (2) 9.31×10^2 MeV

    (3) 9.00×10^{13} J

    (4) 9.00×10^{16} J

11. The subatomic particles that make up both protons and neutrons are called

    (1) electrons   (3) positrons

    (2) leptons   (4) quarks

12. The electron is classified as a

    (1) baryon

    (2) lepton

    (3) meson

    (4) quark

13. If c is the speed of light in a vacuum, which is an acceptable unit for the mass of a subatomic particle?

    (1) GeV

    (2) GeV $\cdot c$

    (3) GeV/c

    (4) GeV/c^2

Base your answers to questions 14 and 15 on the following information, which represents a nuclear reaction.

$$^3_1H + {}^1_1H \rightarrow {}^4_2He + energy$$

The masses of the nuclei are:

$^1_1H = 1.00813$ u

$^3_1H = 3.01695$ u

$^4_2He = 4.00388$ u

14. Which occurs as a result of this reaction?

    (1) Mass is converted into energy.

    (2) Energy is converted into matter.

    (3) Mass and energy are destroyed.

    (4) Mass and energy are created.

15. How much energy is released during the reaction?

    (1) 3.39×10^{-21} MeV

    (2) 2.12×10^{-2} MeV

    (3) 1.97×10^1 MeV

    (4) 1.91×10^{15} MeV

Part B

16. Determine the energy of a photon with a frequency of 5.00×10^{15} hertz. [2]

17. On the axes below sketch a line that represents the relationship between the energy of a photon and its wavelength. [1]

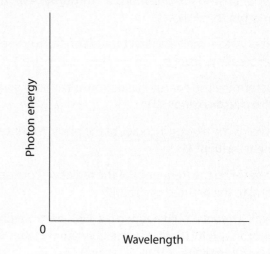

Base your answers to questions 18 through 20 on the following information and diagram.

The diagram represents the collision of an X-ray photon having wavelength λ with an electron -e in an atom. The electron is ejected from the atom, and a photon having a longer wavelength λ' than the incident photon is also emitted.

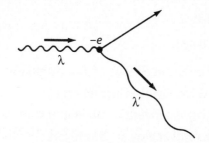

18. Determine the wavelength λ of an incident photon which has a frequency of 1.00×10^{18} hertz. [2]

19. Energy is conserved in the collision. Write an expression in terms of photon wavelength to represent the electron's increase in energy as a result of the collision. [1]

20. Compared to the total momentum of the photon-electron system before the collision, the total momentum of the photon-electron system after the collision is

(1) less

(2) greater

(3) the same

Base your answers to questions 21 through 24 on the information that follows.

A mercury atom makes a direct transition from energy level e to energy level b.

21. Determine the energy in electronvolts that is given off in this transition. [1]

22. What is the energy in joules of the photon emitted in the transition? [1]

23. Determine the frequency of the radiation corresponding to the emitted photon. [2]

24. Explain what would happen if a 4.50-electronvolt photon was incident on a mercury atom in the ground state. [1]

25. The following graph represents the relationship between mass and its energy equivalent.

Energy Equivalent vs. Mass

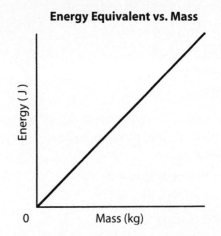

What is the physical signficance of the slope of the line? [1]

26. A proton has a quark content of *uud* and a neutron has a quark content of *udd*. What is the quark content of an antiproton? [1]

Base your answers to questions 27 and 28 on your knowledge of physics.

27. Explain how scientists are able to identify the elements in a star without sending a space probe to it. [1]

28. Show how Planck's constant could be written with the unit kilogram · meter²/second. [1]

Base your answers to questions 29 through 31 on the information in the following chart.

Particle	Rest Mass
proton	1.0073 u
neutron	1.0087 u

29. Determine the energy equivalent of the rest mass of a neutron in megaelectronvolts. [2]

30. A tritium nucleus consists of one proton and two neutrons and has a total mass of 3.0170 universal mass units. Determine the difference in mass between the total mass of the nucleons and the mass of the tritium nucleus. [2]

31. Which force between the proton and the neutrons in a tritium atom has the greatest magnitude?

(1) electrostatic force

(2) gravitational force

(3) magnetic force

(4) nuclear force

Part C

32. According to the *Reference Tables for Physical Setting/Physics,* one universal mass unit is equal to 9.31×10^2 megaelectronvolts. Determine the value for the universal mass unit in kilograms. [2]

33. An alpha particle consists of 2 protons and 2 neutrons. A gold atom has 79 electrons and a nucleus containing 79 protons and 118 neutrons. Determine the force of repulsion between the alpha particle and the gold nucleus when they are separated by a distance of 1.00×10^{-10} meter. [2]

34. The diagram that follows is the energy-level diagram for a fictitious element. Draw arrows on the diagram to represent all possible electron transitions that would cause photons to be emitted from atoms of this element in the $n = 5$ excited state. [2]

35. Determine the approximate number of photons emitted each second by a 150-watt incandescent bulb that produces white light. [3]

Base your answers to questions 36 through 38 on the following information.

According to Bohr's model of the hydrogen atom, the electron can exist only in certain allowed orbits each having radius r_n, which is determined by the energy level n. The equation for calculating this radius is

$r_n = \dfrac{n^2 h^2}{4\pi^2 m_e k e^2}$, where the quantities are represented by the same symbols as in the *Reference Tables for Physical Setting/Physics.*

36. Determine the radius in meters of the hydrogen atom in the ground state. [3]

37. Express the radius of the hydrogen atom in the ground state in nanometers to the proper number of significant digits. [1]

38. Express, in lowest terms, the ratio of the radius of a hydrogen atom in excited state $n = 4$ to the radius of a hydrogen atom in excited state $n = 2$. [1]

Base your answers to questions 39 through 42 on the following statement.

Under certain conditions an electron and a positron can annihilate each other and produce two photons. Annihilation is a process in which a particle and its antiparticle are converted into energy.

39. Determine the combined energy in joules of the photons created when an electron and a positron annihilate each other. [2]

40. Assuming the photons are identical, express the energy of one photon in electronvolts. [1]

41. Assuming the photons are identical, determine the frequency of one photon. [2]

42. According to information in the electromagnetic spectrum chart in the *Reference Tables for Physical Setting/Physics,* how would one of these photons be classified? [1]

Base your answers to questions 43 through 50 on the following information and diagram.

A student performed an experiment using a diffraction grating to measure the wavelengths of the bright lines in mercury's spectrum. A diffraction grating is a device consisting of numerous parallel lines ruled on a glass plate. The device causes light that passes through it from a source to act as individual sources. Where the light interferes constructively, bright lines are produced.

The apparatus used in the experiment included a mercury vapor lamp, exposed by only a thin vertical slit, placed at one corner of a lab table, and a diffraction grating positioned at an adjacent corner. A meter stick was placed at right angles to the line joining the slit and the center of the grating. The rod of a ring stand was used as a guide to mark the distance x of the bright line observed by the student when looking through the grating from the source, as shown. A two-meter stick

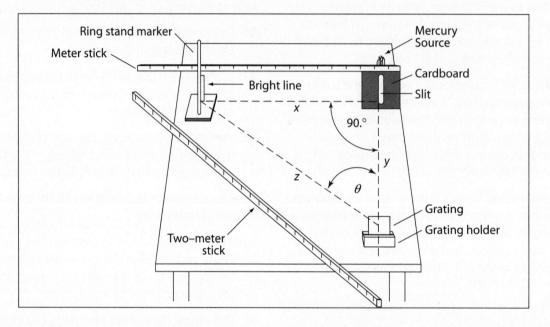

was used to measure the distance z from the grating to the location of the bright line.

The student was told that the equation $\lambda = d \sin \theta$ could be used to determine the wavelength of the bright line. In the equation, d is the distance between the lines on the glass diffraction grating and θ is the angle between the line joining the source and grating and the line joining the bright line and the grating.

The student was given the value of d. She measured x and z three times and recorded the average x and z, as shown below.

$d = 1.67 \times 10^{-4}$ cm

$x = 50.4$ cm

$z = 193.9$ cm

43. Express d in meters. [1]

44. Write an expression that represents the sine of angle θ. [1]

45. Determine the wavelength of the bright line. [2]

46. According to *the Handbook of Chemistry and Physics*, the accepted value for the wavelength of this line is 4358.33 Å (angstrom units). If 1 Å = 10^{-10} m, what is the accepted value for the wavelength in meters? [1]

47. Determine the student's percent error for this bright line measurement. [2]

48. Determine the energy in joules associated with the student's measured wavelength. [2]

49. Express the energy of the measured line in electron-volts. [1]

50. Refer to the energy level diagram for mercury in the *Reference Tables for Physical Setting/Physics*. Which electron transition is most likely to be the one that the student measured? [1]

Appendix 1:
Reference Tables for
Physical Setting/Physics

2003 Edition ◦ Reference Tables for Physical Setting/Physics

List of Physical Constants

Name	Symbol	Value
Universal gravitational constant	G	$6.67 \times 10^{-11} \text{ N} \bullet \text{m}^2/\text{kg}^2$
Acceleration due to gravity	g	9.81 m/s^2
Speed of light in a vacuum	c	$3.00 \times 10^8 \text{ m/s}$
Speed of sound in air at STP		$3.31 \times 10^2 \text{ m/s}$
Mass of Earth		$5.98 \times 10^{24} \text{ kg}$
Mass of the Moon		$7.35 \times 10^{22} \text{ kg}$
Mean radius of Earth		$6.37 \times 10^6 \text{ m}$
Mean radius of the Moon		$1.74 \times 10^6 \text{ m}$
Mean distance—Earth to the Moon		$3.84 \times 10^8 \text{ m}$
Mean distance—Earth to the Sun		$1.50 \times 10^{11} \text{ m}$
Electrostatic constant	k	$8.99 \times 10^9 \text{ N} \bullet \text{m}^2/\text{C}^2$
1 elementary charge	e	$1.60 \times 10^{-19} \text{ C}$
1 coulomb (C)		6.25×10^{18} elementary charges
1 electronvolt (eV)		$1.60 \times 10^{-19} \text{ J}$
Planck's constant	h	$6.63 \times 10^{-34} \text{J} \bullet \text{s}$
1 universal mass unit (u)		$9.31 \times 10^2 \text{ MeV}$
Rest mass of the electron	m_e	$9.11 \times 10^{-31} \text{ kg}$
Rest mass of the proton	m_p	$1.67 \times 10^{-27} \text{ kg}$
Rest mass of the neutron	m_n	$1.67 \times 10^{-27} \text{ kg}$

Prefixes for Powers of 10

Prefix	Symbol	Notation
tera	T	10^{12}
giga	G	10^9
mega	M	10^6
kilo	k	10^3
deci	d	10^{-1}
centi	c	10^{-2}
milli	m	10^{-3}
micro	μ	10^{-6}
nano	n	10^{-9}
pico	p	10^{-12}

Approximate Coefficients of Friction

	Kinetic	Static
Rubber on concrete (dry)	0.68	0.90
Rubber on concrete (wet)	0.58	
Rubber on asphalt (dry)	0.67	0.85
Rubber on asphalt (wet)	0.53	
Rubber on ice	0.15	
Waxed ski on snow	0.05	0.14
Wood on wood	0.30	0.42
Steel on steel	0.57	0.74
Copper on steel	0.36	0.53
Teflon on Teflon	0.04	

Mechanics

$$\bar{v} = \frac{d}{t}$$

$$a = \frac{\Delta v}{t}$$

$$v_f = v_i + at$$

$$d = v_i t + \frac{1}{2}at^2$$

$$v_f^2 = v_i^2 + 2ad$$

$$A_y = A \sin \theta$$

$$A_x = A \cos \theta$$

$$a = \frac{F_{net}}{m}$$

$$F_f = \mu F_N$$

$$F_g = \frac{Gm_1 m_2}{r^2}$$

$$g = \frac{F_g}{m}$$

$$p = mv$$

$$p_{before} = p_{after}$$

$$J = Ft = \Delta p$$

$$F_s = kx$$

$$PE_s = \frac{1}{2}kx^2$$

$$F_c = ma_c$$

$$a_c = \frac{v^2}{r}$$

$$\Delta PE = mg\Delta h$$

$$KE = \frac{1}{2}mv^2$$

$$W = Fd = \Delta E_T$$

$$E_T = PE + KE + Q$$

$$P = \frac{W}{t} = \frac{Fd}{t} = F\bar{v}$$

a = acceleration

a_c = centripetal acceleration

A = any vector quantity

d = displacement/distance

E_T = total energy

F = force

F_c = centripetal force

F_f = force of friction

F_g = weight/force due to gravity

F_N = normal force

F_{net} = net force

F_s = force on a spring

g = acceleration due to gravity or gravitational field strength

G = universal gravitational constant

h = height

J = impulse

k = spring constant

KE = kinetic energy

m = mass

p = momentum

P = power

PE = potential energy

PE_s = potential energy stored in a spring

Q = internal energy

r = radius/distance between centers

t = time interval

v = velocity/speed

$\bar{v}$ = average velocity/average speed

W = work

x = change in spring length from the equilibrium position

Δ = change

θ = angle

μ = coefficient of friction

Electricity

$$F_e = \frac{kq_1q_2}{r^2}$$

$$E = \frac{F_e}{q}$$

$$V = \frac{W}{q}$$

$$I = \frac{\Delta q}{t}$$

$$R = \frac{V}{I}$$

$$R = \frac{\rho L}{A}$$

$$P = VI = I^2R = \frac{V^2}{R}$$

$$W = Pt = VIt = I^2Rt = \frac{V^2t}{R}$$

A = cross-sectional area

E = electric field strength

F_e = electrostatic force

I = current

k = electrostatic constant

L = length of conductor

P = electrical power

q = charge

R = resistance

R_{eq} = equivalent resistance

r = distance between centers

t = time

V = potential difference

W = work (electrical energy)

Δ = change

ρ = resistivity

Series Circuits

$$I = I_1 = I_2 = I_3 = \ldots$$

$$V = V_1 + V_2 + V_3 + \ldots$$

$$R_{eq} = R_1 + R_2 + R_3 + \ldots$$

Parallel Circuits

$$I = I_1 + I_2 + I_3 + \ldots$$

$$V = V_1 = V_2 = V_3 = \ldots$$

$$\frac{1}{R_{eq}} = \frac{1}{R_1} + \frac{1}{R_2} + \frac{1}{R_3} + \ldots$$

Circuit Symbols

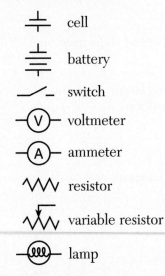

cell

battery

switch

voltmeter

ammeter

resistor

variable resistor

lamp

Resistivities at 20°C	
Material	**Resistivity ($\Omega \bullet m$)**
Aluminum	2.82×10^{-8}
Copper	1.72×10^{-8}
Gold	2.44×10^{-8}
Nichrome	$150. \times 10^{-8}$
Silver	1.59×10^{-8}
Tungsten	5.60×10^{-8}

Waves and Optics

$v = f\lambda$

$T = \dfrac{1}{f}$

$\theta_i = \theta_r$

$n = \dfrac{c}{v}$

$n_1 \sin \theta_1 = n_2 \sin \theta_2$

$\dfrac{n_2}{n_1} = \dfrac{v_1}{v_2} = \dfrac{\lambda_1}{\lambda_2}$

c = speed of light in a vacuum

f = frequency

n = absolute index of refraction

T = period

v = velocity

λ = wavelength

θ = angle

θ_i = angle of incidence

θ_r = angle of reflection

Modern Physics

$E_{photon} = hf = \dfrac{hc}{\lambda}$

$E_{photon} = E_i - E_f$

$E = mc^2$

c = speed of light in a vacuum

E = energy

f = frequency

h = Planck's constant

m = mass

λ = wavelength

Geometry and Trigonometry

Rectangle

$A = bh$

Triangle

$A = \frac{1}{2}bh$

Circle

$A = \pi r^2$

$C = 2\pi r$

Right Triangle

$c^2 = a^2 + b^2$

$\sin \theta = \dfrac{a}{c}$

$\cos \theta = \dfrac{b}{c}$

$\tan \theta = \dfrac{a}{b}$

A = area

b = base

C = circumference

h = height

r = radius

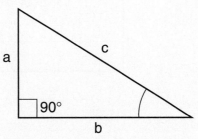

The Electromagnetic Spectrum

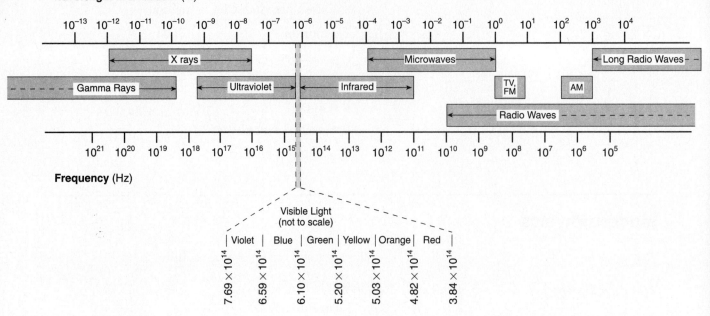

Absolute Indices of Refraction	
($f = 5.09 \times 10^{14}$ Hz)	
Air	1.00
Corn oil	1.47
Diamond	2.42
Ethyl alcohol	1.36
Glass, crown	1.52
Glass, flint	1.66
Glycerol	1.47
Lucite	1.50
Quartz, fused	1.46
Sodium chloride	1.54
Water	1.33
Zircon	1.92

Energy Level Diagrams

Hydrogen

Level		Energy (eV)

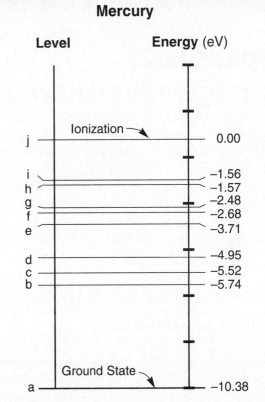

Energy Levels for the Hydrogen Atom

n = ∞   Ionization   0.00
n = 6   −0.38
n = 5   −0.54
n = 4   −0.85
n = 3   −1.51

n = 2   −3.40

n = 1   Ground State   −13.60

Mercury

A Few Energy Levels for the Mercury Atom

j   Ionization   0.00

i   −1.56
h   −1.57
g   −2.48
f   −2.68
e   −3.71

d   −4.95
c   −5.52
b   −5.74

a   Ground State   −10.38

Classification of Matter

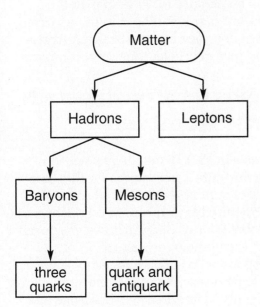

Matter

Hadrons   Leptons

Baryons   Mesons

three quarks   quark and antiquark

Particles of the Standard Model

Quarks

Name	up	charm	top
Symbol	u	c	t
Charge	$+\frac{2}{3}e$	$+\frac{2}{3}e$	$+\frac{2}{3}e$

down	strange	bottom
d	s	b
$-\frac{1}{3}e$	$-\frac{1}{3}e$	$-\frac{1}{3}e$

Leptons

electron	muon	tau
e	μ	τ
−1e	−1e	−1e

electron neutrino	muon neutrino	tau neutrino
ν_e	ν_μ	ν_τ
0	0	0

Note: For each particle there is a corresponding antiparticle with a charge opposite that of its associated particle.

Appendix 2:
Strategies for Answering Test Questions

This appendix provides strategies to help you answer various types of questions on the Regents Examination for The Physical Setting/Physics. Strategies are provided for answering multiple-choice and constructed-response questions as well as for questions based on diagrams, data tables, and graphs and questions that use the *Reference Tables for Physical Setting/Physics*.

Strategies for Multiple-Choice Questions

Multiple-choice questions will likely account for more than 50% of the Regents Examination for The Physical Setting/Physics. Part A is comprised totally of multiple-choice questions, whereas Part B contains some, but not all, multiple-choice questions. Therefore, it is important to be good at deciphering multiple-choice questions. Here are a few helpful strategies. For any one question, not all strategies will need to be used. The numbers are provided for reference, not to specify an order (except for Strategies 1 and 2).

1. Always read the entire question, but wait to read the choices. (See Strategy 4.)

2. Carefully examine any data tables, diagrams, photographs or relevant part(s) of the *Reference Tables for Physical Setting/Physics* associated with the question.

3. Underline key words and phrases in the question that signal what you should be looking for in the answer. This will make you read the question more carefully. This strategy applies mostly to questions with a long introduction.

4. Try to think of an answer to the question before looking at the choices given. If you think you know the answer, write it on a separate piece of paper before reading the choices. Next, read all of the choices and compare them to your answer before making a decision. Do not select the first answer that seems correct. If your answer matches one of the choices, and you are quite sure of your response, you are probably correct. Even if your answer matches one of the choices, carefully consider all of the answers because the obvious choice is not always the correct one. If there are no exact matches, re-read the question and look for the choice that is most similar to your answer.

5. Eliminate any choices that you know are incorrect. Lightly cross out the numbers for those choices on the exam paper. Each choice you can eliminate increases your chances of selecting the correct answer.

6. If the question makes no sense after reading through it several times, leave it for later. After completing the rest of the exam, return to the question. Something you read on the other parts of the exam may give you some ideas about how to answer this question. If you are still unsure, go with your best guess. There is no penalty for guessing, but answers left blank will be counted as wrong. If you employ your best test-taking strategies, you just may select the correct answer.

Strategies for Constructed-Response Questions

Some questions in Part B and all questions in Part C of the Regents Examination for Physical Setting/Physics require a constructed response. You may be required to graph data, complete a data table, label or draw diagrams, design experiments, make calculations, or write short or extended responses. In addition, questions may ask students to hypothesize, interpret, analyze, evaluate data, or apply their scientific knowledge and skills to real-world situations.

The following procedure may prove helpful in answering many constructed-response questions.

1. Read the problem carefully.

2. Reread the problem to make certain you understand what is being asked.

3. Make a sketch of the situation.

4. Include on the sketch all values of quantities given in the statement of the problem. To save time and space, represent quantities with appropriate symbols and be sure to include correct units with the numbers.

5. Include on your sketch quantities that can be inferred from the statement of the problem. For example, if the problem states that "an object falls freely from rest near Earth's surface," it can be inferred that $a = 9.81$ m/s^2 and $v_i = 0$ m/s.

6. Use the proper symbol for the quantity being sought.

7. Refer to the *Reference Tables for Physical Setting/Physics* to help decide which equations are relevant to solving the problem.

8. Solve the appropriate equation(s) for the variable being sought before substituting in any values.

9. Substitute the known values with their correct units into the equation(s). Expressing derived units in terms of fundamental units may help you determine if the answer has the correct unit.

10. Perform the required calculations, paying particular attention to exponents and significant figures. Simplify the units in the answer.

Check the accuracy of your work and the reasonableness of your answer. Be on the lookout for answers that are not physically possible.

Strategies for Questions Based on Diagrams

Both multiple-choice and extended-response questions frequently include diagrams or pictures. Usually the diagrams provide information needed to answer the question. The diagrams may be realistic, or they may be schematic. Schematic draw- ings show the relationships among parts and sometimes the sequence in a system. Follow these steps:

1. First study the diagram and think about what the diagram shows you. Be sure to read any information, such as titles or labels, that go with the diagram.

2. Read the question. Follow the strategies for either multiple-choice or constructed-response questions listed previously.

Strategies for Questions Based on Data Tables

Most data tables contain information that summarizes a topic. A table uses rows and columns to condense information and to present it in an organized way. Rows are the horizontal divisions going from left to right across the table, while columns are vertical divisions going from top to bottom. Column headings name the type of information included in a table. Sometimes different categories of information are listed down the left-hand column of the table. When answering a question with a data table, use the following strategies.

1. Find the title of the table. It is usually located across the top.

2. Determine the number of columns in the table and their purpose.

3. Determine the number of rows and their purpose.

4. Read across the rows and down the columns to determine what the relationships are.

5. Now you are ready to read the question with the data table. Answer the question by using the suggested strategies for multiple-choice or constructed-response questions listed previously.

Strategies for Questions Based on Graphs

Graphs represent relationships in a visual form that is easy to read. Three different types of graphs commonly used on science Regents Examinations are line graphs, bar graphs, and circle graphs. Line graphs are the most common, and they show the relationship between two changing quantities, or variables. When a question is based on any of the three types of graphs, the information you need to correctly answer the question can usually be found on the graph.

When answering a question that includes a graph, first ask yourself these questions:

- What information does the graph provide?
- What are the variables?
- What seems to happen to one variable as the other changes?

After a careful analysis of the graph, use the appropriate strategies for multiple-choice or constructed-response questions.

Use of Reference Tables for Physical Setting/Physics to Help Answer Questions

In recent Regents Examinations between 20% and 35% of the questions have involved the use of the *Reference Tables for Physical Setting/Physics.* You should become thoroughly familiar with all details of these tables. Sometimes the questions will specifically refer you to the reference tables, but most often you will be expected to know what information is included within the reference tables. Listed below are some of the ways these reference tables are used in Regents Examination questions.

- to find a specific fact, such as the value of an electron volt expressed in joules
- using an equation on the reference tables to solve a problem, such as determining the potential energy of a moving object
- graphing or recognizing the correct graph of data on the reference tables, such as the absolute indices of refraction
- decoding a graphic symbol in a question, such as quark or lepton
- performing a procedure using part of the reference tables, such as approximating the wavelength of red light from the frequency data given in the electromagnetic spectrum
- interpretation of data in the reference tables, such as the ionization energies for mercury

Regents Examinations

The following New York Regents Examinations are provided so that you can practice a Regents Examination for The Physical Setting/Physics.

The best way to use these examinations is to take an entire test after you have reviewed the course content. Use the tests to determine if you have reviewed enough to do well on the Regents Examination and to determine where further review will be helpful.

Before beginning a test, make sure you have a copy of the *Reference Tables for Physical Setting/Physics,* a protractor, a centimeter ruler, and a pencil for making graphs and diagrams.

Do not look up any information or answers while you take the examination. Answer each question just as you would during a real test. As you take the examination, use the margin of the paper to note any question where you are just guessing. Leave the more difficult questions for last, but be sure to answer each question. Every point counts so do not skip over a long question that is only worth a point or two. A long question could be easier than it initially appears and a correct answer to it may make the difference between earning an A or a B or between passing and failing.

Many multiple-choice questions and constructed-response questions will have a numerical answer. Although a detailed solution is not required for a multiple-choice question, it is still in your best interest to use the problem-solving skills you have acquired throughout the course to determine the answer. You should represent all known quantities given in the statement with proper symbols and units, and determine the proper symbol for the quantity being sought. Determine the appropriate equation for solving the problem by referring to the *Reference Tables for Physical Setting/Physics.* Solve the equation for the unknown variable and substitute the known quantities with their units. Perform the calculations and simplify the units. You should not merely take values given in a problem and punch numbers into a calculator to determine answers to multiple choice questions. An incorrect answer you may obtain by this careless method will usually be one of the possible answer choices.

When you finish, have your teacher score your examination and help you determine the areas where you need the most work. Also review the "guesses" you noted in the margin to find out what you need to study to ensure that you will be able to answer similar questions on the next test. Once you have determined your weaknesses, you can focus your review on those topics in this book.

Reviewing the areas where you know the least will give you the best chance of improving your final score. Spending time on areas where you are doing quite well will not produce much improvement in your total score, but is still important if time permits.

Physical Setting Physics Sample
Part A

Answer all questions in this part.   [35]

Directions (1–35): For *each* statement or question, select the word or expression that, of those given, best completes the statement or answers the question. Record your answer on the separate answer sheet in accordance with the directions on the front page of this booklet. Some questions may require the use of the *Physical Setting/Physics Reference Tables.*

1   Which is a vector quantity?

   (1)   gravitational field strength of Earth
   (2)   mass of a jogger
   (3)   charge of an electron
   (4)   kinetic energy of a freely falling body

2   A ball starting from rest accelerates uniformly at 5.0 meters per second^2 as it rolls 40. meters down an incline. How much time is required for the ball to roll the 40. meters?

   (1)   2.8 s
   (2)   8.0 s
   (3)   16 s
   (4)   4.0 s

3   The speed of a car is decreased uniformly from 30. meters per second to 10. meters per second in 4.0 seconds. The magnitude of the car's acceleration is

   (1)   5.0 m/s^2
   (2)   10. m/s^2
   (3)   20. m/s^2
   (4)   40. m/s^2

4   Objects *A* and *B* are dropped from rest near Earth's surface. Object *A* has mass *m* and object *B* has mass 2*m*. After 2 seconds of free fall, object *A* has a speed *v* and has fallen a distance *d*. What are the speed and distance of fall of object *B* after 2 seconds of free fall?

   (1)   speed = $\frac{v}{2}$; distance = $\frac{d}{2}$

   (2)   speed = *v*; distance = *d*

   (3)   speed = $\frac{v}{2}$; distance = 2*d*

   (4)   speed = 2*v*; distance = 2*d*

5   A ball is thrown horizontally from the top of a building with an initial velocity of 15 meters per second. At the same instant, a second ball is dropped from the top of the building. The two balls have the same

   (1)   path as they fall
   (2)   final velocity as they reach the ground
   (3)   initial horizontal velocity
   (4)   initial vertical velocity

6   In the diagram below, the upward drag force acting on a parachute is equal in magnitude but opposite in direction to the weight of the parachutist and equipment.

As a result of the forces shown, the parachutist may be moving

(1) downward with decreasing speed
(2) downward at constant speed
(3) upward with decreasing speed
(4) upward with constant acceleration

7   The diagram below shows a 2.0-kilogram block being moved across a frictionless horizontal surface by a 6.0-newton horizontal force.

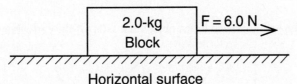

What is the magnitude of the acceleration of the block?

(1) 0.33 m/s^2
(2) 6.0 m/s^2
(3) 3.0 m/s^2
(4) 12 m/s^2

8   The magnitude of the acceleration due to gravity on the surface of planet A is twice as great as on the surface of planet B. What is the ratio of the weight of mass X on the surface of planet A to its weight on the surface of planet B?

(1)   1:2
(2)   2:1
(3)   1:4
(4)   4:1

Base your answers to questions 9 and 10 on the information and diagram below.

A roller coaster cart starts from rest and accelerates, due to gravity, down a track. The cart starts at a height that enables it to complete a loop in the track. [Neglect friction.]

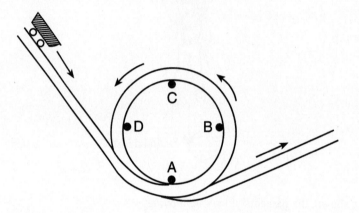

9   The magnitude of the centripetal force keeping the cart in circular motion would be greatest at point

(1) A
(2) B
(3) C
(4) D

10   Which diagram best represents the path followed by an object that falls off the cart when the cart is at point D?

(1)   (2)   (3)   (4)

11   The diagram below shows two carts initially at rest on a horizontal frictionless surface being pushed apart when a compressed spring attached to one of the carts is released.

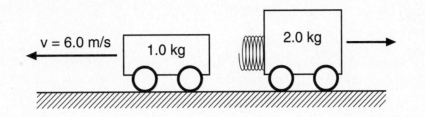

If the 1.0-kilogram cart moves to the left with a speed of 6.0 meters per second, then the 2.0-kilogram cart moves to the right with a speed of

(1)   6.0 m/s
(2)   2.0 m/s
(3)   3.0 m/s
(4)   12 m/s

12   A mother pushes her 120-newton child, who is sitting on a swing. If the mother exerts a 10.-newton force on the child for 0.50 second, what is the magnitude of the impulse imparted to the child by the mother?

(1)   5.0 N•s
(2)   20. N/s
(3)   60. N•s
(4)   240 N/s

Note that question 13 has only three choices.

13   A ball having mass m is struck by a bat having mass $9m$. Compared to the magnitude of the force exerted by the bat on the ball, the magnitude of the force exerted by the ball on the bat is

(1)   less
(2)   greater
(3)   the same

14   Gravitational force F exists between point objects A and B separated by distance R. If the mass of A is doubled and distance R is tripled, what is the new gravitational force between A and B?

(1) $\frac{2}{9}$ F

(2) $\frac{2}{3}$ F

(3) $\frac{3}{2}$ F

(4) $\frac{9}{2}$ F

15   At point P in an electric field, the magnitude of the electrostatic force on a proton is 4.0×10^{-10} newton. What is the magnitude of the electric field intensity at point P?

(1) 6.4×10^{-29} N/C
(2) 1.6×10^{-19} N/C
(3) 4.0×10^{-10} N/C
(4) 2.5×10^{9} N/C

16   The diagram below shows two negatively charged balloons suspended from nonconducting strings being held by a student.

What occurs as the student brings the balloons closer to each other without allowing them to touch?

(1)   The magnitude of the electrostatic force between the balloons decreases, and they attract each other.
(2)   The magnitude of the electrostatic force between the balloons decreases, and they repel each other.
(3)   The magnitude of the electrostatic force between the balloons increases, and they attract each other.
(4)   The magnitude of the electrostatic force between the balloons increases, and they repel each other.

17   A 500.-newton girl lifts a 10.-newton box vertically upward a distance of 0.50 meter. The work done on the box is

(1)   5.0 J
(2)   50. J
(3)   250 J
(4)   2500 J

18   The diagram below shows a 5.0-kilogram mass sliding 9.0 meters down an incline from a height of 2.0 meters in 3.0 seconds. The object gains 90. joules of kinetic energy while sliding.

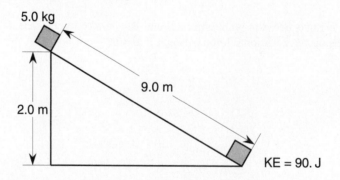

How much work is done against friction as the mass slides the 9.0 meters?

(1)   0 J
(2)   8 J
(3)   45 J
(4)   90. J

19   A motor having a power rating of 500. watts is used to lift an object weighing 100. newtons. How much time does the motor take to lift the object a vertical distance of 10.0 meters?

(1)   0.500 s   (3)   5.00 s
(2)   2.00 s   (4)   50.0 s

20   If 1.0 joule of work is required to move a charge of 1.0 coulomb between two points in an electric field, the potential difference between these two points is

(1)   1.0 V
(2) 1.6×10^{-19} V
(3) 9.0×10^9 V
(4) 6.3×10^{18} V

21   A microwave oven operating at 120 volts is used to heat a hot dog. If the oven draws 12.5 amperes of current for 45 seconds, what is the power dissipated by the oven?

(1)   33 W
(2) 1.5×10^3 W
(3) 5.4×10^3 W
(4) 6.8×10^4 W

22   For which quantities are values needed to calculate the amount of energy supplied to an operating toaster?

(1)   applied voltage and resistance, only
(2)   applied voltage and operation time, only
(3)   applied voltage, current drawn, and resistance
(4)   applied voltage, current drawn, and operation time

23   Two electrically neutral metal spheres, A and B, on insulating stands are placed in contact with each other. A negatively charged rod is brought near, but does *not* touch the spheres, as shown in the diagram below.

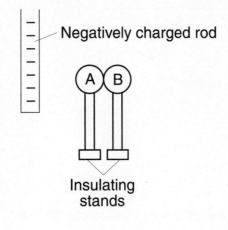

How are the spheres now charged?

(1) A is positive and B is positive.
(2) A is positive and B is negative.
(3) A is negative and B is positive.
(4) A is negative and B is negative.

24 In a television set, an electron beam with a current of 5.0×10^{-6} ampere is directed at the screen. Approximately how many electrons are transferred to the screen in 60. seconds?

(1) 1.2×10^7
(2) 5.3×10^{11}
(3) 1.9×10^{15}
(4) 6.3×10^{18}

25 The diagram below represents a periodic wave generated during a 1.5-second interval.

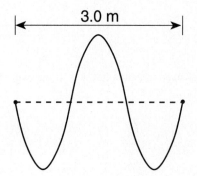

The frequency of the wave is

(1) 1.0 Hz
(2) 2.0 Hz
(3) 0.50 Hz
(4) 4.5 Hz

26 The diagram below represents a periodic wave.

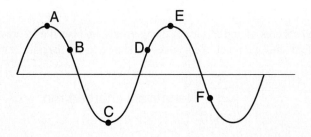

Which two points on the wave are in phase?

(1) A and E
(2) A and C
(3) B and D
(4) D and F

27 What is the frequency of a light wave with a wavelength of 6.0×10^{-7} meter traveling through space?

(1) 2.0×10^{-15} Hz
(2) 5.0×10^1 Hz
(3) 1.8×10^{14} Hz
(4) 5.0×10^{14} Hz

28   The diagram below shows a wave phenomenon.

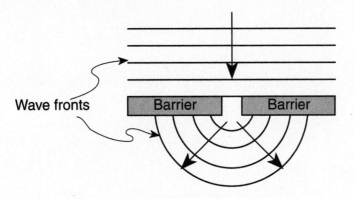

Wave fronts

The pattern of waves shown behind the barriers is the result of

(1)   reflection
(2)   diffraction
(3)   refraction
(4)   absorption

29   An astronomical body emitting high-intensity pulses of green light is moving toward Earth at high velocity. To an observer on Earth, this light may appear

(1)   red
(2)   blue
(3)   orange
(4)   yellow

30   The diagram below shows a light ray in air incident on a crown glass block.

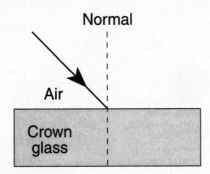

As the light ray enters the crown glass block, it will

(1)   slow down and bend toward the normal
(2)   slow down and bend away from the normal
(3)   speed up and bend toward the normal
(4)   speed up and bend away from the normal

31   If a small sphere possesses an excess of 5 electrons, the net charge on the sphere is

   (1) -3.2×10^{-20} C
   (2) -8.0×10^{-19} C
   (3) -8.0×10^{19} C
   (4) -3.2×10^{20} C

32   A baryon may have a charge of

   (1) $-\frac{1}{3}$ e
   (2) 0 e
   (3) $+\frac{2}{3}$ e
   (4) $+\frac{4}{3}$ e

33   What is the energy equivalent of a mass of 0.026 kilogram?

   (1) 2.34×10^{15} J
   (2) 2.3×10^{15} J
   (3) 2.34×10^{17} J
   (4) 2.3×10^{17} J

Note that questions 34 and 35 have only three choices.

Base your answers to questions 34 and 35 on the diagrams below, which show a photon and an electron before and after their collision.

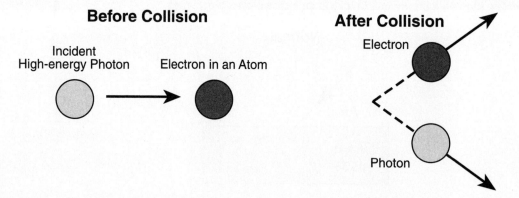

34   Compared to the wavelength of the photon before its collision with the electron, the wavelength of the photon after the collision is

   (1)   shorter
   (2)   longer
   (3)   the same

35   Compared to the total momentum of the photon-electron system before the collision, the total momentum of the photon-electron system after the collision is

   (1)   less
   (2)   greater
   (3)   the same

Part B–1

Answer all questions in this part.

Directions (36–48): For *each* statement or question, write on the separate answer sheet the number of the word or expression that, of those given, best completes the statement or answers the question. Some questions may require the use of the *Physical Setting/Physics Reference Tables*.

36 The thickness of one page of this test booklet is closest to

    (1) 10^{-4} m

    (2) 10^{-2} m

    (3) 10^{0} m

    (4) 10^{2} m

37 The diagram below represents two forces acting concurrently on an object at point *P*.

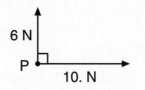

Which diagram best represents the resultant of these two forces?

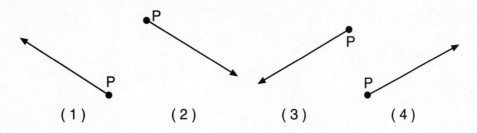

38 Two students are pushing a car. What should be the angle of each student's arms with respect to the flat ground to maximize the horizontal component of the force?

    (1) 0°

    (2) 30°

    (3) 45°

    (4) 90°

39 A student performed a laboratory investigation to determine the spring constant of a spring. The force applied to the spring was varied and the resulting elongation of the spring measured. The student graphed the data collected, as shown below.

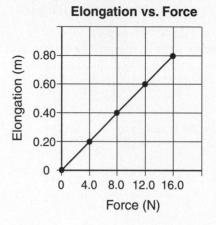

According to the student's graph, what is the spring constant for this spring?

(1) 0.050 m/N
(2) 9.8 N/kg
(3) 13 N•m
(4) 20. N/m

40 The diagram below shows a golf ball being struck by a club. The ball leaves the club with a speed of 40. meters per second at an angle of 60.° with the horizontal.

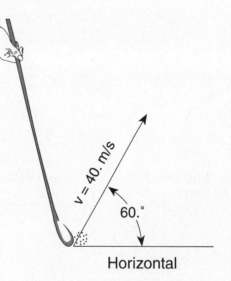

If the ball strikes the ground 7.1 seconds later, how far from the golfer does the ball land? [Assume level ground and neglect air resistance.]

(1) 35 m
(2) 71 m
(3) 140 m
(4) 280 m

41   A student sprinkled iron filings around a bar magnet and observed that the filings formed the pattern shown below.

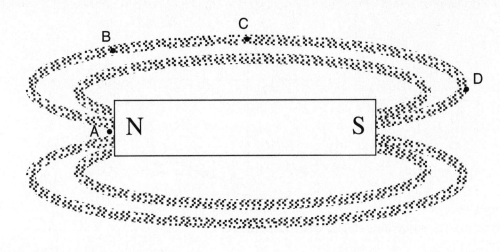

The magnetic field is strongest at point

(1) A
(2) B
(3) C
(4) D

42   Which graph best represents the kinetic energy KE of an object as a function of its speed v?

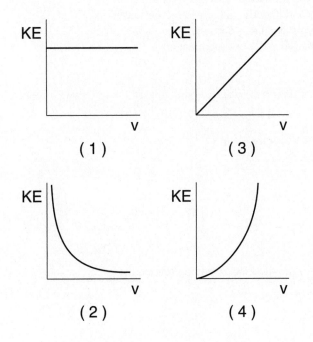

43 The diagram below shows three positions, *A, B,* and *C,* in the swing of a pendulum, released from rest at point *A.* [Neglect friction.]

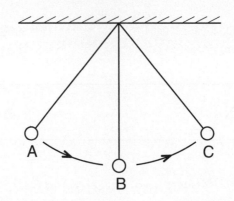

Which statement is true about this swinging pendulum?

(1) The potential energy at *A* equals the kinetic energy at *C.*
(2) The speed of the pendulum at *A* equals the speed of the pendulum at *B.*
(3) The potential energy at *B* equals the potential energy at *C.*
(4) The potential energy at *A* equals the kinetic energy at *B.*

44 A manufacturer recommends that the longer the extension cord used with an electric drill, the thicker (heavier gauge) the extension cord should be. This recommendation is made because the resistance of a wire varies

(1) directly with length and inversely with cross-sectional area
(2) inversely with length and directly with cross-sectional area
(3) directly with both length and cross-sectional area
(4) inversely with both length and cross-sectional area

45 The diagram below shows a transverse wave moving toward the left along a rope.

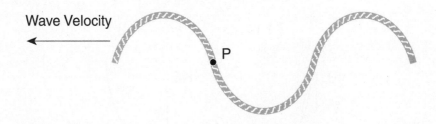

At the instant shown, point *P* on the rope is moving toward the

(1) bottom of the page
(2) top of the page
(3) left of the page
(4) right of the page

46   A light ray passes from air into glass as shown in the diagram below.

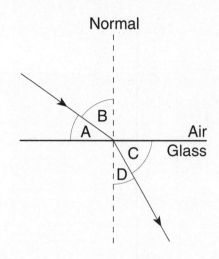

Which relationship represents the index of refraction of the glass?

(1) $\dfrac{\sin A}{\sin C}$

(2) $\dfrac{\sin A}{\sin D}$

(3) $\dfrac{\sin B}{\sin C}$

(4) $\dfrac{\sin B}{\sin D}$

47   The diagram below shows two pulses approaching each other from opposite directions in the same medium. Pulse A has an amplitude of 0.20 meter and pulse B has an amplitude of 0.10 meter.

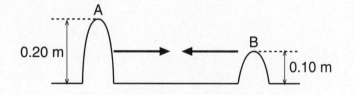

After the pulses have passed through each other, what will be the amplitude of each of the two pulses?

(1) $A = 0.10$ m; $B = 0.20$ m
(2) $A = 0.20$ m; $B = 0.10$ m
(3) $A = 0.30$ m; $B = 0.30$ m
(4) $A = 0.15$ m; $B = 0.15$ m

48   The diagram below shows a light ray being reflected from a plane mirror.

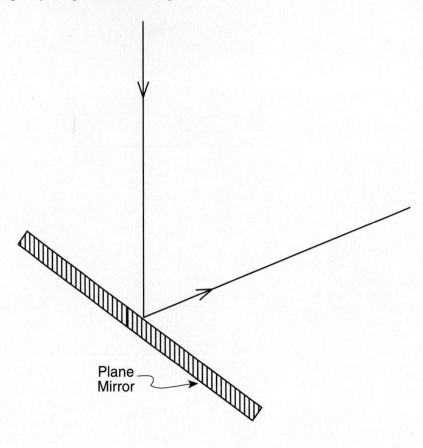

Plane
Mirror

What is the angle of incidence?

(1)   20.°
(2)   35°
(3)   55°
(4)   70.°

Part B–2

Answer all questions in this part.

Directions (49–64): Record your answers in the spaces provided in your answer booklet.

49   The diagram below shows a 5.0-kilogram block accelerating at 6.0 meters per second^2 along a rough horizontal surface by the application of a horizontal force, F, of 50. newtons.

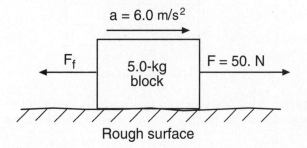

What is the magnitude in newtons of the force of friction, F_f, acting on the block?   [1]

Base your answers to questions 50 through 53 on the data table below, which describes the motion of an object moving in a straight line.

Data Table

Time (s)	Speed (m/s)
0.0	0.0
1.0	1.2
2.0	2.7
3.0	3.3
4.0	5.0
5.0	5.6

Directions (50–53): Using the information in the data table, construct a graph on the grid provided *on your answer paper*, following the directions below. The grid below is provided for practice purposes only. Be sure your final answer appears on your answer paper.

50 Plot the data points. [1]

51 Draw the line of best-fit. [1]

52 On the same grid, sketch a line representing an object decelerating uniformly in a straight line. [1]

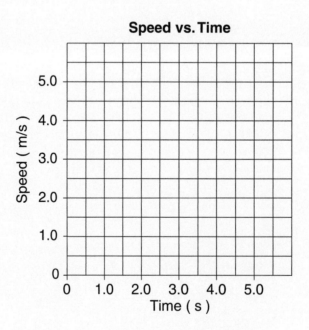

53 Based on your line of best-fit, what is the acceleration of the object? [1]

Base your answers to questions 54 and 55 on the information below.

A student conducted a series of experiments to investigate the effect of mass, length, and amplitude (angle of release) on a simple pendulum. The table below shows the initial conditions for a series of trials.

Trial	Mass (kg)	Length (m)	Angle of release (°)
R	2	3	10.
S	3	2	15
T	3	2	10.
U	1	3	10.
V	3	2	5
W	2	2	15
X	2	1	15
Y	3	3	10.
Z	2	3	15

54   Which three trials should the student use to test the effect of mass on the period of the pendulum?   [1]

55   Which three trials should the student use to test the effect of length on the period of the pendulum?   [1]

---

56   The circuit shown below contains two resistors, R_1 and R_2.

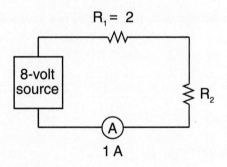

What is the resistance of resistor R_2?   [1]

Base your answers to questions 57 through 60 on the information and diagram below.

A wave generator having a constant frequency of 15 hertz produces a standing wave pattern in a stretched string.

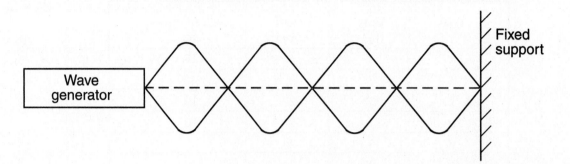

57 Using a ruler, measure the amplitude of the wave shown. Record the value to the *nearest tenth of a centimeter* on your answer paper. [1]

58 Using a ruler, measure the wavelength of the wave shown. Record the value to the *nearest tenth of a centimeter* on your answer paper. [1]

59 State what would happen to the wavelength of the wave if the frequency of the wave were increased. [1]

60 How many antinodes are shown in the diagram? [1]

Base your answers to questions 61 through 64 on the information below.

When an electron in an excited hydrogen atom falls from a higher to a lower energy level, a photon having a wavelength of 6.58×10^{-7} meter is emitted.

61 Calculate the energy of a photon of this light wave in joules. [Show all calculations, including the equation and substitution with units.] [2]

62 Convert the energy of the photon to electronvolts. [1]

63 Determine which *two* energy levels the electron has fallen between to emit this photon. [1]

64 Is this photon an x-ray photon? Justify your answer. [1]

Part C

Answer all questions in this part.

Directions (65–74): Record your answers in the spaces provided in your answer booklet.

65   Four small metal spheres *R*, *S*, *T*, and *U* on insulating stands act on each other by means of electrostatic forces.

It was known that sphere *S* is negatively charged. The following observations were made:

   Sphere *S* attracts all the other spheres.
   Spheres *T* and *U* repel each other.
   Sphere *R* attracts all the other spheres.

Determine the charge on each sphere and complete the table *on your answer paper* noting for each sphere if it is positive (+), negative (–), or neutral (0). The chart below is provided for practice purposes only. Be sure your final answer appears *on your answer paper*. [3]

Sphere	Charge
R	
T	
U	

66   A box of mass *m* is held motionless on a frictionless inclined plane by a rope that is parallel to the surface of the plane. On the diagram provided *on your answer paper*, draw and label all of the force vectors acting on the box. The diagram below is provided for practice purposes only. Be sure your final answer appears *on your answer paper*. [3]

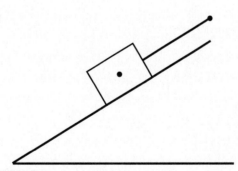

Base your answers to questions 67 and 68 on the information and diagram below.

A block of mass m starts from rest at height h on a frictionless incline. The block slides down the incline across a frictionless level surface and comes to rest by compressing a spring through distance x, as shown in the diagram below.

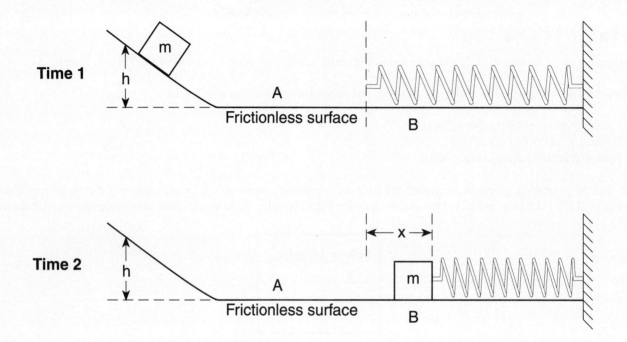

67   Name the forms of mechanical energy possessed by the system when the block is in position A and in position B.   [2]

68   Determine the spring constant, k, in terms of g, h, m, and x. [Show all work including formulas and an algebraic solution for k.]   [2]

Base your answers to questions 69 through 71 on the information below.

You are given a 12-volt battery, ammeter *A*, voltmeter *V*, resistor R_1, and resistor R_2.
Resistor R_2 has a value of 3.0 ohms.

69   Using appropriate symbols from the *Reference Tables for Physical Setting/Physics*, draw and label a complete circuit showing:

• resistors R_1 and R_2 connected in parallel with the battery   [1]
• the ammeter connected to measure the current through resistor R_1, only   [1]
• the voltmeter connected to measure the potential drop across resistor R_1 [1]

70   If the total current in the circuit is 6.0 amperes, determine the equivalent resistance of the circuit.   [1]

71   If the total current in the circuit is 6.0 amperes, determine the resistance of resistor R_1. [Show all calculations, including the equation and substitution with units.]   [2]

_____

Base your answers to questions 72 through 74 on the passage below and on your knowledge of physics.

Forces of Nature

Our understanding of the fundamental forces has evolved along with our growing knowledge of the particles of matter. Many everyday phenomena seemed to be governed by a long list of unique forces. Observations identified the gravitational, electric, and magnetic forces as distinct. A large step toward simplification came in the mid-19th century with Maxwell's unification of the electric and magnetic forces into a single electromagnetic force. Fifty years later came the recognition that the electromagnetic force also governed atoms. By the late 1800s, all commonly observed phenomena could be understood with only the electromagnetic and gravitational forces.

Particle Physics–Perspectives and Opportunities (adapted)

A hydrogen atom, consisting of an electron in orbit about a proton, has an approximate radius of 10^{-10} meter.

72 Determine the order of magnitude of the electrostatic force between the electron and the proton. [1]

73 Determine the order of magnitude of the gravitational force between the electron and the proton. [1]

74 In the above passage there is an apparent contradiction. The author stated that "the electromagnetic force also governed atoms." He concluded with "all commonly observed phenomena could be understood with only the electromagnetic and gravitational forces."

Use your responses to questions 72 and 73 to explain why the gravitational interaction is negligible for the hydrogen atom. [2]

_____

49 _____ N

61

50 - 52

Speed vs. Time

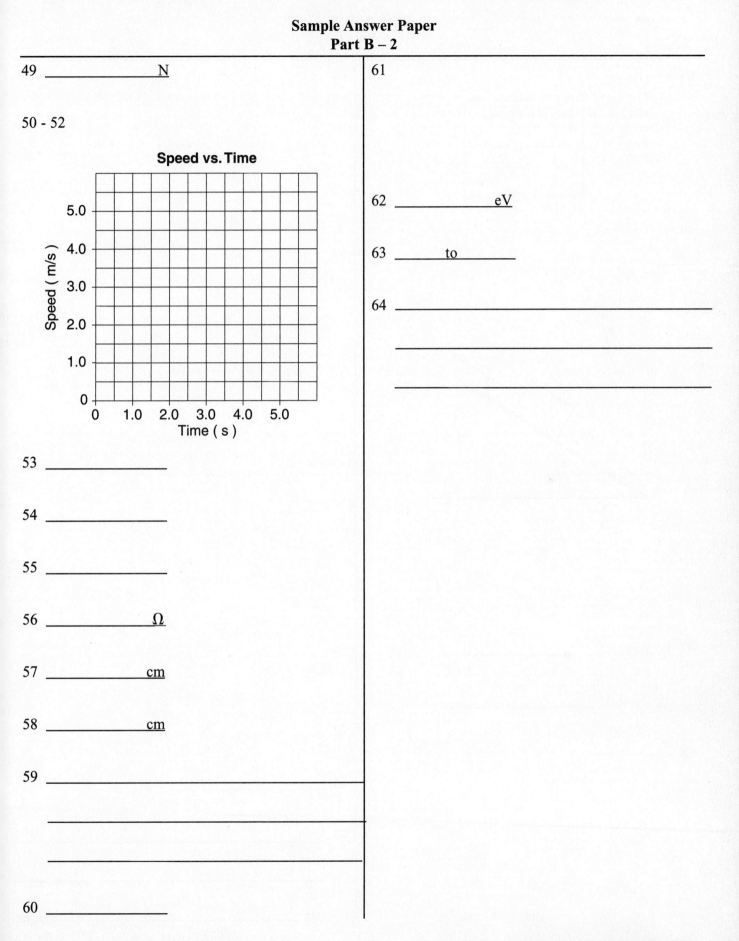

62 _____ eV

63 _____ to _____

64 _____

_____

_____

53 _____

54 _____

55 _____

56 _____ Ω

57 _____ cm

58 _____ cm

59 _____

_____

_____

60 _____

65

Sphere	Charge
R	
T	
U	

66

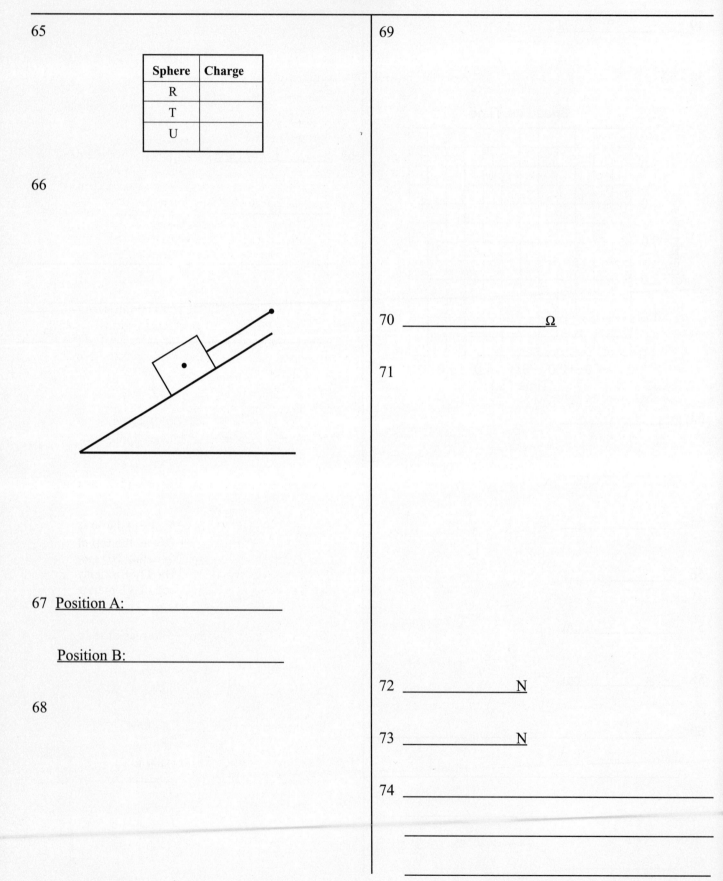

67 <u>Position A:</u> _____

    <u>Position B:</u> _____

68

69

70 _____ Ω

71

72 _____ N

73 _____ N

74 _____

    _____

    _____

Physical Setting Physics June, 2003

Part A

Answer all questions in this part.

Directions (1–35): For *each* statement or question, write on the separate answer sheet, the *number* of the word or expression that, of those given, best completes the statement or answers the question.

1 The diagram below shows a 50.-kilogram crate on a frictionless plane at angle θ to the horizontal. The crate is pushed at constant speed up the incline from point A to point B by force F.

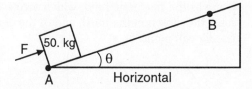

If angle θ were increased, what would be the effect on the magnitude of force F and the total work W done on the crate as it is moved from A to B?

(1) W would remain the same and the magnitude of F would decrease.

(2) W would remain the same and the magnitude of F would increase.

(3) W would increase and the magnitude of F would decrease.

(4) W would increase and the magnitude of F would increase.

2 A vector makes an angle, θ, with the horizontal. The horizontal and vertical components of the vector will be equal in magnitude if angle θ is

(1) 30°   (3) 60°

(2) 45°   (4) 90°

3 A car initially traveling at a speed of 16 meters per second accelerates uniformly to a speed of 20. meters per second over a distance of 36 meters. What is the magnitude of the car's acceleration?

(1) 0.11 m/s²   (3) 0.22 m/s²

(2) 2.0 m/s²   (4) 9.0 m/s²

4 A ball is thrown at an angle of 38° to the horizontal. What happens to the magnitude of the ball's vertical acceleration during the total time interval that the ball is in the air?

(1) It decreases, then increases.

(2) It decreases, then remains the same.

(3) It increases, then decreases.

(4) It remains the same.

5 A man standing on a scale in an elevator notices that the scale reads 30 newtons greater than his normal weight. Which type of movement of the elevator could cause this greater-than-normal reading?

(1) accelerating upward

(2) accelerating downward

(3) moving upward at constant speed

(4) moving downward at constant speed

Base your answers to questions 6 and 7 on the information below.

Projectile A is launched horizontally at a speed of 20. meters per second from the top of a cliff and strikes a level surface below, 3.0 seconds later. Projectile B is launched horizontally from the same location at a speed of 30. meters per second.

6 The time it takes projectile B to reach the level surface is

(1) 4.5 s   (3) 3.0 s

(2) 2.0 s   (4) 10. s

7 Approximately how high is the cliff?

(1) 29 m   (3) 60. m

(2) 44 m   (4) 104 m

M = 60 kg

8 A 60-kilogram skydiver is falling at a constant speed near the surface of Earth. The magnitude of the force of air friction acting on the skydiver is approximately

(1) 0 N   (3) 60 N
(2) 6 N   (4) 600 N

$g = \frac{F_g}{m}$

9 An astronaut weighs 8.00×10^2 newtons on the surface of Earth. What is the weight of the astronaut 6.37×10^6 meters above the surface of Earth?

(1) 0.00 N   (3) 1.60×10^3 N
(2) 2.00×10^2 N   (4) 3.20×10^3 N

10 A 10.-newton force is required to hold a stretched spring 0.20 meter from its rest position. What is the potential energy stored in the stretched spring?

(1) 1.0 J   (3) 5.0 J
(2) 2.0 J   (4) 50. J

11 When a 12-newton horizontal force is applied to a box on a horizontal tabletop, the box remains at rest. The force of static friction acting on the box is

(1) 0 N
(2) between 0 N and 12 N
(3) 12 N
(4) greater than 12 N

12 Ball A of mass 5.0 kilograms moving at 20. meters per second collides with ball B of unknown mass moving at 10. meters per second in the same direction. After the collision, ball A moves at 10. meters per second and ball B at 15 meters per second, both still in the same direction. What is the mass of ball B?

(1) 6.0 kg   (3) 10. kg
(2) 2.0 kg   (4) 12 kg

13 A 1.5-kilogram lab cart is accelerated uniformly from rest to a speed of 2.0 meters per second in 0.50 second. What is the magnitude of the force producing this acceleration?

(1) 0.70 N   (3) 3.0 N
(2) 1.5 N   (4) 6.0 N

14 The diagram below represents the magnetic field near point P.

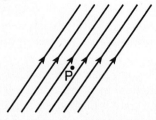

If a compass is placed at point P in the same plane as the magnetic field, which arrow represents the direction the north end of the compass needle will point?

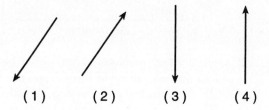

15 Which person has the greatest inertia?

(1) a 110-kg wrestler resting on a mat
(2) a 90-kg man walking at 2 m/s
(3) a 70-kg long-distance runner traveling at 5 m/s
(4) a 50-kg girl sprinting at 10 m/s

16 A child is riding on a merry-go-round. As the speed of the merry-go-round is doubled, the magnitude of the centripetal force acting on the child

(1) remains the same   (3) is halved
(2) is doubled   (4) is quadrupled

17 The magnitude of the electrostatic force between two point charges is F. If the distance between the charges is doubled, the electrostatic force between the charges will become

(1) $\frac{F}{4}$ (3) $\frac{F}{2}$
(2) $2F$ (4) $4F$

Note that question 18 has only three choices.

18 As a ball falls freely (without friction) toward the ground, its total mechanical energy

(1) decreases
(2) increases
(3) remains the same

19 A 0.50-kilogram ball is thrown vertically upward with an initial kinetic energy of 25 joules. Approximately how high will the ball rise? [Neglect air resistance.]

(1) 2.6 m   (3) 13 m
(2) 5.1 m   (4) 25 m

20 What is the average power developed by a motor as it lifts a 400.-kilogram mass at constant speed through a vertical distance of 10.0 meters in 8.0 seconds?

(1) 320 W   (3) 4,900 W
(2) 500 W   (4) 32,000 W

21 If 4.8×10^{-17} joule of work is required to move an electron between two points in an electric field, what is the electric potential difference between these points?

(1) 1.6×10^{-19} V   (3) 3.0×10^2 V
(2) 4.8×10^{-17} V   (4) 4.8×10^2 V

Note that question 22 has only three choices.

22 The diagram below shows a wire moving to the right at speed v through a uniform magnetic field that is directed into the page.

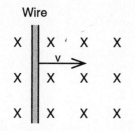

Wire

Magnetic field directed into page

As the speed of the wire is increased, the induced potential difference will

(1) decrease
(2) increase
(3) remain the same

23 A change in the speed of a wave as it enters a new medium produces a change in

(1) frequency   (3) wavelength
(2) period   (4) phase

24 Two identical resistors connected in parallel have an equivalent resistance of 40. ohms. What is the resistance of each resistor?

(1) 20. Ω   (3) 80. Ω
(2) 40. Ω   (4) 160 Ω

25 A tuning fork oscillates with a frequency of 256 hertz after being struck by a rubber hammer. Which phrase best describes the sound waves produced by this oscillating tuning fork?

(1) electromagnetic waves that require no medium for transmission
(2) electromagnetic waves that require a medium for transmission
(3) mechanical waves that require no medium for transmission
(4) mechanical waves that require a medium for transmission

26 In a vacuum, all electromagnetic waves have the same

(1) wavelength   (3) speed
(2) frequency   (4) amplitude

27 The speed of light ($f = 5.09 \times 10^{14}$ Hz) in a transparent material is 0.75 times its speed in air. The absolute index of refraction of the material is approximately

(1) 0.75   (3) 2.3
(2) 1.3   (4) 4.0

28 Waves pass through a 10.-centimeter opening in a barrier without being diffracted. This observation provides evidence that the wavelength of the waves is

(1) much shorter than 10. cm
(2) equal to 10. cm
(3) longer than 10. cm, but shorter than 20. cm
(4) longer than 20. cm

29 Standing waves in water are produced most often by periodic water waves

(1) being absorbed at the boundary with a new medium
(2) refracting at a boundary with a new medium
(3) diffracting around a barrier
(4) reflecting from a barrier

Note that question 30 has only three choices.

30 A sound of constant frequency is produced by the siren on top of a firehouse. Compared to the frequency produced by the siren, the frequency observed by a firefighter approaching the firehouse is

(1) lower
(2) higher
(3) the same

31 White light is passed through a cloud of cool hydrogen gas and then examined with a spectroscope. The dark lines observed on a bright background are caused by

(1) the hydrogen emitting all frequencies in white light
(2) the hydrogen absorbing certain frequencies of the white light
(3) diffraction of the white light
(4) constructive interference

32 Compared to a photon of red light, a photon of blue light has a

(1) greater energy
(2) longer wavelength
(3) smaller momentum
(4) lower frequency

33 Protons and neutrons are examples of

(1) positrons   (3) mesons
(2) baryons   (4) quarks

34 The strong force is the force of

(1) repulsion between protons
(2) attraction between protons and electrons
(3) repulsion between nucleons
(4) attraction between nucleons

35 If a deuterium nucleus has a mass of 1.53×10^{-3} universal mass units less than its components, this mass represents an energy of

(1) 1.38 MeV   (3) 1.53 MeV
(2) 1.42 MeV   (4) 3.16 MeV

Part B–1

Answer all questions in this part.

Directions (36–47): For *each* statement or question, write on the separate answer sheet the *number* of the word or expression that, of those given, best completes the statement or answers the question.

36 Forces *A* and *B* have a resultant *R*. Force *A* and resultant *R* are represented in the diagram below.

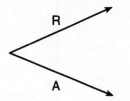

Which vector best represents force *B*?

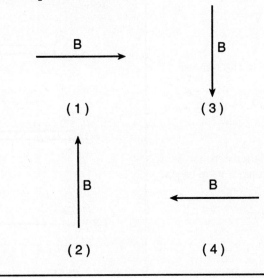

37 An object with a net charge of 4.80×10^{-6} coulomb experiences an electrostatic force having a magnitude of 6.00×10^{-2} newton when placed near a negatively charged metal sphere. What is the electric field strength at this location?

(1) 1.25×10^4 N/C directed away from the sphere
(2) 1.25×10^4 N/C directed toward the sphere
(3) 2.88×10^{-8} N/C directed away from the sphere
(4) 2.88×10^{-8} N/C directed toward the sphere

38 What is the approximate width of a person's little finger?

(1) 1 m   (3) 0.01 m
(2) 0.1 m   (4) 0.001 m

39 The diagram below represents a ray of mono-chromatic light ($f = 5.09 \times 10^{14}$ Hz) passing from medium X ($n = 1.46$) into fused quartz.

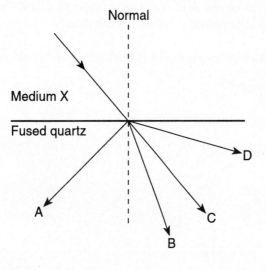

Which path will the ray follow in the quartz?

(1) A (3) C

(2) B (4) D

40 The graph below shows the relationship between the work done by a student and the time of ascent as the student runs up a flight of stairs.

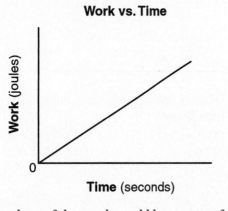

The slope of the graph would have units of

(1) joules   (3) watts

(2) seconds   (4) newtons

41 In the diagram below, two positively charged spheres, A and B, of masses m_A and m_B are located a distance d apart.

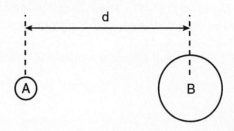

Which diagram best represents the directions of the gravitational force, F_g, and the electrostatic force, F_e, acting on sphere A due to the mass and charge of sphere B? [Vectors are not drawn to scale.]

(1)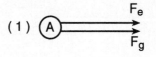

(2)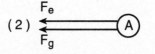

(3)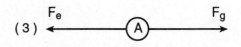

(4)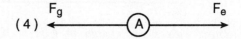

42 Which graph best represents the relationship between the kinetic energy, *KE*, and the velocity of an object accelerating in a straight line?

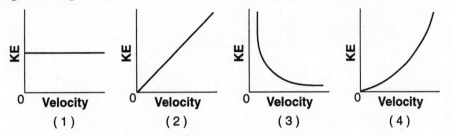

43 Which circuit diagram below correctly shows the connection of ammeter *A* and voltmeter *V* to measure the current through and potential difference across resistor *R*?

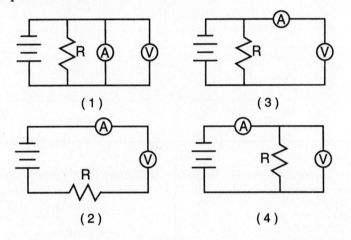

44 Identical resistors (*R*) are connected across the same 12-volt battery. Which circuit uses the greatest power?

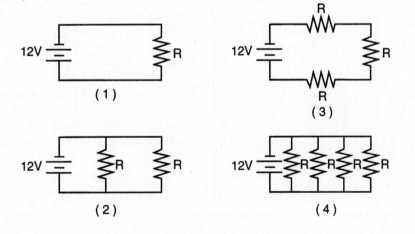

45 The diagram below shows two pulses, *A* and *B*, approaching each other in a uniform medium.

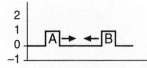

Which diagram best represents the superposition of the two pulses?

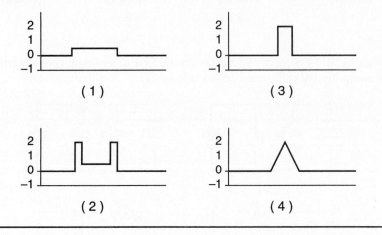

(1)   (3)

(2)   (4)

46 Which graph best represents the motion of an object that is *not* in equilibrium as it travels along a straight line?

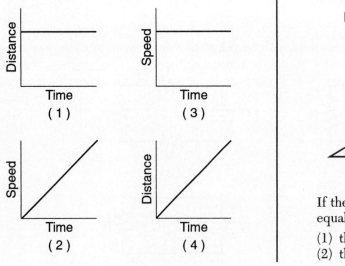

47 Three forces act on a box on an inclined plane as shown in the diagram below. [Vectors are not drawn to scale.]

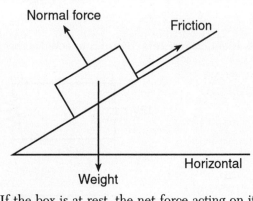

If the box is at rest, the net force acting on it is equal to

(1) the weight   (3) friction
(2) the normal force   (4) zero

Part B–2

Answer all questions in this part.

Directions (48–63): Record your answers in the spaces provided in your answer booklet.

48 The diagram below represents a wire conductor, *RS*, positioned perpendicular to a uniform magnetic field directed into the page.

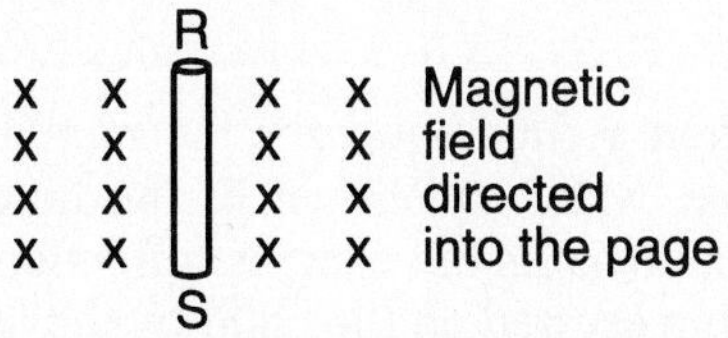

Describe the direction in which the wire could be moved to produce the maximum potential difference across its ends, *R* and *S*. [1]

49 Rubbing a moistened finger around the rim of a water glass transfers energy to the glass at the natural frequency of the glass. Which wave phenomenon is responsible for this effect? [1]

50 Explain why a hydrogen atom in the ground state can absorb a 10.2-electronvolt photon, but can *not* absorb an 11.0-electronvolt photon. [1]

Base your answers to questions 51 and 52 on the information below.

A hiker walks 5.00 kilometers due north and then 7.00 kilometers due east.

51 What is the magnitude of her resultant displacement? [1]

52 What total distance has she traveled? [1]

53 What is the magnitude of the charge, in coulombs, of a lithium nucleus containing three protons and four neutrons? [1]

54 A light bulb attached to a 120.-volt source of potential difference draws a current of 1.25 amperes for 35.0 seconds. Calculate how much electrical energy is used by the bulb. [Show all work, including the equation and substitution with units.] [2]

55 Calculate the wavelength in a vacuum of a radio wave having a frequency of 2.2×10^6 hertz. [Show all work, including the equation and substitution with units.] [2]

56 Two monochromatic, coherent light beams of the same wavelength converge on a screen. The point at which the beams converge appears dark. Which wave phenomenon best explains this effect? [1]

57 Exposure to ultraviolet radiation can damage skin. Exposure to visible light does not damage skin. State *one* possible reason for this difference. [1]

Base your answers to questions 58 through 61 on the information and data table below.

In an experiment, a student measured the length and period of a simple pendulum. The data table lists the length (ℓ) of the pendulum in meters and the square of the period (T^2) of the pendulum in seconds^2.

Length (ℓ) (meters)	Square of Period (T^2) (seconds^2)
0.100	0.410
0.300	1.18
0.500	1.91
0.700	2.87
0.900	3.60

Directions (58–59): Using the information in the data table, construct a graph on the grid *provided in your answer booklet*, following the directions below.

58 Plot the data points for the square of period versus length. [1]

59 Draw the best-fit straight line. [1]

60 Using your graph, determine the time in seconds it would take this pendulum to make one complete swing if it were 0.200 meter long. [1]

61 The period of a pendulum is related to its length by the formula: $T^2 = \left(\dfrac{4\pi^2}{g}\right) \cdot \ell$ where g represents the acceleration due to gravity. Explain how the graph you have drawn could be used to calculate the value of g. [You do *not* need to perform any actual calculations.] [1]

62 A student is given two pieces of iron and told to determine if one or both of the pieces are magnets. First, the student touches an end of one piece to one end of the other. The two pieces of iron attract. Next, the student reverses one of the pieces and again touches the ends together. The two pieces attract again. What does the student definitely know about the initial magnetic properties of the two pieces of iron? [1]

63 When a child squeezes the nozzle of a garden hose, water shoots out of the hose toward the east. What is the compass direction of the force being exerted on the child by the nozzle? [1]

Part C

Answer all questions in this part.

Directions (64–76): Record your answers in the spaces provided in your answer booklet.

Base your answers to questions 64 through 68 on the information and data table below.

Three lamps were connected in a circuit with a battery of constant potential. The current, potential difference, and resistance for each lamp are listed in the data table below. [There is negligible resistance in the wires and the battery.]

	Current (A)	Potential Difference (V)	Resistance (Ω)
lamp 1	0.45	40.1	89
lamp 2	0.11	40.1	365
lamp 3	0.28	40.1	143

64 Using the circuit symbols found in the *Reference Tables for Physical Setting/Physics,* draw a circuit showing how the lamps and battery are connected. [2]

65 What is the potential difference supplied by the battery? [1]

66 Calculate the equivalent resistance of the circuit. [Show all work, including the equation and substitution with units.] [2]

67 If lamp 3 is removed from the circuit, what would be the value of the potential difference across lamp 1 after lamp 3 is removed? [1]

68 If lamp 3 is removed from the circuit, what would be the value of the current in lamp 2 after lamp 3 is removed? [1]

Base your answers to questions 69 through 71 on the information and diagram below.

A ray of light passes from air into a block of transparent material X as shown in the diagram below.

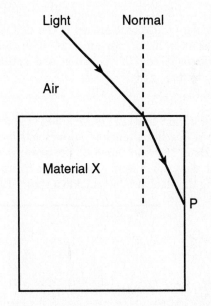

69 Measure the angles of incidence and refraction to the nearest degree for this light ray at the air into material X boundary and write your answers in the appropriate spaces *in your answer booklet.* [2]

70 Calculate the absolute index of refraction of material X. [Show all work, including the equation and substitution with units.] [2]

71 The refracted light ray is reflected from the material X–air boundary at point P. Using a protractor and straightedge, on the diagram *in your answer booklet,* draw the reflected ray from point P. [1]

Base your answers to questions 72 through 74 on the information below.

A 50.-kilogram child running at 6.0 meters per second jumps onto a stationary 10.-kilogram sled. The sled is on a level frictionless surface.

72 Calculate the speed of the sled with the child after she jumps onto the sled. [Show all work, including the equation and substitution with units.] [2]

73 Calculate the kinetic energy of the sled with the child after she jumps onto the sled. [Show all work, including the equation and substitution with units.] [2]

74 After a short time, the moving sled with the child aboard reaches a rough level surface that exerts a constant frictional force of 54 newtons on the sled. How much work must be done by friction to bring the sled with the child to a stop? [1]

Base your answers to questions 75 and 76 on the information below.

Louis de Broglie extended the idea of wave-particle duality to all of nature with his matter-wave equation, $\lambda = \frac{h}{mv}$, where λ is the particle's wavelength, m is its mass, v is its velocity, and h is Planck's constant.

75 Using this equation, calculate the de Broglie wavelength of a helium nucleus (mass = 6.7×10^{-27} kg) moving with a speed of 2.0×10^6 meters per second. [Show all work, including the equation and substitution with units.] [2]

76 The wavelength of this particle is of the same order of magnitude as which type of electromagnetic radiation? [1]

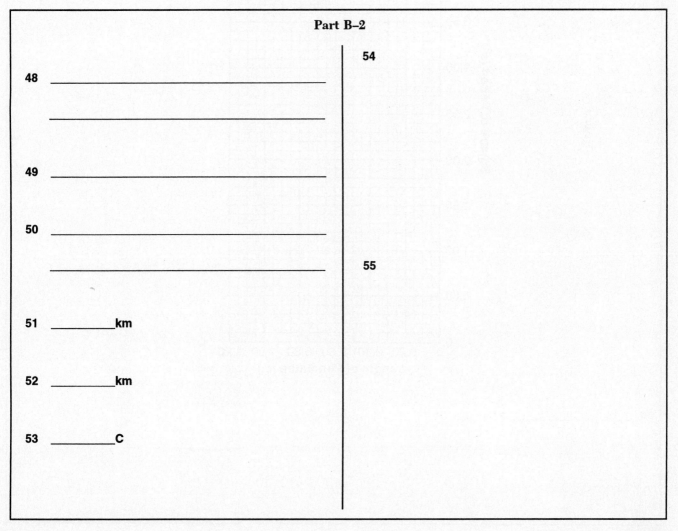

Part B–2

48 _____

_____

49 _____

50 _____

_____

51 _____ km

52 _____ km

53 _____ C

54

55

[a]

[OVER]

56 _____

57 _____

_____

58–59

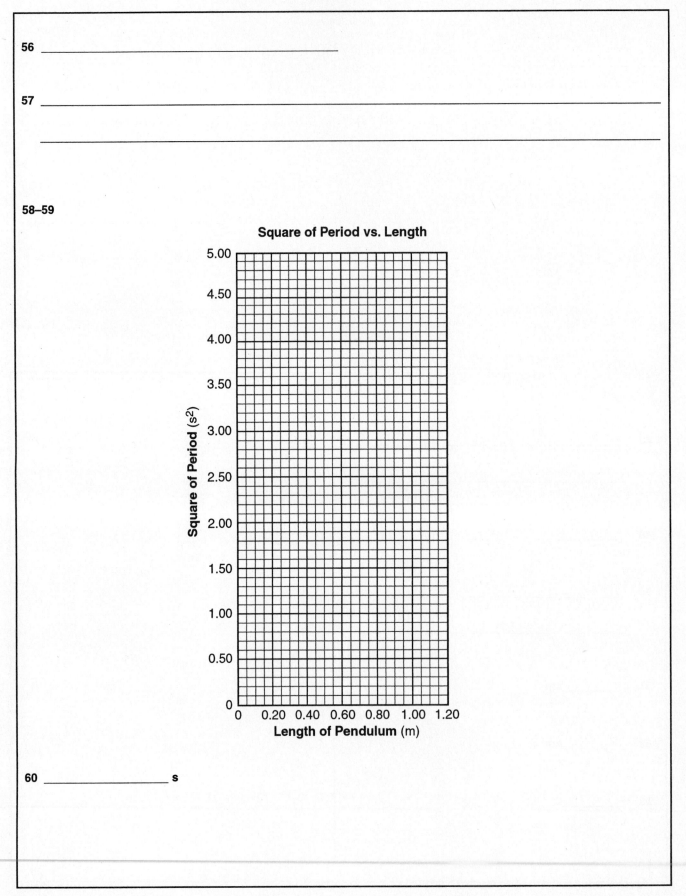

Square of Period vs. Length

60 _____ s

61 _____

_____

_____

_____

62 _____

_____

63 _____

Part C

64

65 _____v

66

[c]

67 _____ v

68 _____ A

69 angle of incidence = _____ °

    angle of refraction = _____ °

70

71

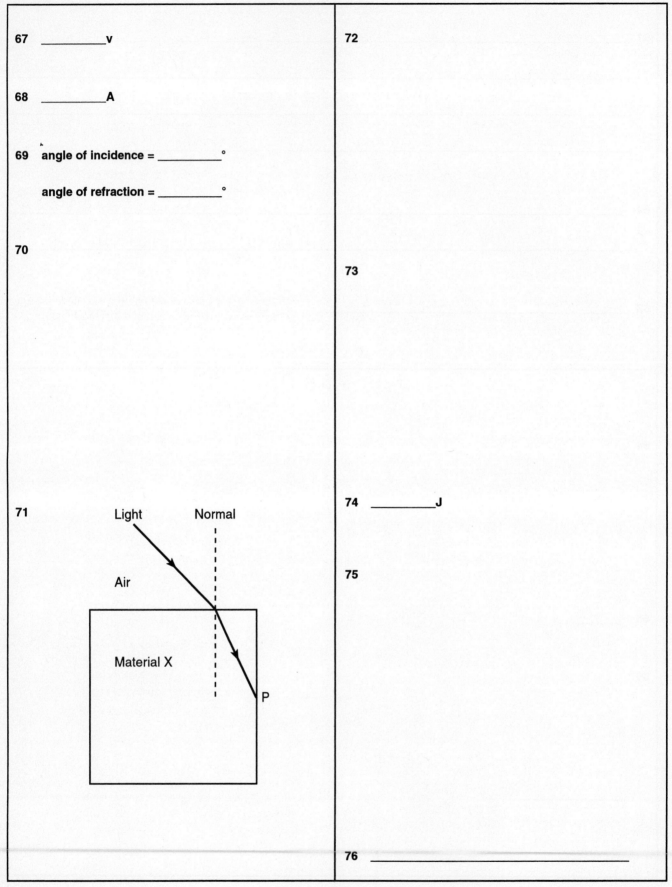

72

73

74 _____ J

75

76 _____

Physical Setting Physics January, 2003

Part A

Answer all questions in this part.

Directions (1–35): For *each* statement or question, write on the separate answer sheet, the *number* of the word or expression that, of those given, best completes the statement or answers the question.

1 The diagram below shows a worker using a rope to pull a cart.

The worker's pull on the handle of the cart can best be described as a force having

(1) magnitude, only
(2) direction, only
(3) both magnitude and direction
(4) neither magnitude nor direction

2 A car travels 90. meters due north in 15 seconds. Then the car turns around and travels 40. meters due south in 5.0 seconds. What is the magnitude of the average velocity of the car during this 20.-second interval?

(1) 2.5 m/s   (3) 6.5 m/s
(2) 5.0 m/s   (4) 7.0 m/s

3 How far will a brick starting from rest fall freely in 3.0 seconds?

(1) 15 m   (3) 44 m
(2) 29 m   (4) 88 m

4 If the sum of all the forces acting on a moving object is zero, the object will

(1) slow down and stop
(2) change the direction of its motion
(3) accelerate uniformly
(4) continue moving with constant velocity

5 A net force of 10. newtons accelerates an object at 5.0 meters per second^2. What net force would be required to accelerate the same object at 1.0 meter per second^2?

(1) 1.0 N   (3) 5.0 N
(2) 2.0 N   (4) 50. N

6 The graph below represents the relationship between gravitational force and mass for objects near the surface of Earth.

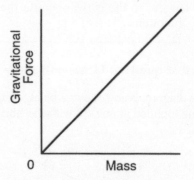

The slope of the graph represents the

(1) acceleration due to gravity
(2) universal gravitational constant
(3) momentum of objects
(4) weight of objects

7 A 1,200-kilogram car traveling at 10. meters per second hits a tree and is brought to rest in 0.10 second. What is the magnitude of the average force acting on the car to bring it to rest?

(1) 1.2×10^2 N   (3) 1.2×10^4 N
(2) 1.2×10^3 N   (4) 1.2×10^5 N

8 A spring scale reads 20. newtons as it pulls a 5.0-kilogram mass across a table. What is the magnitude of the force exerted by the mass on the spring scale?

(1) 49 N   (3) 5.0 N
(2) 20. N   (4) 4.0 N

Base your answers to questions 9 and 10 on the information below.

A 2.0×10^3-kilogram car travels at a constant speed of 12 meters per second around a circular curve of radius 30. meters.

9 What is the magnitude of the centripetal acceleration of the car as it goes around the curve?

(1) 0.40 m/s²
(2) 4.8 m/s²
(3) 800 m/s²
(4) 9,600 m/s²

10 As the car goes around the curve, the centripetal force is directed

(1) toward the center of the circular curve
(2) away from the center of the circular curve
(3) tangent to the curve in the direction of motion
(4) tangent to the curve opposite the direction of motion

___

Note that question 11 has only three choices.

11 The diagram below shows a block sliding down a plane inclined at angle θ with the horizontal.

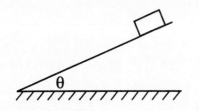

As angle θ is increased, the coefficient of kinetic friction between the bottom surface of the block and the surface of the incline will

(1) decrease
(2) increase
(3) remain the same

12 The amount of work done against friction to slide a box in a straight line across a uniform, horizontal floor depends most on the

(1) time taken to move the box
(2) distance the box is moved
(3) speed of the box
(4) direction of the box's motion

13 A 1.2-kilogram block and a 1.8-kilogram block are initially at rest on a frictionless, horizontal surface. When a compressed spring between the blocks is released, the 1.8-kilogram block moves to the right at 2.0 meters per second, as shown.

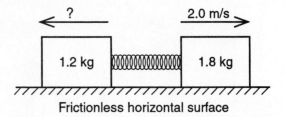

Frictionless horizontal surface

What is the speed of the 1.2-kilogram block after the spring is released?

(1) 1.4 m/s
(2) 2.0 m/s
(3) 3.0 m/s
(4) 3.6 m/s

14 An object weighs 100. newtons on Earth's surface. When it is moved to a point one Earth radius above Earth's surface, it will weigh

(1) 25.0 N
(2) 50.0 N
(3) 100. N
(4) 400. N

15 An object weighing 15 newtons is lifted from the ground to a height of 0.22 meter. The increase in the object's gravitational potential energy is approximately

(1) 310 J
(2) 32 J
(3) 3.3 J
(4) 0.34 J

Note that question 16 has only three choices.

16 As an object falls freely, the kinetic energy of the object

(1) decreases
(2) increases
(3) remains the same

17 Moving 2.5×10^{-6} coulomb of charge from point A to point B in an electric field requires 6.3×10^{-4} joule of work. The potential difference between points A and B is approximately

(1) 1.6×10^{-9} V
(2) 4.0×10^{-3} V
(3) 2.5×10^2 V
(4) 1.0×10^{14} V

18 A 3.0-kilogram block is initially at rest on a frictionless, horizontal surface. The block is moved 8.0 meters in 2.0 seconds by the application of a 12-newton horizontal force, as shown in the diagram below.

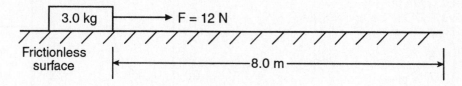

What is the average power developed while moving the block?
(1) 24 W   (3) 48 W
(2) 32 W   (4) 96 W

19 The diagram below shows three neutral metal spheres, x, y, and z, in contact and on insulating stands.

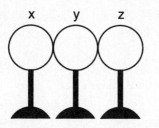

Which diagram best represents the charge distribution on the spheres when a positively charged rod is brought near sphere x, but does not touch it?

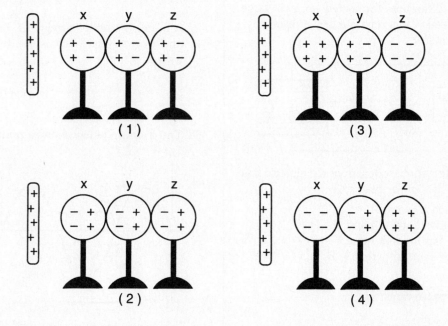

20 Which graph best represents the electrostatic force between an alpha particle with a charge of +2 elementary charges and a positively charged nucleus as a function of their distance of separation?

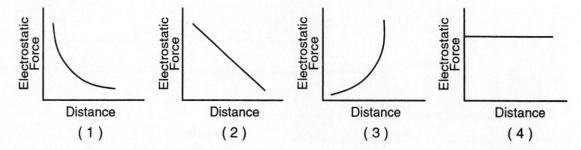

21 When a neutral metal sphere is charged by contact with a positively charged glass rod, the sphere

  (1) loses electrons   (3) loses protons
  (2) gains electrons   (4) gains protons

22 If 10. coulombs of charge are transferred through an electric circuit in 5.0 seconds, then the current in the circuit is

  (1) 0.50 A   (3) 15 A
  (2) 2.0 A   (4) 50. A

23 The diagram below represents a source of potential difference connected to two large, parallel metal plates separated by a distance of 4.0×10^{-3} meter.

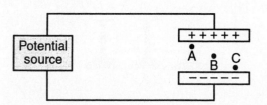

Which statement best describes the electric field strength between the plates?

  (1) It is zero at point B.
  (2) It is a maximum at point B.
  (3) It is a maximum at point C.
  (4) It is the same at points A, B, and C.

24 A periodic wave transfers

  (1) energy, only
  (2) mass, only
  (3) both energy and mass
  (4) neither energy nor mass

Note that question 25 has only three choices.

25 As the potential difference across a given resistor is increased, the power expended in moving charge through the resistor

  (1) decreases
  (2) increases
  (3) remains the same

26 An electric iron operating at 120 volts draws 10. amperes of current. How much heat energy is delivered by the iron in 30. seconds?

  (1) 3.0×10^2 J   (3) 3.6×10^3 J
  (2) 1.2×10^3 J   (4) 3.6×10^4 J

27 A motor is used to produce 4.0 waves each second in a string. What is the frequency of the waves?

  (1) 0.25 Hz   (3) 25 Hz
  (2) 15 Hz   (4) 4.0 Hz

28 The diagram below shows a periodic wave.

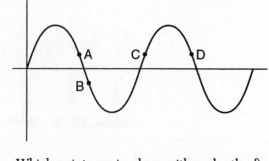

Which points are in phase with each other?

  (1) A and C (3) B and C
  (2) A and D (4) C and D

29 A surfacing whale in an aquarium produces water wave crests having an amplitude of 1.2 meters every 0.40 second. If the water wave travels at 4.5 meters per second, the wavelength of the wave is

(1) 1.8 m
(2) 2.4 m
(3) 3.0 m
(4) 11 m

30 In a certain material, a beam of monochromatic light ($f = 5.09 \times 10^{14}$ hertz) has a speed of 2.25×10^8 meters per second. The material could be

(1) crown glass
(2) flint glass
(3) glycerol
(4) water

31 Orange light has a frequency of 5.0×10^{14} hertz in a vacuum. What is the wavelength of this light?

(1) 1.5×10^{23} m
(2) 1.7×10^6 m
(3) 6.0×10^{-7} m
(4) 2.0×10^{-15} m

32 A radar gun can determine the speed of a moving automobile by measuring the difference in frequency between emitted and reflected radar waves. This process illustrates

(1) resonance
(2) the Doppler effect
(3) diffraction
(4) refraction

33 The diagram below shows a standing wave.

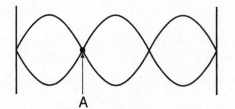

Point A on the standing wave is

(1) a node resulting from constructive interference
(2) a node resulting from destructive interference
(3) an antinode resulting from constructive interference
(4) an antinode resulting from destructive interference

34 An object possessing an excess of 6.0×10^6 electrons has a net charge of

(1) 2.7×10^{-26} C
(2) 5.5×10^{-24} C
(3) 3.8×10^{-13} C
(4) 9.6×10^{-13} C

35 One watt is equivalent to one

(1) N•m
(2) N/m
(3) J•s
(4) J/s

Part B–1

Answer all questions in this part.

Directions (36–50): For *each* statement or question, write on the separate answer sheet, the *number* of the word or expression that, of those given, best completes the statement or answers the question.

36 Which pair of forces acting concurrently on an object will produce the resultant of greatest magnitude?

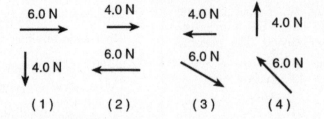

Note that question 37 has only three choices.

37 The diagram below shows a force of magnitude F applied to a mass at angle θ relative to a horizontal frictionless surface.

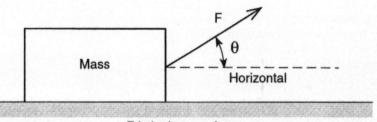

As angle θ is increased, the horizontal acceleration of the mass

(1) decreases
(2) increases
(3) remains the same

38 The mass of a high school football player is approximately

(1) 10^0 kg   (3) 10^2 kg
(2) 10^1 kg   (4) 10^3 kg

39 A constant force is used to keep a block sliding at constant velocity along a rough horizontal track. As the block slides, there could be an increase in its

(1) gravitational potential energy, only
(2) internal energy, only
(3) gravitational potential energy and kinetic energy
(4) internal energy and kinetic energy

40 A photon of which electromagnetic radiation has the most energy?

(1) ultraviolet   (3) infrared
(2) x ray   (4) microwave

41 The spring of a toy car is wound by pushing the car backward with an average force of 15 newtons through a distance of 0.50 meter. How much elastic potential energy is stored in the car's spring during this process?

(1) 1.9 J   (3) 30. J
(2) 7.5 J   (4) 56 J

42 The graph below shows the relationship between the potential difference across a metallic conductor and the electric current through the conductor at constant temperature T_1.

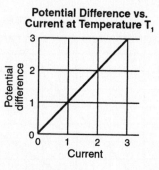

Potential Difference vs. Current at Temperature T_1

Which graph best represents the relationship between potential difference and current for the same conductor maintained at a higher constant temperature, T_2?

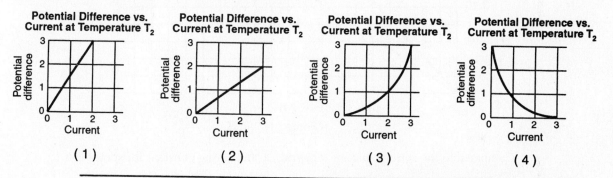

Potential Difference vs. Current at Temperature T_2

(1)

Potential Difference vs. Current at Temperature T_2

(2)

Potential Difference vs. Current at Temperature T_2

(3)

Potential Difference vs. Current at Temperature T_2

(4)

---

43 The diagram below shows a circuit with two resistors.

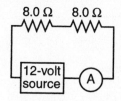

What is the reading on ammeter A?

(1) 1.3 A   (3) 3.0 A
(2) 1.5 A   (4) 0.75 A

44 The diagram below shows a bar magnet.

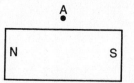

Which arrow best represents the direction of the needle of a compass placed at point A?

(1) ↑   (3) →
(2) ↓   (4) ←

45 Which graph best represents the motion of a block accelerating uniformly down an inclined plane?

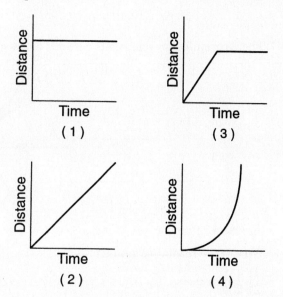

(1)

(3)

(2)

(4)

Note that question 46 has only three choices.

46 The graph below shows elongation as a function of the applied force for two springs, *A* and *B*.

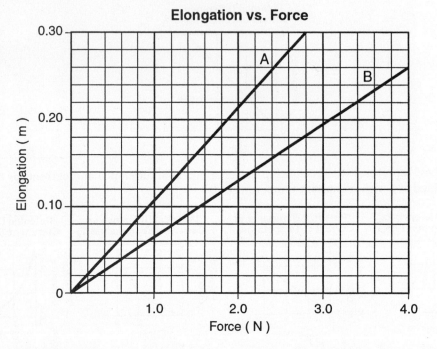

Compared to the spring constant for spring *A*, the spring constant for spring *B* is

(1) smaller
(2) larger
(3) the same

47 The diagram below represents currents in a segment of an electric circuit.

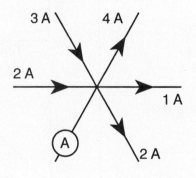

What is the reading of ammeter *A*?

(1) 1 A   (3) 3 A
(2) 2 A   (4) 4 A

Base your answers to questions 48 and 49 on the diagram below, which represents a light ray traveling from air to Lucite to medium Y and back into air.

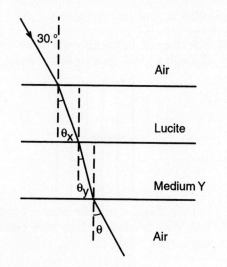

48 The sine of angle θ_x is

(1) 0.333   (3) 0.707
(2) 0.500   (4) 0.886

49 Light travels *slowest* in

(1) air, only
(2) Lucite, only
(3) medium Y, only
(4) air, Lucite, and medium Y

50 The diagram below shows two pulses traveling toward each other in a uniform medium.

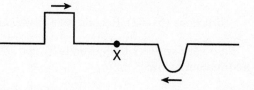

Which diagram best represents the medium when the pulses meet at point X?

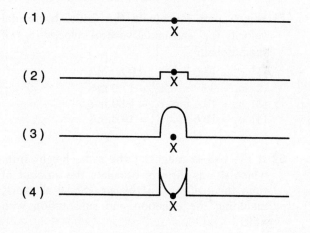

Part B–2

Answer all questions in this part.

Directions (51–62): Record your answers in the spaces provided in your answer booklet.

Base your answers to questions 51 and 52 on the information below.

An outfielder throws a baseball to the first baseman at a speed of 19.6 meters per second and an angle of 30.° above the horizontal.

51 Which pair represents the initial horizontal velocity (v_x) and initial vertical velocity (v_y) of the baseball?

(1) $v_x = 17.0$ m/s, $v_y = 9.80$ m/s
(2) $v_x = 9.80$ m/s, $v_y = 17.0$ m/s
(3) $v_x = 19.4$ m/s, $v_y = 5.90$ m/s
(4) $v_x = 19.6$ m/s, $v_y = 19.6$ m/s

52 If the ball is caught at the same height from which it was thrown, calculate the amount of time the ball was in the air. [Show all work, including the equation and substitution with units.] [2]

Base your answers to questions 53 and 54 on the circuit diagram below, which shows two resistors connected to a 24-volt source of potential difference.

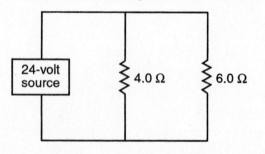

53 On the diagram *in your answer booklet,* use the appropriate circuit symbol to indicate a correct placement of a voltmeter to determine the potential difference across the circuit. [1]

54 What is the total resistance of the circuit?

(1) 0.42 Ω   (3) 5.0 Ω
(2) 2.4 Ω   (4) 10. Ω

55 The diagram below shows a plane wave passing through a small opening in a barrier.

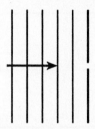

On the diagram *in your answer booklet,* sketch four wave fronts after they have passed through the barrier. [1]

56 What prevents the nucleus of a helium atom from flying apart? [1]

Base your answers to questions 57 and 58 on the information below.

A 1.00-meter length of nichrome wire with a cross-sectional area of 7.85×10^{-7} meter² is connected to a 1.50-volt battery.

57 Calculate the resistance of the wire. [Show all work, including the equation and substitution with units.] [2]

58 Determine the current in the wire. [1]

Base your answers to questions 59 through 62 on the information and table below.

In a laboratory exercise, a student kept the mass and amplitude of swing of a simple pendulum constant. The length of the pendulum was increased and the period of the pendulum was measured. The student recorded the data in the table below.

Length (meters)	Period (seconds)
0.05	0.30
0.20	0.90
0.40	1.30
0.60	1.60
0.80	1.80
1.00	2.00

Directions (59–61): Using the information in the table, construct a graph on the grid provided *in your answer booklet*, following the directions below.

59 Label each axis with the appropriate physical quantity and unit. Mark an appropriate scale on each axis.   [2]

60 Plot the data points for period versus pendulum length.   [1]

61 Draw the best-fit line or curve for the data graphed.   [1]

62 Using your graph, determine the period of a pendulum whose length is 0.25 meter.   [1]

Part C

Answer all questions in this part.

Directions (63–78): Record your answers in the spaces provided in your answer booklet.

Base your answers to questions 63 through 65 on the information and diagram below.

A mass, M, is hung from a spring and reaches equilibrium at position B. The mass is then raised to position A and released. The mass oscillates between positions A and C. [Neglect friction.]

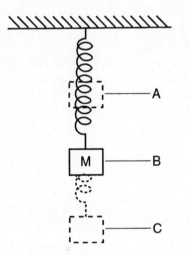

63 At which position, A, B, or C, is mass M located when the kinetic energy of the system is at a maximum? Explain your choice.   [1]

64 At which position, A, B, or C, is mass M located when the gravitational potential energy of the system is at a maximum? Explain your choice.   [1]

65 At which position, A, B, or C, is mass M located when the elastic potential energy of the system is at a maximum? Explain your choice.   [1]

Base your answers to questions 66 through 69 on the information below.

A force of 6.0×10^{-15} newton due south and a force of 8.0×10^{-15} newton due east act concurrently on an electron, e^-.

66 On the diagram *in your answer booklet*, draw a force diagram to represent the *two* forces acting on the electron. (The electron is represented by a dot.) Use a metric ruler and the scale of 1.0 centimeter = 1.0×10^{-15} newton. Begin each vector at the dot representing the electron and label its magnitude in newtons.   [2]

67 *In your answer booklet,* determine the resultant force on the electron, *graphically*. Label the resultant vector R.   [1]

68 Determine the magnitude of the resultant vector R.   [1]

69 Determine the angle between the resultant and the 6.0×10^{-15}-newton vector.   [1]

Base your answers to questions 70 through 74 on the information below.

A force of 10. newtons toward the right is exerted on a wooden crate initially moving to the right on a horizontal wooden floor. The crate weighs 25 newtons.

70 Calculate the magnitude of the force of friction between the crate and the floor. [Show all work, including the equation and substitution with units.] [2]

71 On the diagram *in your answer booklet,* draw and label all vertical forces acting on the crate. [1]

72 On the diagram *in your answer booklet,* draw and label all horizontal forces acting on the crate. [1]

73 What is the magnitude of the net force acting on the crate? [1]

74 Is the crate accelerating? Explain your answer. [1]

Base your answers to questions 75 through 78 on the information below.

An electron in a hydrogen atom drops from the $n = 3$ energy level to the $n = 2$ energy level.

75 What is the energy, in electronvolts, of the emitted photon? [1]

76 What is the energy, in joules, of the emitted photon? [1]

77 Calculate the frequency of the emitted radiation. [Show all work, including the equation and substitution with units.] [2]

78 Calculate the wavelength of the emitted radiation. [Show all work, including the equation and substitution with units.] [2]

51 _____

52

53

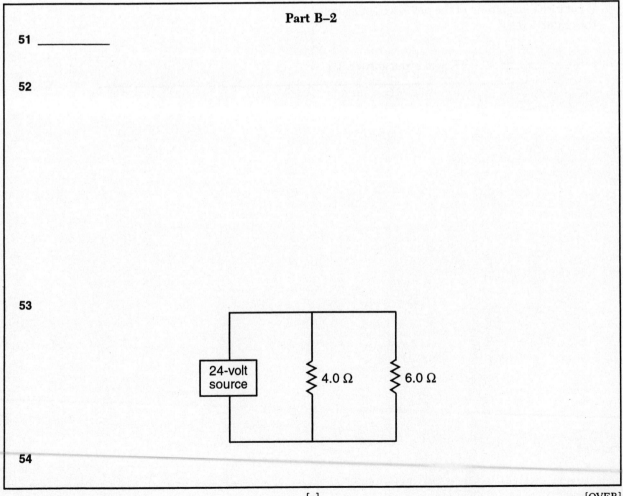

24-volt source   4.0 Ω   6.0 Ω

54

[a]

[OVER]

55

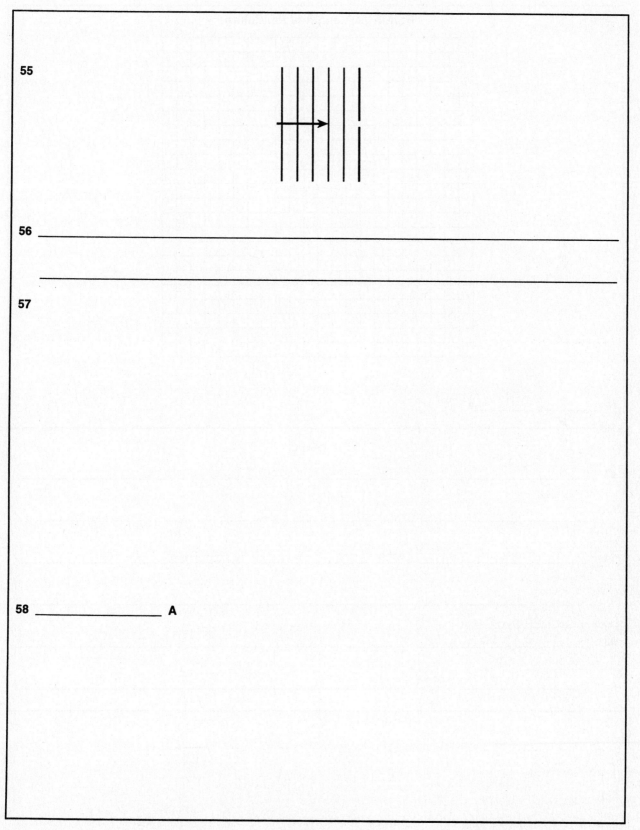

56 _____

_____

57

58 _____ **A**

[b]

59–61

Period vs. Length of Pendulum

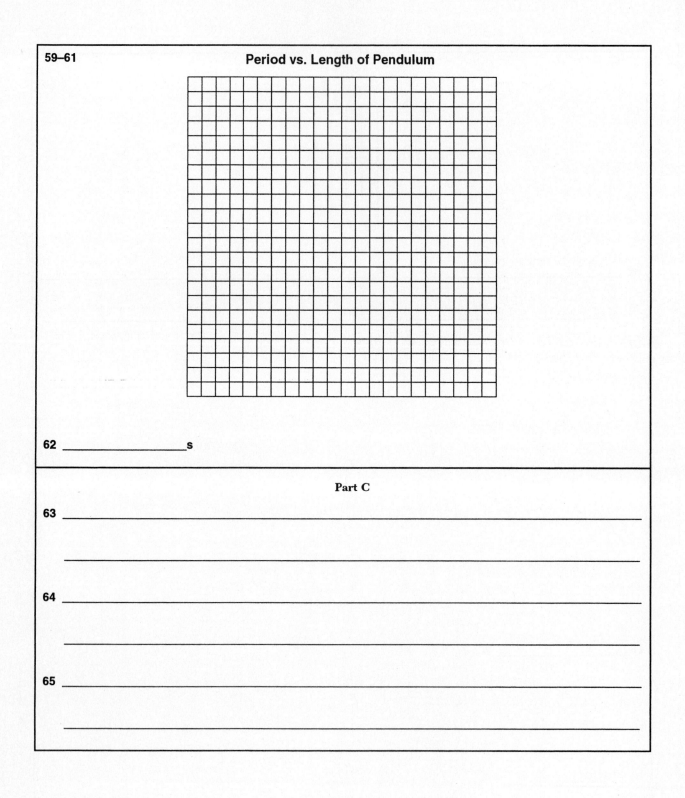

62 _____ s

Part C

63 _____

_____

64 _____

_____

65 _____

_____

[c]

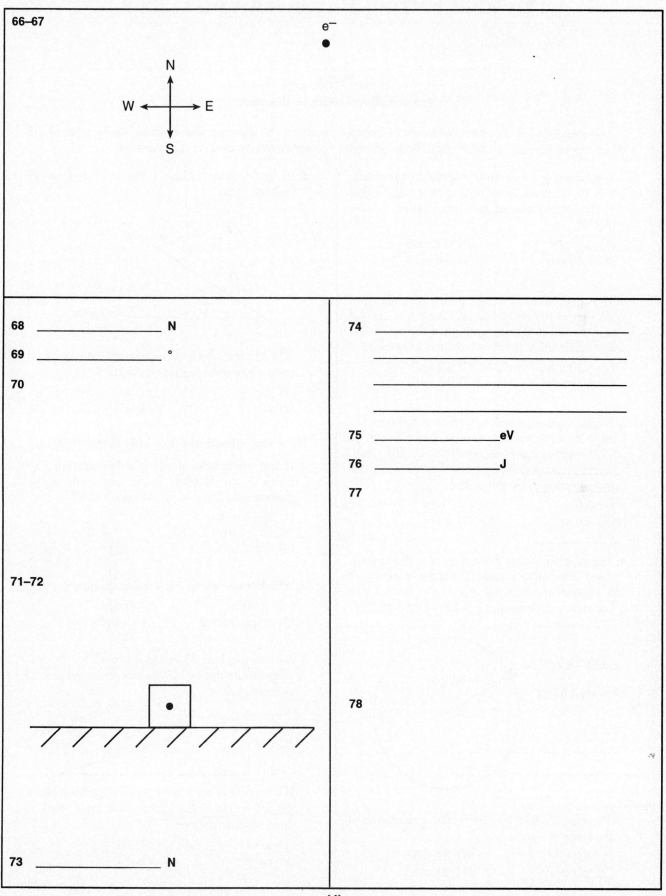

66–67

e⁻
●

N
W ←—→ E
S

68 _____ **N**

69 _____ °

70

71–72

●

73 _____ **N**

74 _____

_____

_____

_____

75 _____ **eV**

76 _____ **J**

77

78

Physical Setting Physics August, 2002

Part A

Answer all questions in this part.

Directions (1–35): For *each* statement or question, write on the separate anwser sheet, the *number* of the word or expression that, of those given, best completes the statement or answers the question.

1. A net force of 25 newtons is applied horizontally to a 10.-kilogram block resting on a table. What is the magnitude of the acceleration of the block?

    (1) 0.0 m/s^2 (3) 0.40 m/s^2
    (2) 0.26 m/s^2 (4) 2.5 m/s^2

2. The speed of a car is increased uniformly from 20. meters per second to 30. meters per second in 4.0 seconds. The magnitude of the car's average acceleration in this 4.0-second interval is

    (1) 0.40 m/s^2.   (3) 10 m/s^2.
    (2) 2.5 m/s^2.   (4) 13 m/s^2.

3. A roller coaster, traveling with an initial speed of 15 meters per second, decelerates uniformly at −7.0 meters per second^2 to a full stop. Approximately how far does the roller coaster travel during its deceleration?

    (1) 1.0 m   (3) 16 m
    (2) 2.0 m   (4) 32 m

4. The diagram below represents a 0.40-kilogram stone attached to a string. The stone is moving at a constant speed of 4.0 meters per second in a horizontal circle having a radius of 0.80 meters.

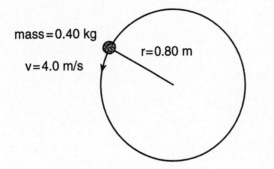

    mass=0.40 kg
    v=4.0 m/s
    r=0.80 m

The magnitude of the centripetal acceleration of the stone is

    (1) 0.0 m/s^2.   (3) 5.0 m/s^2.
    (2) 2.0 m/s^2.   (4) 20. m/s^2.

5. In the diagram below, a box is at rest on an inclined plane.

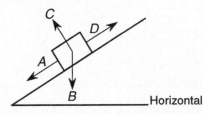

Horizontal

Which vector best represents the direction of the normal force acting on the box?

    (1) A   (3) C
    (2) B   (4) D

Note that question 6 has only three choices.

6. If the magnitude of the gravitational force of Earth on the Moon is F, the magnitude of the gravitational force of the Moon on Earth is

    (1) smaller than F.
    (2) larger than F.
    (3) equal to F.

7. Which term represents a scalar quantity?

    (1) distance   (3) force
    (2) displacement   (4) weight

8. A block weighing 15 newtons is pulled to the top of an incline that is 0.20 meters above the ground, as shown below.

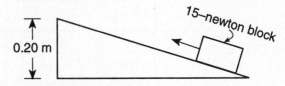

    0.20 m
    15-newton block

If 4.0 joules of work are needed to pull the block the full length of the incline, how much work is done against friction?

    (1) 1.0 J   (3) 3.0 J
    (2) 0.0 J   (4) 7.0 J

9. A 1.0-kilogram rubber ball traveling east at 4.0 meters per second hits a wall and bounces back toward the west at 2.0 meters per second. Compared to the kinetic energy of the ball before it hits the wall, the kinetic energy of the ball after it bounces off the wall is

(1) one-fourth as great.   (3) the same.
(2) one-half as great.   (4) four times as great.

Note that questions 10 and 11 have only three choices.

10. As a spring is stretched, its elastic potential energy
(1) decreases.
(2) increases.
(3) remains the same.

11. An electroscope is a device with a metal knob, a metal stem, and freely hanging metal leaves used to detect charges. The diagram below shows a positively charged leaf electroscope.

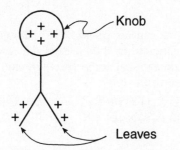

As a positively charged glass rod is brought near the knob of the electroscope, the separation of the electroscope leaves will

(1) decrease.
(2) increase.
(3) remain the same.

12. A catapult with a spring constant of 1.0×10^4 newtons per meter is required to launch an airplane from the deck of an aircraft carrier. The plane is released when it has been displaced 0.50 meters from its equilibrium position by the catapult. The energy acquired by the airplane from the catapult during takeoff is approximately

(1) 1.3×10^3 J.   (3) 2.5×10^3 J.
(2) 2.0×10^4 J.   (4) 1.0×10^4 J.

13. A 10.-ohm resistor and a 20.-ohm resistor are connected in series to a voltage source. When the current through the 10.-ohm resistor is 2.0 amperes, what is the current through the 20.-ohm resistor?

(1) 1.0 A   (3) 0.50 A
(2) 2.0 A   (4) 4.0 A

14. In the circuit diagram below, what are the correct readings of voltmeters V_1 and V_2?

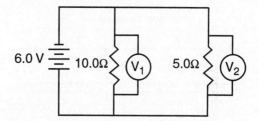

(1) V_1 reads 2.0 V and V_2 reads 4.0 V
(2) V_1 reads 4.0 V and V_2 reads 2.0 V
(3) V_1 reads 3.0 V and V_2 reads 3.0 V
(4) V_1 reads 6.0 V and V_2 reads 6.0 V

15. A physics student notices that 4.0 waves arrive at the beach every 20. seconds. The frequency of these waves is

(1) 0.20 Hz.   (3) 16 Hz.
(2) 5.0 Hz.   (4) 80. Hz.

16. An electric guitar is generating a sound of constant frequency. An increase in which sound wave characteristic would result in an increase in loudness?

(1) speed   (3) wavelength
(2) period   (4) amplitude

17. The diagram below shows two points, A and B, on a wave train.

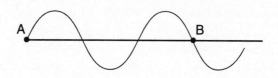

How many wavelengths separate point A and point B?

(1) 1.0   (3) 3.0
(2) 1.5   (4) 0.75

18. In a demonstration, a vibrating tuning fork causes a nearby second tuning fork to begin to vibrate with the same frequency. Which wave phenomenon is illustrated by this demonstration?

    (1) the Doppler effect   (3) resonance
    (2) nodes   (4) interference

19. The diagram below shows wave fronts spreading into the region behind a barrier.

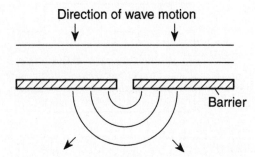

Direction of wave motion

Barrier

Which wave phenomenon is represented in the diagram?

    (1) reflection   (3) diffraction
    (2) refraction   (4) standing waves

20. The diagram below represents the wave pattern produced by two sources located at points A and B.

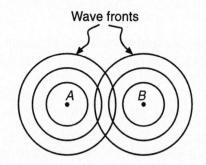

Wave fronts

Which phenomenon occurs at the intersections of the circular wave fronts?

    (1) diffraction   (3) refraction
    (2) interference   (4) reflection

21. How much work is required to move a single electron through a potential difference of 100. volts?

    (1) 1.6×10^{-21} J   (3) 1.6×10^{-17} J
    (2) 1.6×10^{-19} J   (4) 1.0×10^{2} J

22. An object can *not* have a charge of

    (1) 3.2×10^{-19} C   (3) 8.0×10^{-19} C
    (2) 4.5×10^{-19} C   (4) 9.6×10^{-19} C

23. After electrons in hydrogen atoms are excited to the $n = 3$ energy state, how many different frequencies of radiation can be emitted as the electrons return to the ground state?

    (1) 1   (3) 3
    (2) 2   (4) 4

24. What type of nuclear force holds the protons and neutrons in an atom together?

    (1) a strong force that acts over a short range
    (2) a strong force that acts over a long range
    (3) a weak force that acts over a short range
    (4) a weak force that acts over a long range

25. Which is an acceptable unit for impulse?

    (1) N • m   (3) J • s
    (2) J/s   (4) kg • m/s

26. The centers of two 15.0-kilogram spheres are separated by 3.00 meters. The magnitude of the gravitational force between the two spheres is approximately

    (1) 1.11×10^{-10} N.   (3) 1.67×10^{-9} N.
    (2) 3.34×10^{-10} N.   (4) 5.00×10^{-9} N.

27. During a collision, an 84-kilogram driver of a car moving at 24 meters per second is brought to rest by an inflating air bag in 1.2 seconds. The magnitude of the force exerted on the driver by the air bag is approximately

    (1) 7.0×10^{1} N.   (3) 1.7×10^{3} N.
    (2) 8.2×10^{2} N.   (4) 2.0×10^{3} N.

28. An apple weighing 1 newton on the surface of Earth has a mass of approximately

    (1) 1×10^{-1} kg.   (3) 1×10^{1} kg.
    (2) 1×10^{0} kg.   (4) 1×10^{2} kg.

29. In raising an object vertically at a constant speed of 2.0 meters per second, 10. watts of power is developed. The weight of the object is

    (1) 5.0 N.   (3) 40. N.
    (2) 20. N.   (4) 50. N.

30. Which diagram best represents magnetic flux lines around a bar magnet?

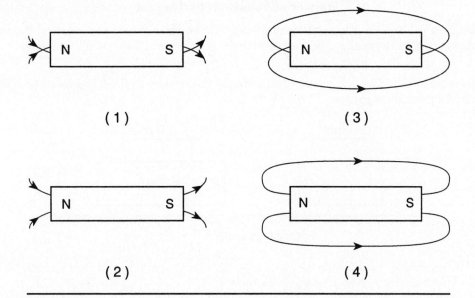

(1)

(3)

(2)

(4)

31. In which situation is the net force on the object equal to zero?

 (1) a satellite moving at constant speed around Earth in a circular orbit
 (2) an automobile braking to a stop
 (3) a bicycle moving at constant speed on a straight, level road
 (4) a pitched baseball being hit by a bat

Base your answers to questions 32 and 33 on the information below.

A 2.00×10^6-hertz radio signal is sent a distance of 7.30×10^{10} meters from Earth to a spaceship orbiting Mars.

32. Approximately how much time does it take the radio signal to travel from Earth to the spaceship?

 (1) 4.11×10^{-3} s   (3) 2.19×10^8 s
 (2) 2.43×10^2 s   (4) 1.46×10^{17} s

Note that question 33 has only three choices.

33. The spaceship is moving away from Earth when the radio signal is received. Compared to the frequency of the signal sent from Earth, the frequency of the signal received by the spaceship is

 (1) lower.
 (2) higher.
 (3) the same.

34. What is the total resistance of the circuit segment shown in the diagram below?

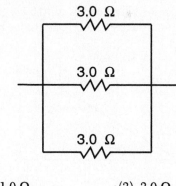

 (1) 1.0 Ω   (3) 3.0 Ω
 (2) 9.0 Ω   (4) 27 Ω

35. What is the approximate electrostatic force between two protons separated by a distance of 1.0×10^{-6} meter?

 (1) 2.3×10^{-16} N and repulsive
 (2) 2.3×10^{-16} N and attractive
 (3) 9.0×10^{21} N and repulsive
 (4) 9.0×10^{21} N and attractive

Part B–1

Answer all questions in this part.

Directions (36–47): For *each* statement or question, write on the separate answer sheet the *number* of the word or expression that, of those given, best completes the statement or answers the question.

36. The diagram below shows a 4.0-kilogram cart moving to the right and a 6.0-kilogram cart moving to the left on a horizontal frictionless surface.

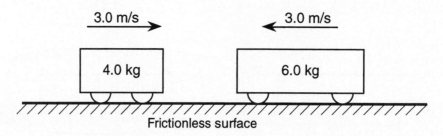

When the two carts collide they lock together. The magnitude of the total momentum of the two-cart system after the collision is

(1) 0.0 kg • m/s.

(2) 6.0 kg • m/s.

(3) 15 kg • m/s.

(4) 30. kg • m/s.

---

37. The diagram below shows a 10.0-kilogram mass held at rest on a frictionless 30.0° incline by force *F*.

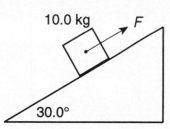

What is the approximate magnitude of force *F*?

(1) 9.81 N

(3) 85.0 N

(2) 49.1 N

(4) 98.1 N

38. An archer uses a bow to fire two similar arrows with the same string force. One arrow is fired at an angle of 60.° with the horizontal, and the other is fired at an angle of 45° with the horizontal. Compared to the arrow fired at 60.°, the arrow fired at 45° has a

(1) longer flight time and longer horizontal range.

(2) longer flight time and shorter horizontal range.

(3) shorter flight time and longer horizontal range.

(4) shorter flight time and shorter horizontal range.

39. The graph below shows the velocity of a race car moving along a straight line as a function of time.

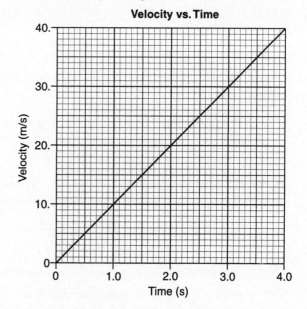

What is the magnitude of the displacement of the car from *t* = 2.0 seconds to *t* = 4.0 seconds?

(1) 20. m

(3) 60. m

(2) 40. m

(4) 80. m

40. Which vector diagram represents the greatest magnitude of displacement for an object?

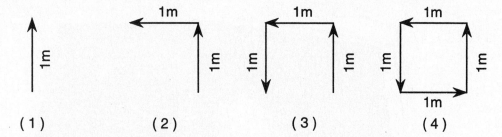

(1)   (2)   (3)   (4)

41. Which circuit diagram shows voltmeter V and ammeter A correctly positioned to measure the total potential difference of the circuit and the current through each resistor?

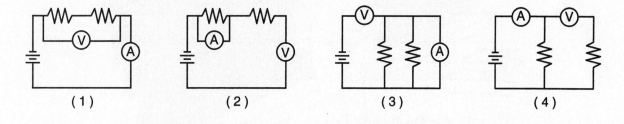

(1)   (2)   (3)   (4)

42. A monochromatic ray of light ($f = 5.09 \times 10^{14}$ hertz) traveling in air is incident upon medium A at an angle of 45°. If the angle of refraction is 29°, medium A could be

(1) water.
(2) fused quartz.
(3) Lucite.
(4) flint glass.

43. What is the total electrical energy used by a 1500-watt hair dryer operating for 6.0 minutes?

(1) 4.2 J
(2) 250 J
(3) 9.0×10^3 J
(4) 5.4×10^5 J

44. Which combination of quarks would produce a neutral baryon?

(1) uud
(2) udd
(3) $\overline{u}\,\overline{u}d$
(4) $\overline{u}dd$

45. A 12.0-meter length of copper wire has a resistance of 1.50 ohms. How long must an aluminum wire with the same cross-sectional area be to have the same resistance?

(1) 7.32 m
(2) 8.00 m
(3) 12.0 m
(4) 19.7 m

46. A 0.500-meter length of wire with a cross-sectional area of 3.14×10^{-6} meters squared is found to have a resistance of 2.53×10^{-3} ohms. According to the resistivity chart, the wire could be made of

(1) aluminum.
(2) copper.
(3) nichrome.
(4) silver.

Base your answer to question 47 on the cartoon below and your knowledge of physics.

47. In the cartoon, Einstein is contemplating the equation for the principle that
   (1) the fundamental source of all energy is the conversion of mass into energy.
   (2) energy is emitted or absorbed in discrete packets called photons.
   (3) mass always travels at the speed of light in a vacuum.
   (4) the energy of a photon is proportional to its frequency.

Part B–2

Answer all questions in this part.

Directions (48–60): Record your answers in the spaces provided in your answer booklet.

Base your answers to questions 48 through 52 on the information and data table below.

A variable resistor was connected to a battery. As the resistance was adjusted, the current and power in the circuit were determined. The data are recorded in the table below.

Current (amperes)	Power (watts)
0.75	2.27
1.25	3.72
2.25	6.75
3.00	9.05
4.00	11.9

48–49. Using the information in the data table, construct a line graph on the grid provided *in your answer booklet,* following the directions below. The grid below is provided for practice purposes only. Be sure your final answer appears *in your answer booklet*.

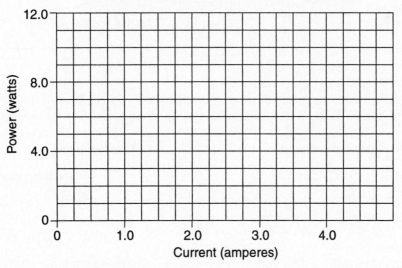

Power vs. Current for a Variable Resistor

48. Plot the data points for power versus current.   [1]

49. Draw the best-fit line.   [1]

50. Using your graph, determine the power delivered to the circuit at a current of 3.5 amperes.   [1]

51. Calculate the slope of the graph. [Show all calculations, including the equation and substitution with units.]   [2]

52. What is the physical significance of the slope of the graph?   [1]

Base your answers to questions 53 through 55 on the diagram below which shows a ray of monochromatic light ($f = 5.09 \times 10^{14}$ hertz) passing through a flint glass prism. [The same diagram appears in your answer booklet.]

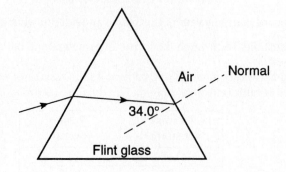

53. Calculate the angle of refraction (in degrees) of the light ray as it enters the air from the flint glass prism. [Show all calculations, including the equation and substitution with units.]   [2]

54. Using a protractor and a straightedge, construct the refracted light ray in the air on the diagram *in your answer booklet.*   [2]

55. What is the speed of the light ray in flint glass?
   (1) 5.53×10^{-9} m/s
   (2) 1.81×10^{8} m/s
   (3) 3.00×10^{8} m/s
   (4) 4.98×10^{8} m/s

Base your answers to questions 56 and 57 on the information and diagram below. The diagram shows the collision of an incident photon having a frequency of 2.00×10^{19} hertz with an electron initially at rest.

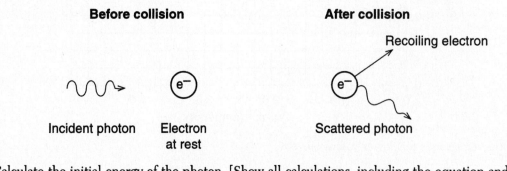

56. Calculate the initial energy of the photon. [Show all calculations, including the equation and substitution with units.] [2]

57. What is the total energy of the two-particle system after the collision? [1]

58. Determine the color of a ray of light with a wavelength of 6.21×10^{-7} meter. [1]

Base your answers to questions 59 and 60 on the information below.

A periodic transverse wave has an amplitude of 0.20 meter and a wavelength of 3.0 meters.

59. On the grid provided *in your answer booklet*, draw at least one cycle of this periodic wave. [2]

60. If the frequency of this wave is 12 Hz, what is its speed?
   (1) 0.25 m/s   (3) 36 m/s
   (2) 12 m/s   (4) 4.0 m/s

_____

Part C

Answer all questions in this part.

Directions (61–68): Record your answers in the spaces provided in your answer booklet.

Base your answers to questions 61 through 63 on the information and diagram below.

A child is flying a kite, *K*. A student at point *B*, located 100. meters away from point *A* (directly underneath the kite), measures the angle of elevation of the kite from the ground as 30.°.

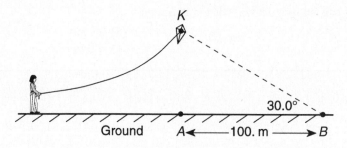

61. *In your answer booklet,* use a metric ruler and protractor to draw a triangle representing the positions of the kite, *K*, and point *A* relative to point *B* that is given. Label points *A* and *K*. Use a scale of 1.0 centimeter = 10. meters.   [2]

62. Use a metric ruler and your scale diagram to determine the height, *AK*, of the kite.   [1]

63. A small lead sphere is dropped from the kite. Calculate the amount of time required for the sphere to fall to the ground. [Show all calculations, including the equation and substitution with units. Neglect air resistance.]   [2] _____

Base your answers to questions 64 and 65 on the information given below.

Friction provides the centripetal force that allows a car to round a circular curve.

64. Find the minimum coefficient of friction needed between the tires and the road to allow a 1600-kilogram car to round a curve of radius 80. meters at a speed of 20. meters per second. [Show all work, including formulas and substitutions with units.]   [4]

65. If the mass of the car were increased, how would that affect the maximum speed at which it could round the curve?   [1] _____

Base your answers to questions 66 and 67 on the information below and on your knowledge of physics.

Using a spring toy like the one shown in the diagram, a physics teacher pushes on the toy, compressing the spring, causing the suction cup to stick to the base of the toy.

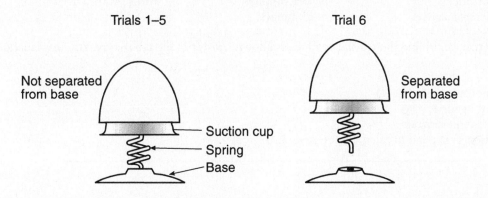

Trials 1–5   Trial 6

Not separated from base   Separated from base

Suction cup
Spring
Base

When the teacher removes her hand, the toy pops straight up and just brushes against the ceiling. She does this demonstration five times, always with the same result.

When the teacher repeats the demonstration for the sixth time the toy crashes against the ceiling with considerable force. The students notice that in this trial, the spring and toy separated from the base at the moment the spring released.

The teacher puts the toy back together, repeats the demonstration and the toy once again just brushes against the ceiling.

66. Describe the conversions that take place between pairs of the three forms of mechanical energy, beginning with the work done by the teacher on the toy and ending with the form(s) of energy possessed by the toy as it hits the ceiling. [Neglect friction.]   [3]

67. Explain, in terms of mass and energy, why the spring toy hits the ceiling in the sixth trial and not in the other trials.   [2]

68. Your school's physics laboratory has the following equipment available for conducting experiments:

accelerometers	lasers	stopwatches
ammeters	light bulbs	thermometers
bar magnets	meter sticks	voltmeters
batteries	power supplies	wires
electromagnets	spark timers	

Explain how you would find the resistance of an unknown resistor in the laboratory. Your explanation must include:

a. Measurements required   [1]
b. Equipment needed   [1]
c. Complete circuit diagram   [2]
d. Any equation(s) needed to calculate the resistance   [1]

August 2002 Answer Paper
Part B–2

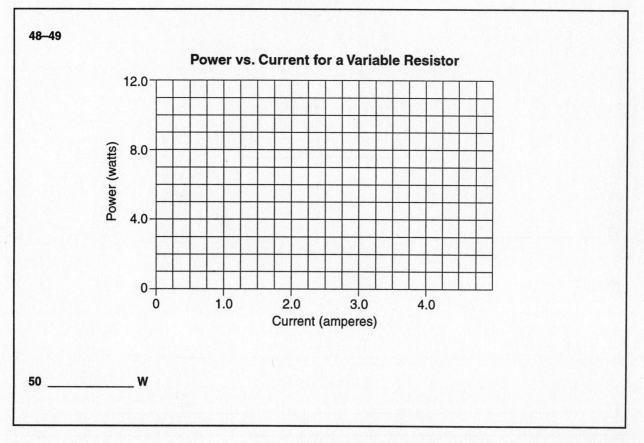

Power vs. Current for a Variable Resistor

50 _____ **W**

[a]

51

52 _____

53

54

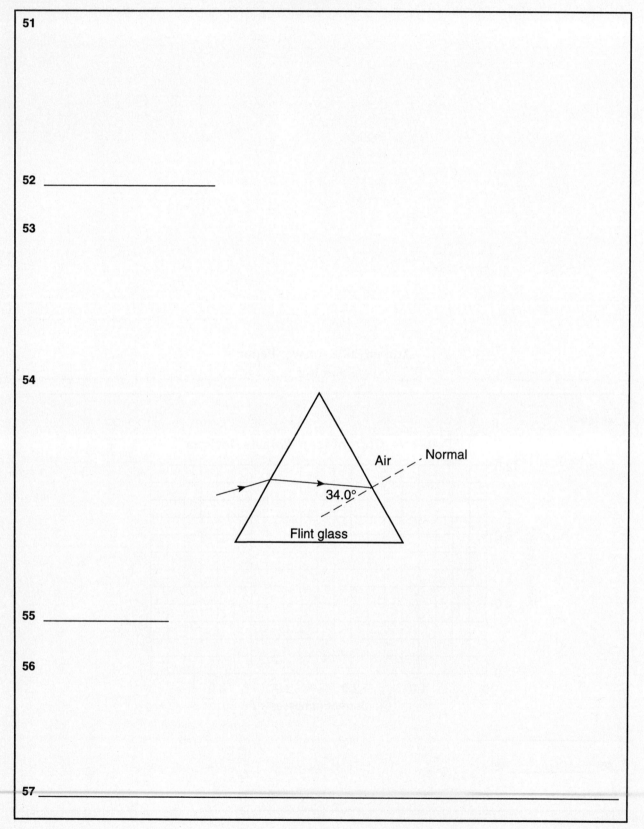

55 _____

56

57 _____

[b]

58 _____

59

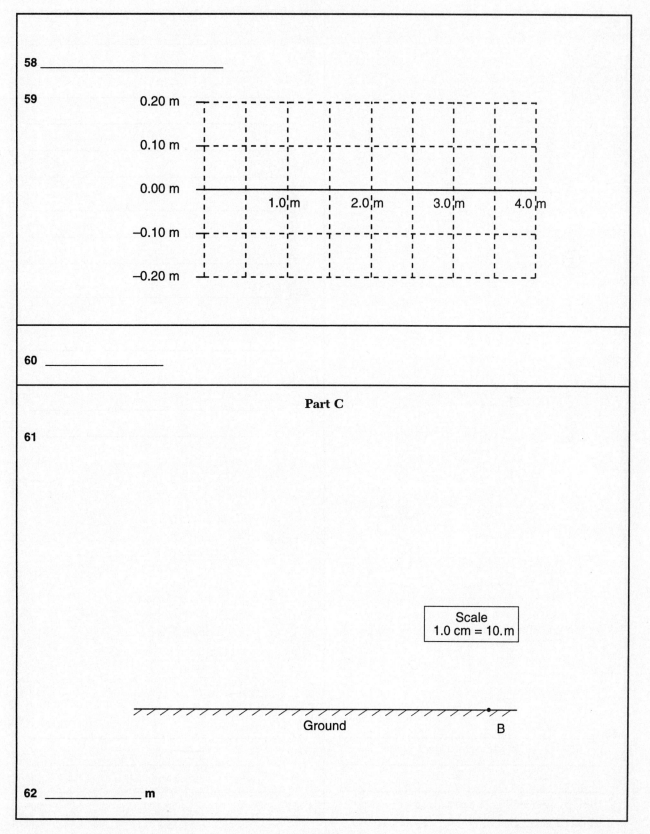

0.20 m

0.10 m

0.00 m   1.0 m   2.0 m   3.0 m   4.0 m

−0.10 m

−0.20 m

60 _____

Part C

61

Scale
1.0 cm = 10. m

Ground   B

62 _____ **m**

[c]

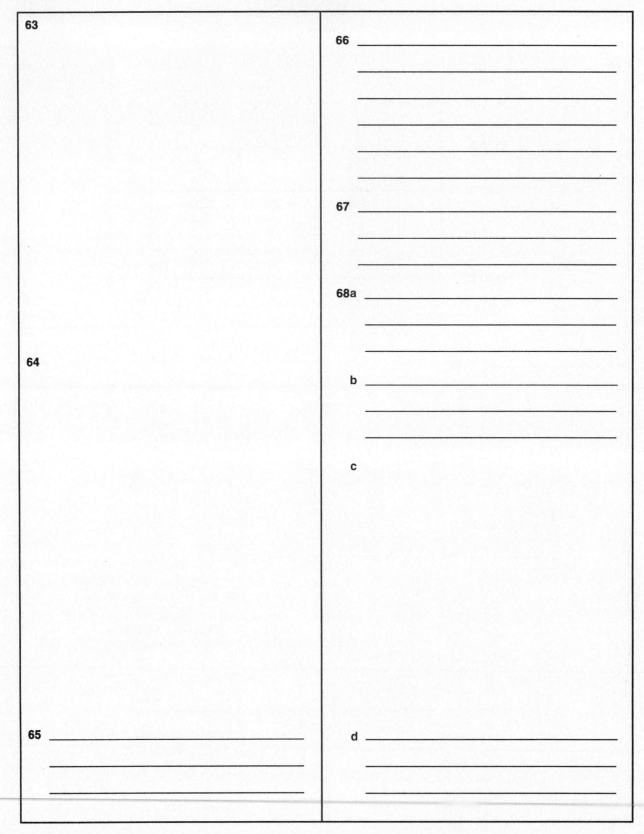

[d]

Part A

Answer all questions in this part.

Directions (1–35): For *each* statement or question, write on the separate anwser sheet, the *number* of the word or expression that, of those given, best completes the statement or answers the question.

1 Which is a vector quantity?

(1) distance   (3) power

(2) speed   (4) force

2 The diagram below shows a granite block being slid at constant speed across a horizontal concrete floor by a force parallel to the floor.

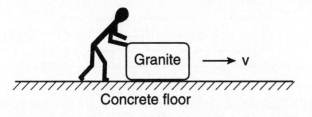

Concrete floor

Which pair of quantities could be used to determine the coefficient of friction for the granite on the concrete?

(1) mass and speed of the block

(2) mass and normal force on the block

(3) frictional force and speed of the block

(4) frictional force and normal force on the block

3 An object with an initial speed of 4.0 meters per second accelerates uniformly at 2.0 meters per second² in the direction of its motion for a distance of 5.0 meters. What is the final speed of the object?

(1) 6.0 m/s   (3) 14 m/s

(2) 10. m/s   (4) 36 m/s

4 After a model rocket reached its maximum height, it then took 5.0 seconds to return to the launch site. What is the approximate maximum height reached by the rocket? [Neglect air resistance.]

(1) 49 m   (3) 120 m

(2) 98 m   (4) 250 m

5 The diagram below shows a student throwing a baseball horizontally at 25 meters per second from a cliff 45 meters above the level ground.

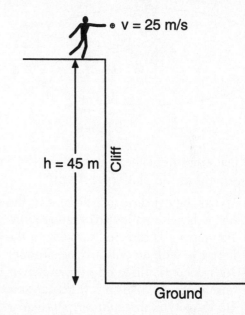

Approximately how far from the base of the cliff does the ball hit the ground? [Neglect air resistance.]

(1) 45 m   (3) 140 m

(2) 75 m   (4) 230 m

6 A projectile is fired from a gun near the surface of Earth. The initial velocity of the projectile has a vertical component of 98 meters per second and a horizontal component of 49 meters per second. How long will it take the projectile to reach the highest point in its path?

(1) 5.0 s   (3) 20. s

(2) 10. s   (4) 100. s

7 A 70.-kilogram astronaut has a weight of 560 newtons on the surface of planet Alpha. What is the acceleration due to gravity on planet Alpha?

(1) 0.0 m/s²   (3) 9.8 m/s²

(2) 8.0 m/s²   (4) 80. m/s²

Base your answers to questions 8 and 9 on the diagram and information below.

The diagram shows a student seated on a rotating circular platform, holding a 2.0-kilogram block with a spring scale. The block is 1.2 meters from the center of the platform. The block has a constant speed of 8.0 meters per second. [Frictional forces on the block are negligible.]

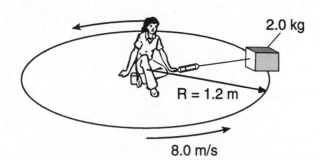

8 Which statement best describes the block's movement as the platform rotates?

(1) Its velocity is directed tangent to the circular path, with an inward acceleration.
(2) Its velocity is directed tangent to the circular path, with an outward acceleration.
(3) Its velocity is directed perpendicular to the circular path, with an inward acceleration.
(4) Its velocity is directed perpendicular to the circular path, with an outward acceleration.

9 The reading on the spring scale is approximately

(1) 20. N   (3) 110 N
(2) 53 N   (4) 130 N

10 The diagram below shows a horizontal 8.0-newton force applied to a 4.0-kilogram block on a frictionless table.

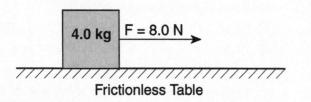

Frictionless Table

What is the magnitude of the block's acceleration?

(1) 0.50 m/s²   (3) 9.8 m/s²
(2) 2.0 m/s²   (4) 32 m/s²

11 A 0.10-kilogram model rocket's engine is designed to deliver an impulse of 6.0 newton-seconds. If the rocket engine burns for 0.75 second, what average force does it produce?

(1) 4.5 N   (3) 45 N
(2) 8.0 N   (4) 80. N

Base your answers to questions 12 and 13 on the information and diagram below.

The diagram shows a compressed spring between two carts initially at rest on a horizontal frictionless surface. Cart A has a mass of 2 kilograms and cart B has a mass of 1 kilogram. A string holds the carts together.

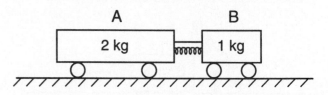

12 What occurs when the string is cut and the carts move apart?

(1) The magnitude of the acceleration of cart A is one-half the magnitude of the acceleration of cart B.
(2) The length of time that the force acts on cart A is twice the length of time the force acts on cart B.
(3) The magnitude of the force exerted on cart A is one-half the magnitude of the force exerted on cart B.
(4) The magnitude of the impulse applied to cart A is twice the magnitude of the impulse applied to cart B.

13 After the string is cut and the two carts move apart, the magnitude of which quantity is the same for both carts?

(1) momentum   (3) inertia
(2) velocity   (4) kinetic energy

14 An object moving at a constant speed of 25 meters per second possesses 450 joules of kinetic energy. What is the object's mass?

(1) 0.72 kg   (3) 18 kg
(2) 1.4 kg   (4) 36 kg

15 The diagram below shows a moving, 5.00-kilogram cart at the foot of a hill 10.0 meters high. For the cart to reach the top of the hill, what is the minimum kinetic energy of the cart in the position shown? [Neglect energy loss due to friction.]

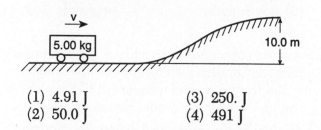

(1) 4.91 J   (3) 250. J
(2) 50.0 J   (4) 491 J

16 A constant force of 1900 newtons is required to keep an automobile having a mass of 1.0×10^3 kilograms moving at a constant speed of 20. meters per second. The work done in moving the automobile a distance of 2.0×10^3 meters is

(1) 2.0×10^4 J   (3) 2.0×10^6 J
(2) 3.8×10^4 J   (4) 3.8×10^6 J

17 The energy required to move one elementary charge through a potential difference of 5.0 volts is

(1) 8.0 J   (3) 8.0×10^{-19} J
(2) 5.0 J   (4) 1.6×10^{-19} J

18 The diagram below shows two identical metal spheres, A and B, on insulated stands. Each sphere possesses a net charge of -3×10^{-6} coulomb.

-3×10^{-6} C -3×10^{-6} C

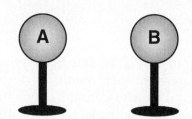

If the spheres are brought into contact with each other and then separated, the charge on sphere A will be

(1) 0 C   (3) -3×10^{-6} C
(2) $+3 \times 10^{-6}$ C   (4) -6×10^{-6} C

19 In a vacuum, light with a frequency of 5.0×10^{14} hertz has a wavelength of

(1) 6.0×10^{-21} m   (3) 1.7×10^6 m
(2) 6.0×10^{-7} m   (4) 1.5×10^{23} m

20 In the diagram below, 400. joules of work is done raising a 72-newton weight a vertical distance of 5.0 meters.

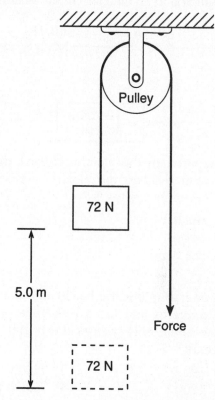

How much work is done to overcome friction as the weight is raised?

(1) 40. J   (3) 400. J
(2) 360 J   (4) 760 J

21 An incandescent light bulb is supplied with a constant potential diference of 120 volts. As the filament of the bulb heats up, its resistance

(1) increases and the current through it decreases
(2) increases and the current through it increases
(3) decreases and the current through it decreases
(4) decreases and the current through it increases

22 During a thunderstorm, a lightning strike transfers 12 coulombs of charge in 2.0×10^{-3} second. What is the average current produced in this strike?

(1) 1.7×10^{-4} A   (3) 6.0×10^3 A
(2) 2.4×10^{-2} A   (4) 9.6×10^3 A

Note that question 23 has only three choices.

23 A 30.-ohm resistor and a 60.-ohm resistor are connected in an electric circuit as shown below.

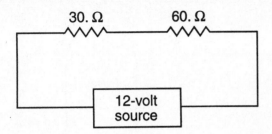

Compared to the electric current through the 30.-ohm resistor, the electric current through the 60.-ohm resistor is

(1) smaller
(2) larger
(3) the same

24 An operating electric heater draws a current of 10. amperes and has a resistance of 12 ohms. How much energy does the heater use in 60. seconds?

(1) 120 J   (3) 7200 J
(2) 1200 J   (4) 72,000 J

25 If the charge on each of two small charged metal spheres is doubled and the distance between the spheres remains fixed, the magnitude of the electric force between the spheres will be

(1) the same   (3) one-half as great
(2) two times as great (4) four times as great

26 The diagram below represents a periodic wave.

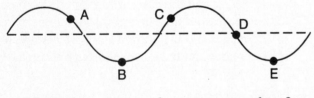

Which two points on the wave are in phase?

(1) A and C   (3) A and D
(2) B and D   (4) B and E

27 A beam of monochromatic light travels through flint glass, crown glass, Lucite, and water. The speed of the light beam is slowest in

(1) flint glass   (3) Lucite
(2) crown glass   (4) water

28 A standing wave pattern is produced when a guitar string is plucked. Which characteristic of the standing wave immediately begins to decrease?

(1) speed   (3) frequency
(2) wavelength   (4) amplitude

29 A source of sound waves approaches a stationary observer through a uniform medium. Compared to the frequency and wavelength of the emitted sound, the observer would detect waves with a

(1) higher frequency and shorter wavelength
(2) higher frequency and longer wavelength
(3) lower frequency and shorter wavelength
(4) lower frequency and longer wavelength

30 What is the smallest electric charge that can be put on an object?

(1) 9.11×10^{-31} C   (3) 9.00×10^9 C
(2) 1.60×10^{-19} C   (4) 6.25×10^{18} C

31 Which characteristic of electromagnetic radiation is directly proportional to the energy of a photon?

(1) wavelength   (3) frequency
(2) period   (4) path

32 What is the maximum height to which a 1200-watt motor could lift an object weighing 200. newtons in 4.0 seconds?

(1) 0.67 m   (3) 6.0 m
(2) 1.5 m   (4) 24 m

33 A spring of negligible mass has a spring constant of 50. newtons per meter. If the spring is stretched 0.40 meter from its equilibrium position, how much potential energy is stored in the spring?

(1) 20. J   (3) 8.0 J
(2) 10. J   (4) 4.0 J

34 How much current flows through a 12-ohm flashlight bulb operating at 3.0 volts?

(1) 0.25 A   (3) 3.0 A
(2) 0.75 A   (4) 4.0 A

35 Which diagram below best represents the phenomenon of diffraction?

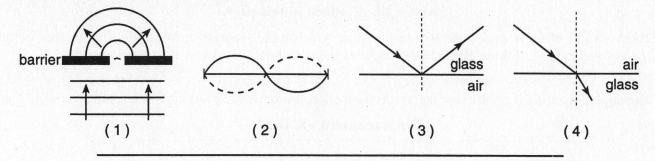

(1)   (2)   (3)   (4)

Part B–1

Answer all questions in this part.

Directions (36–45): For *each* statement or question, write on the separate answer sheet the *number* of the word or expression that, of those given, best completes the statement or answers the question.

36 The displacement-time graph below represents the motion of a cart initially moving forward along a straight line.

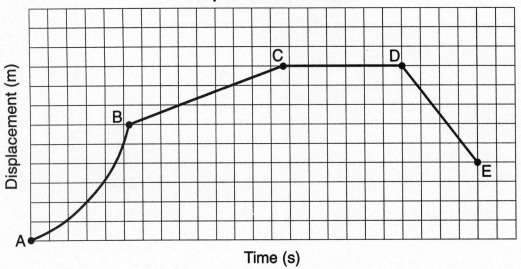

Displacement vs. Time

During which interval is the cart moving forward at constant speed?

(1) *AB*   (3) *CD*

(2) *BC*   (4) *DE*

37 The diagram below represents shallow water waves of wavelength λ passing through two small openings, *A* and *B*, in a barrier.

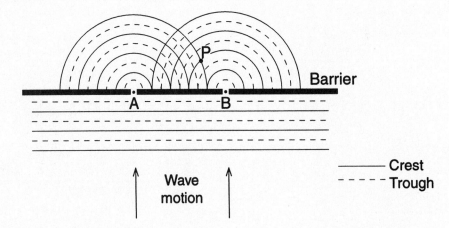

How much longer is the length of path *AP* than the length of path *BP*?

(1) 1λ   (3) 3λ

(2) 2λ   (4) 4λ

Note that question 38 has only three choices.

38 In the diagram below, lamps L_1 and L_2 are connected to a constant voltage power supply.

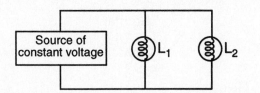

If lamp L_1 burns out, the brightness of L_2 will
(1) decrease
(2) increase
(3) remain the same

39 What is the approximate mass of a pencil?
(1) 5.0×10^{-3} kg   (3) 5.0×10^0 kg
(2) 5.0×10^{-1} kg   (4) 5.0×10^1 kg

40 What is the minimum energy needed to ionize a hydrogen atom in the n = 2 energy state?
(1) 13.6 eV   (3) 3.40 eV
(2) 10.2 eV   (4) 1.89 eV

41 The potential difference applied to a circuit element remains constant as the resistance of the element is varied. Which graph best represents the relationship between power (P) and resistance (R) of this element?

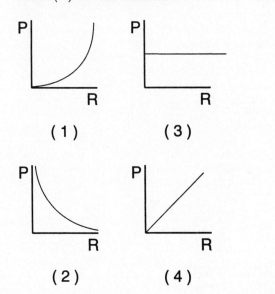

42 Which graph best represents the elastic potential energy stored in a spring (PE_s) as a function of its elongation, x?

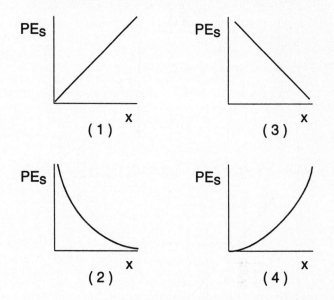

43 Which graph best represents the relationship between the gravitational potential energy of a freely falling object and the object's height above the ground near the surface of Earth?

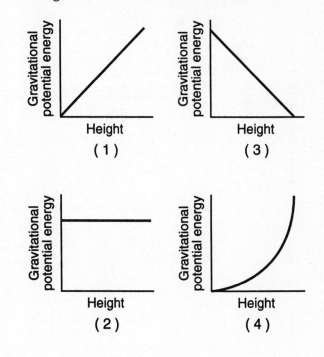

44 A force vector was resolved into two perpendicular components, F_1 and F_2, as shown in the diagram below.

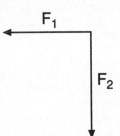

Which vector best represents the original force?

(1)   (3)

(2)   (4)

45 A beam of monochromatic light ($f = 5.09 \times 10^{14}$ hertz) passes through parallel sections of glycerol, medium X, and medium Y as shown in the diagram below.

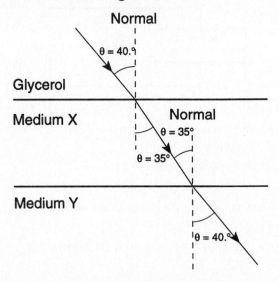

What could medium X and medium Y be?

(1) X could be flint glass and Y could be corn oil.
(2) X could be corn oil and Y could be flint glass.
(3) X could be water and Y could be glycerol.
(4) X could be glycerol and Y could be water.

Directions (46–59): Record your answers in the spaces provided in your answer booklet.

46 The diagram below shows two compasses located near the ends of a bar magnet. The north pole of compass *X* points toward end *A* of the magnet.

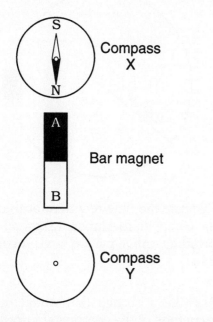

On the diagram provided *in your answer booklet*, draw the correct orientation of the needle of compass *Y* and label its polarity.   [1]

47 A ray of light traveling in air is incident on an air-water boundary as shown below.

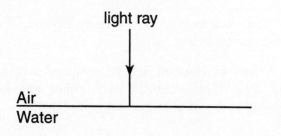

On the diagram provided *in your answer booklet*, draw the path of the ray in the water.   [1]

Base your answers to questions 48 and 49 on the information and diagram below.

A 160.-newton box sits on a 10.-meter-long frictionless plane inclined at an angle of 30.° to the horizontal as shown. Force (*F*) applied to a rope attached to the box causes the box to move with a constant speed up the incline.

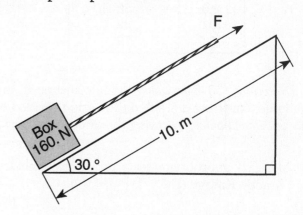

48 On the diagram *in your answer booklet*, construct a vector to represent the weight of the box. Use a metric ruler and a scale of 1.0 centimeter = 40. newtons. Begin the vector at point *B* and label its magnitude in newtons.   [2]

49 Calculate the amount of work done in moving the box from the bottom to the top of the inclined plane. [Show all work, including the equation and substitution with units.]   [2]

Base your answers to questions 50 through 53 on the information and table below.

The table lists the kinetic energy of a 4.0-kilogram mass as it travels in a straight line for 12.0 seconds.

Time (seconds)	Kinetic Energy (joules)
0.0	0.0
2.0	8.0
4.0	18
6.0	32
10.0	32
12.0	32

Directions (50–51): Using the information in the data table, construct a graph on the grid provided *in your answer booklet*, following the directions below.

50 Mark an appropriate scale on the axis labeled "Kinetic Energy (J)." [1]

51 Plot the data points for kinetic energy versus time. [1]

52 Calculate the speed of the mass at 10.0 seconds. [Show all work, including the equation and substitution with units.] [2]

53 Compare the speed of the mass at 6.0 seconds to the speed of the mass at 10.0 seconds. [1]

───────────────

54 Using dimensional analysis, show that the expression v^2/d has the same units as acceleration. [Show all the steps used to arrive at your answer.] [2]

Base your answers to questions 55 through 57 on the information and diagram below.

A 1.50-kilogram cart travels in a horizontal circle of radius 2.40 meters at a constant speed of 4.00 meters per second.

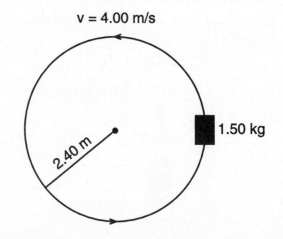

55 Calculate the time required for the cart to make one complete revolution. [Show all work, including the equation and substitution with units.] [2]

56 Describe a change that would quadruple the magnitude of the centripetal force. [1]

57 On the diagram *in your answer booklet*, draw an arrow to represent the direction of the acceleration of the cart in the position shown. Label the arrow *a*. [1]

───────────────

Base your answers to questions 58 and 59 on the information below.

When an electron and its antiparticle (positron) combine, they annihilate each other and become energy in the form of gamma rays.

58 The positron has the same mass as the electron. Calculate how many joules of energy are released when they annihilate. [Show all work, including the equation and substitution with units.] [2]

59 What conservation law prevents this from happening with two electrons? [1]

Part C

Answer all questions in this part.

Directions (60–69): Record your answers in the spaces provided in your answer booklet.

Base your answers to questions 60 and 61 on the diagram below, which shows some energy levels for an atom of an unknown substance.

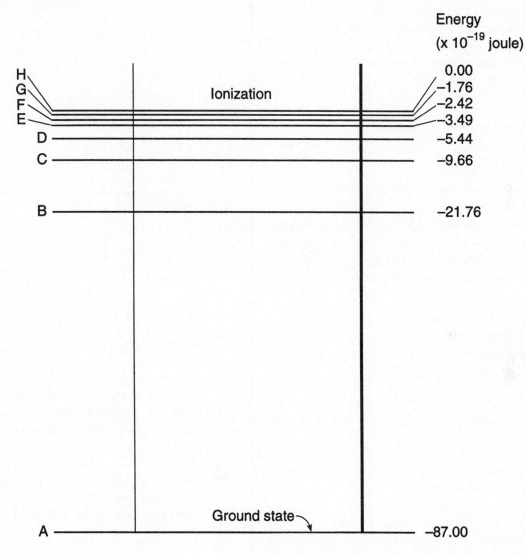

60 Determine the minimum energy necessary for an electron to change from the *B* energy level to the *F* energy level. [1]

61 Calculate the frequency of the photon emitted when an electron in this atom changes from the *F* energy level to the *B* energy level. [Show all work, including the equation and substitution with units.] [2]

Base your answers to questions 62 and 63 on the information below.

An electric circuit contains two 3.0-ohm resistors connected in parallel with a battery. The circuit also contains a voltmeter that reads the potential difference across one of the resistors.

62 In the space provided *in your answer booklet,* draw a diagram of this circuit, using the symbols from the *Reference Tables for Physical Setting/Physics.* [Assume availability of any number of wires of negligible resistance.]   [2]

63 Calculate the total resistance of the circuit. [Show all work, including the equation and substitution with units.]   [2]

_____

64 Explain how to find the coefficient of kinetic friction between a wooden block of unknown mass and a tabletop in the laboratory. Include the following in your explanation:

- Measurements required   [1]
- Equipment needed   [1]
- Procedure   [1]
- Equation(s) needed to calculate the coefficient of friction   [1]

Base your answers to questions 65 and 66 on the information below.

A toaster having a power rating of 1050 watts is operated at 120. volts.

65 Calculate the resistance of the toaster. [Show all work, including the equation and substitution with units.]   [2]

66 The toaster is connected in a circuit protected by a 15-ampere fuse. (The fuse will shut down the circuit if it carries more than 15 amperes.) Is it possible to simultaneously operate the toaster and a microwave oven that requires a current of 10.0 amperes on this circuit? Justify your answer mathematically.   [2]

Base your answers to questions 67 through 69 on the information and diagram below. A monochromatic beam of yellow light, *AB*, is incident upon a Lucite block in air at an angle of 33°.

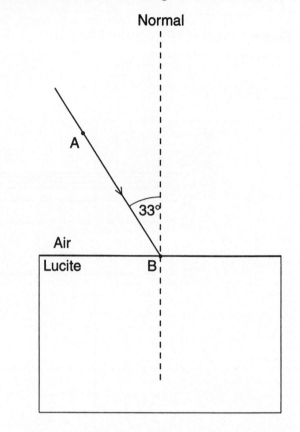

67 Calculate the angle of refraction for incident beam *AB*. [Show all work, including the equation and substitution with units.]   [2]

68 Using a straightedge, a protractor, and your answer from question 67, draw an arrow to represent the path of the refracted beam.   [2]

69 Compare the speed of the yellow light in air to the speed of the yellow light in Lucite.   [1]

46

47

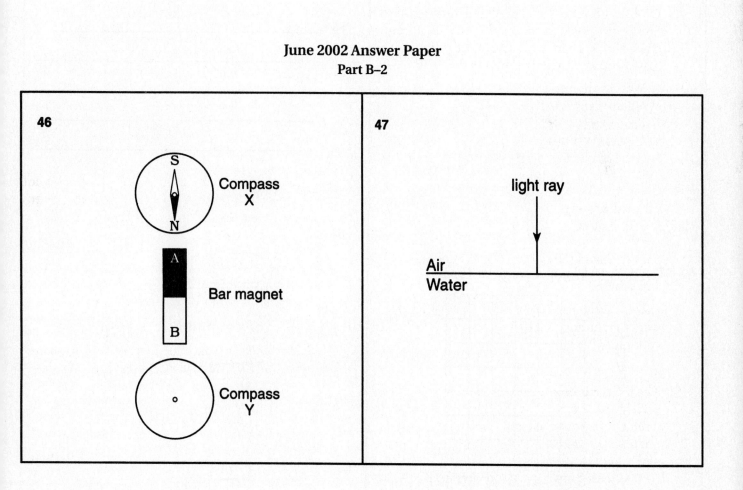

48

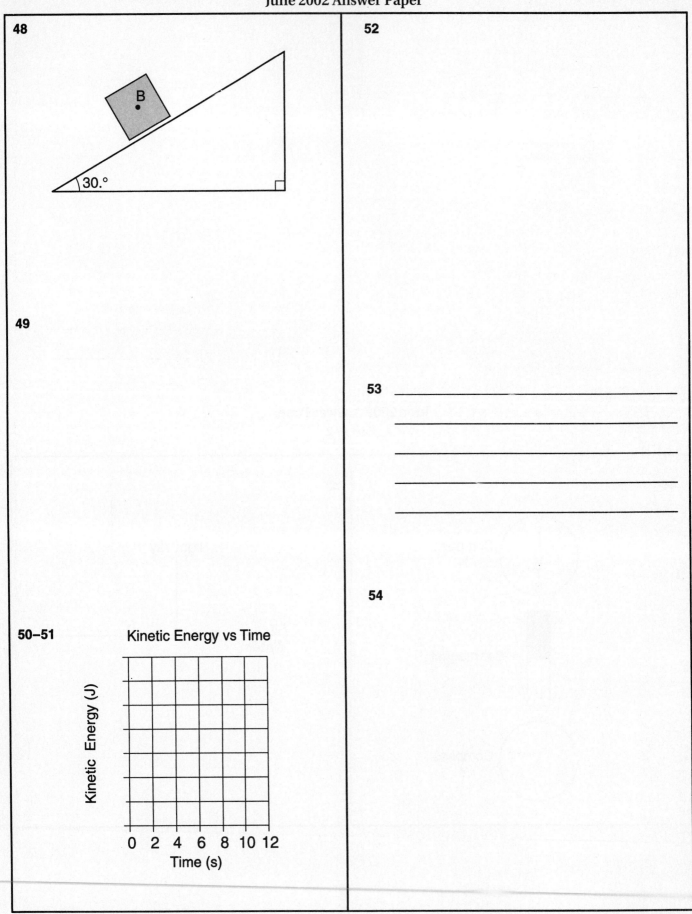

49

50–51

Kinetic Energy vs Time

52

53 _____

_____

_____

_____

_____

54

55

58

56 _____
_____
_____
_____
_____

59 _____
_____

Part C

60 _____ **J**

61

57

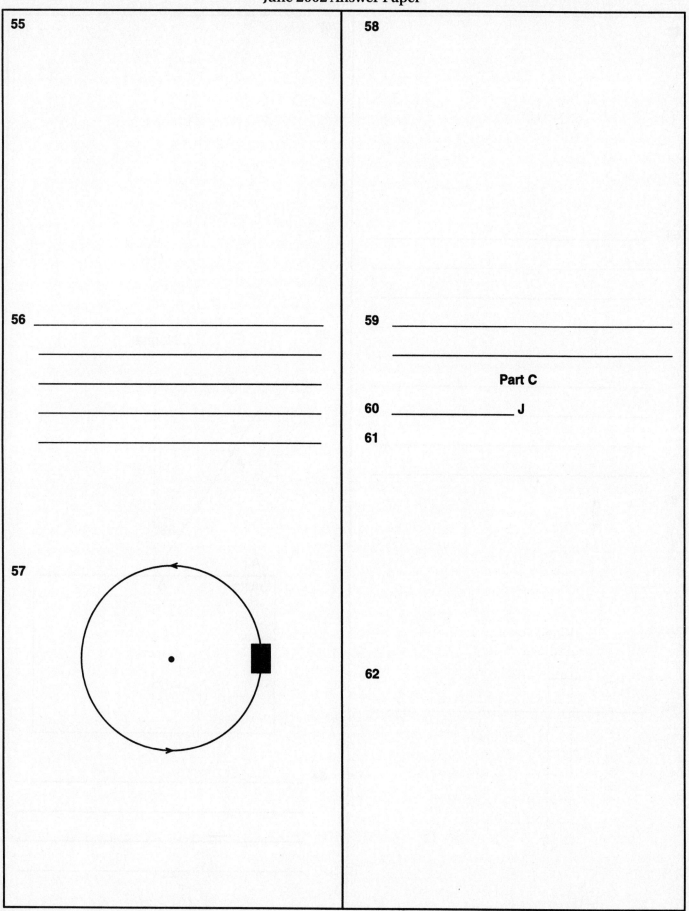

62

63

64 _____

_____

_____

_____

_____

_____

_____

_____

_____

65

66 _____

67

68

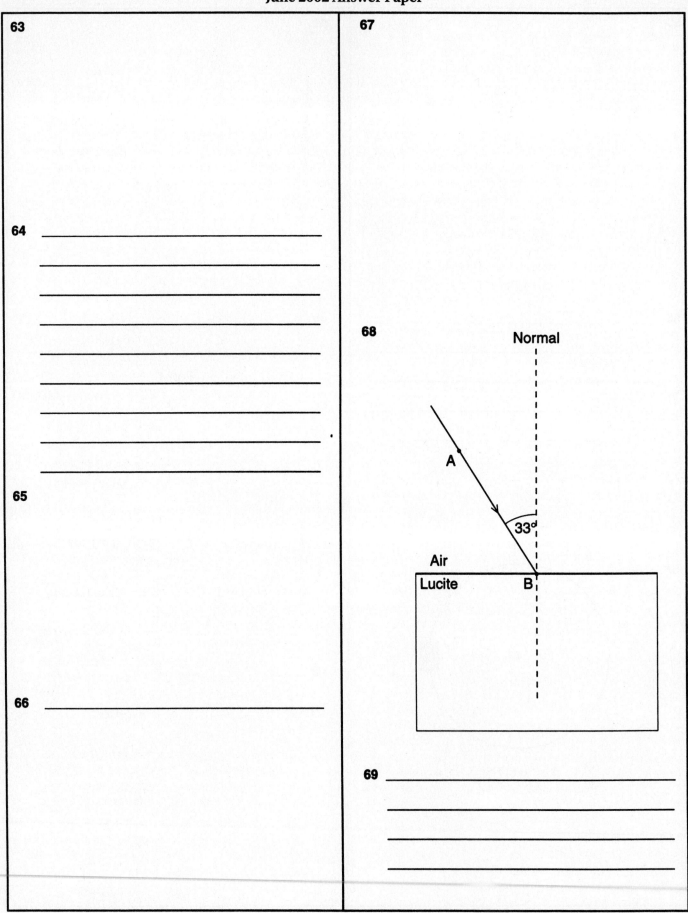

Normal

A

33ᵈ

Air

Lucite   B

69 _____

_____

_____

_____

[d]

Part I

Answer all 55 questions in this part. [65]

Directions (1–55): For *each* statement or question, select the word or expression that, of those given, best completes the statement or answers the question. Record your answer on the separate answer paper in accordance with the directions on the front page of this booklet.

1 What is the total displacement of a student who walks 3 blocks east, 2 blocks north, 1 block west, and then 2 blocks south?

(1) 0　　　　　　　　(3) 2 blocks west
(2) 2 blocks east　　　(4) 8 blocks

2 Which measurement of an average classroom door is closest to 1 meter?

(1) thickness　　　(3) height
(2) width　　　　　(4) surface area

3 A group of bike riders took a 4.0-hour trip. During the first 3.0 hours, they traveled a total of 50. kilometers, but during the last hour they traveled only 10. kilometers. What was the group's average speed for the entire trip?

(1) 15 km/hr　　　(3) 40. km/hr
(2) 30. km/hr　　　(4) 60. km/hr

4 A skier starting from rest skis straight down a slope 50. meters long in 5.0 seconds. What is the magnitude of the acceleration of the skier?

(1) 20. m/s^2　　　(3) 5.0 m/s^2
(2) 9.8 m/s^2　　　(4) 4.0 m/s^2

5 An object falls freely from rest near the surface of Earth. What is the speed of the object after having fallen a distance at 4.90 meters?

(1) 4.90 m/s　　　(3) 24.0 m/s
(2) 9.80 m/s　　　(4) 96.1 m/s

6 Which two terms represent a vector quantity and the scalar quantity of the vector's magnitude, respectively?

(1) acceleration and velocity
(2) weight and force
(3) speed and time
(4) displacement and distance

7 A 4.0-kilogram rock and a 1.0-kilogram stone fall freely from rest from a height of 100 meters. After they fall for 2.0 seconds, the ratio of the rock's speed to the stone's speed is

(1) 1:1　　　(3) 2:1
(2) 1:2　　　(4) 4:1

8 Two concurrent forces have a maximum resultant of 45 newtons and a minimum resultant of 5 newtons. What is the magnitude of each of these forces?

(1) 0 N and 45 N　　　(3) 20. N and 25 N
(2) 5 N and 9 N　　　(4) 0 N and 50. N

9 In the diagram below, a box is on a frictionless horizontal surface with forces F_1 and F_2 acting as shown.

Frictionless surface

If the magnitude of F_1 is greater than the magnitude of F_2, then the box is

(1) moving at constant speed in the direction of F_1
(2) moving at constant speed in the direction of F_2
(3) accelerating in the direction of F_1
(4) accelerating in the direction of F_2

10 When a satellite is a distance R from the center of Earth, the force due to gravity on the satellite is F. What is the force due to gravity on the satellite when its distance from the center of Earth is $3R$?

(1) $\dfrac{F}{9}$　　　　(3) F

(2) $\dfrac{F}{3}$　　　　(4) $9F$

11 Which two graphs represent the motion of an object on which the net force is zero?

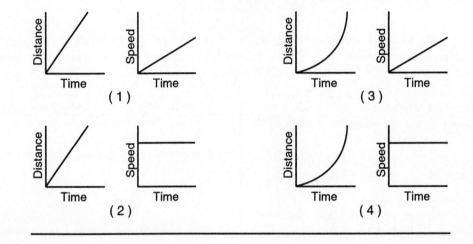

12 The table below lists the coefficients of kinetic friction for four materials sliding over steel.

Material	Coefficient of Kinetic Friction
aluminum	0.47
brass	0.44
copper	0.36
steel	0.57

A 10.-kilogram block of each of these materials is pulled horizontally across a steel floor at constant velocity. Which block requires the *smallest* applied force to keep it moving at constant velocity?

(1) aluminum   (3) copper
(2) brass   (4) steel

13 The magnitude of the force that a baseball bat exerts on a ball is 50. newtons. The magnitude of the force that the ball exerts on the bat is

(1) 5.0 N   (3) 50. N
(2) 10. N   (4) 250 N

14 A bullet traveling at 5.0×10^2 meters per second is brought to rest by an impulse of 50. newton•seconds. What is the mass of the bullet?

(1) 1.0×10^{-2} kg   (3) 1.0×10^1 kg
(2) 1.0×10^{-1} kg   (4) 2.5×10^4 kg

15 Which graph best represents the relationship between acceleration due to gravity and mass for objects near the surface of Earth? [Neglect air resistance.]

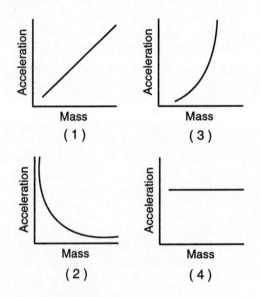

16 What is an essential characteristic of an object in equilibrium?

(1) zero velocity
(2) zero acceleration
(3) zero potential energy
(4) zero kinetic energy

17 The diagram below shows two carts that were initially at rest on a horizontal, frictionless surface being pushed apart when a compressed spring attached to one of the carts is released. Cart A has a mass of 3.0 kilograms and cart B has a mass of 5.0 kilograms.

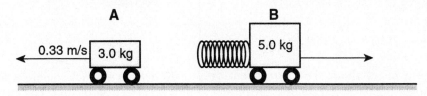

If the speed of cart A is 0.33 meter per second after the spring is released, what is the approximate speed of cart B after the spring is released?

(1) 0.12 m/s   (3) 0.33 m/s

(2) 0.20 m/s   (4) 0.55 m/s

18 Which graph best represents the relationship between the kinetic energy of a moving object and its velocity?

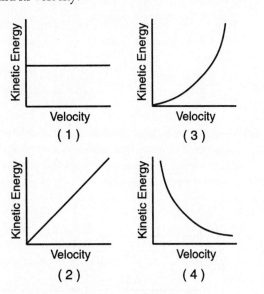

19 How much work is done on a downhill skier by an average braking force of 9.8×10^2 newtons to stop her in a distance of 10. meters?

(1) 1.0×10^1 J   (3) 1.0×10^3 J

(2) 9.8×10^1 J   (4) 9.8×10^3 J

20 A spring has a spring constant of 120 newtons per meter. How much potential energy is stored in the spring as it is stretched 0.20 meter?

(1) 2.4 J   (3) 12 J

(2) 4.8 J   (4) 24 J

21 The graph below shows the relationship between the elongation of a spring and the force applied to the spring causing it to stretch.

Elongation vs. Applied Force

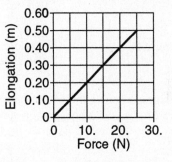

What is the spring constant for this spring?

(1) 0.020 N/m   (3) 25 N/m

(2) 2.0 N/m   (4) 50. N/m

22 Which quantity and unit are correctly paired?

(1) velocity — m/s^2

(2) momentum — $\dfrac{kg \cdot m}{s^2}$

(3) energy — $\dfrac{kg \cdot m^2}{s^2}$

(4) work — kg/m

23 A 10.-newton force is required to move a 3.0-kilogram box at constant speed. How much power is required to move the box 8.0 meters in 2.0 seconds?

(1) 40. W   (3) 15 W

(2) 20. W   (4) 12 W

24 A 0.10-kilogram ball dropped vertically from a height of 1.00 meter above the floor bounces back to a height of 0.80 meter. The mechanical energy lost by the ball as it bounces is

(1) 0.080 J   (3) 0.30 J
(2) 0.20 J   (4) 0.78 J

25 The diagram below shows the arrangement of three charged hollow metal spheres, A, B, and C. The arrows indicate the direction of the electric forces acting between the spheres. At least two of the spheres are positively charged.

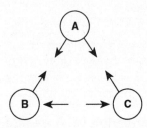

Which sphere, if any, could be negatively charged?

(1) sphere A (3) sphere C
(2) sphere B (4) no sphere

26 The diagram below shows proton P located at point A near a positively charged sphere.

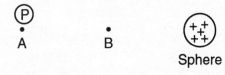

If 6.4×10^{-19} joule of work is required to move the proton from point A to point B, the potential difference between A and B is

(1) 6.4×10^{-19} V   (3) 6.4 V
(2) 4.0×10^{-19} V   (4) 4.0 V

27 An electrostatic force of magnitude F exists between two metal spheres having identical charge q. The distance between their centers is r. Which combination of changes would produce *no* change in the electrostatic force between the spheres?

(1) doubling q on one sphere while doubling r
(2) doubling q on both spheres while doubling r
(3) doubling q on one sphere while halving r
(4) doubling q on both spheres while halving r

28 What is the magnitude of the electrostatic force acting on an electron located in an electric field having a strength of 5.0×10^3 newtons per coulomb?

(1) 3.1×10^{22} N   (3) 8.0×10^{-16} N
(2) 5.0×10^3 N   (4) 3.2×10^{-23} N

29 A charge of 5.0 coulombs moves through a circuit in 0.50 second. The current in the circuit is

(1) 2.5 A   (3) 7.0 A
(2) 5.0 A   (4) 10. A

30 An operating electric iron draws a current of 5 amperes and has a resistance of 20 ohms. The amount of energy used by the iron in 40 seconds is

(1) 1×10^2 J   (3) 4×10^3 J
(2) 5×10^2 J   (4) 2×10^4 J

31 What is the net static electric charge on a metal sphere having an excess of +3 elementary charges?

(1) 1.60×10^{-19} C   (3) 3.00×10^0 C
(2) 4.80×10^{-19} C   (4) 4.80×10^{19} C

32 Which graph best represents the relationship between the potential difference across a conductor and the current through the conductor at constant temperature?

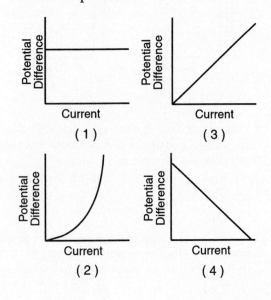

33 Which diagram below best represents the magnetic field near a bar magnet?

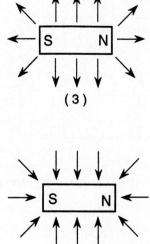

34 Which diagram shows correct current direction in a segment of an electric circuit?

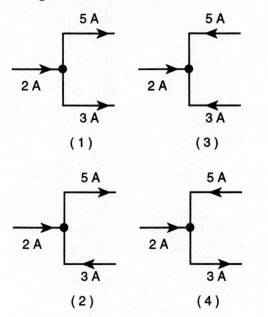

35 While operating at 120 volts, an electric toaster has a resistance of 15 ohms. The power used by the toaster is

(1) 8.0 W   (3) 960 W
(2) 120 W   (4) 1,800 W

36 In the circuit shown below, voltmeter V_2 reads 80. volts.

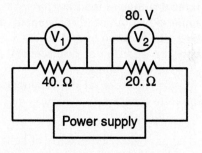

What is the reading of voltmeter V_1?

(1) 160 V   (3) 40. V
(2) 80. V   (4) 20. V

37 A physics student is given three 12-ohm resistors with instructions to create the circuit that would have the lowest possible resistance. The correct circuit would be a

(1) series circuit with an equivalent resistance of 36 Ω
(2) series circuit with an equivalent resistance of 4.0 Ω
(3) parallel circuit with an equivalent resistance of 36 Ω
(4) parallel circuit with an equivalent resistance of 4.0 Ω

38 Two resistors are connected to a source of voltage as shown in the diagram below.

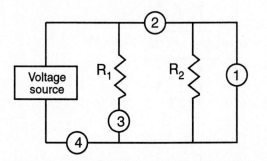

At which position should an ammeter be placed to measure the current passing only through resistor R_1?

(1) 1   (3) 3
(2) 2   (4) 4

39 Two points on a transverse wave that have the same magnitude of displacement from equilibrium are in phase if the points also have the

(1) same direction of displacement and the same direction of motion
(2) same direction of displacement and the opposite direction of motion
(3) opposite direction of displacement and the same direction of motion
(4) opposite direction of displacement and the opposite direction of motion

40 The diagram below shows a ray of light passing from medium X into air.

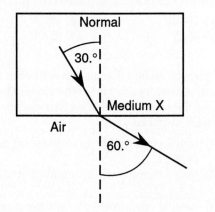

What is the absolute index of refraction of medium X?

(1) 0.500   (3) 1.73
(2) 2.00   (4) 0.577

41 What is the frequency of a wave if its period is 0.25 second?

(1) 1.0 Hz   (3) 12 Hz
(2) 0.25 Hz   (4) 4.0 Hz

42 What occurs when light passes from water into flint glass?

(1) Its speed decreases, its wavelength becomes shorter, and its frequency remains the same.
(2) Its speed decreases, its wavelength becomes shorter, and its frequency increases.
(3) Its speed increases, its wavelength becomes longer, and its frequency remains the same.
(4) Its speed increases, its wavelength becomes longer, and its frequency decreases.

43 The diagram below shows straight wave fronts passing through an opening in a barrier.

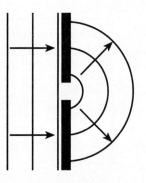

This wave phenomenon is called

(1) reflection   (3) polarizaton
(2) refraction   (4) diffraction

44 The speed of light in a material is 2.50×10^8 meters per second. What is the absolute index of refraction of the material?

(1) 1.20   (3) 7.50
(2) 2.50   (4) 0.833

45 An opera singer's voice is able to break a thin crystal glass when the singer's voice and the vibrating glass have the same

(1) frequency   (3) amplitude
(2) speed   (4) wavelength

46 The periodic wave in the diagram below has a frequency of 40. hertz.

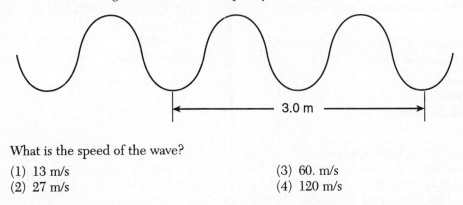

What is the speed of the wave?

(1) 13 m/s
(2) 27 m/s

(3) 60. m/s
(4) 120 m/s

47 The diagram below represents a rope along which two pulses of equal amplitude, A, approach point P.

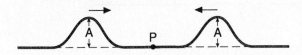

As the two pulses pass through point P, the maximum vertical displacement of the rope at point P will be

(1) A   (3) 0

(2) 2A   (4) $\frac{A}{2}$

48 As shown in the diagram below, a transverse wave is moving with velocity v along a rope.

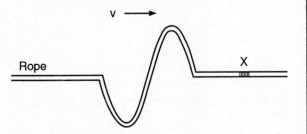

In which direction will segment X move as the wave passes through it?

(1) down, only
(2) up, only
(3) down, then up, then down
(4) up, then down, then up

49 How many nodes are represented in the standing wave diagram below?

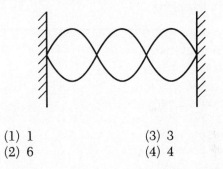

(1) 1
(2) 6

(3) 3
(4) 4

50 Which phenomenon can *not* be exhibited by longitudinal waves?

(1) reflection
(2) refraction

(3) diffraction
(4) polarization

51 An electron in a hydrogen atom drops from the $n = 3$ energy level to the $n = 2$ energy level. The energy of the emitted photon is

(1) 1.51 eV
(2) 1.89 eV

(3) 3.40 eV
(4) 4.91 eV

52 What is the energy of a photon with a frequency of 5.00×10^{14} hertz?

(1) 3.32 eV
(2) 3.20×10^{-6} eV

(3) 3.00×10^{48} J
(4) 3.32×10^{-19} J

Note that questions 53 through 55 have only three choices.

53 If the diameter of a wire were decreased, its electrical resistance would

(1) decrease
(2) increase
(3) remain the same

54 An astronomer on Earth studying light coming from a star notes that the observed light frequencies are lower than the actual emitted frequencies. The astronomer concludes that the distance between the star and Earth is

(1) decreasing
(2) increasing
(3) unchanging

55 Compared to the wavelength of red light, the wavelength of yellow light is

(1) shorter
(2) longer
(3) the same

Part II

This part consists of six groups, each containing ten questions. Each group tests an optional area of the course. Choose two of these six groups. Be sure that you answer all ten questions in each group chosen. Record the answers to the questions in accordance with the directions on the front page of this booklet. [20]

Group 1 — Motion in a Plane

If you choose this group, be sure to answer questions 56–65.

Base your answers to question 56 through 58 on the information and diagram below.

A ball is thrown horizontally with an initial velocity of 20.0 meters per second from the top of a tower 60.0 meters high.

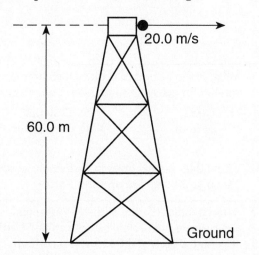

56 What is the initial vertical velocity of the ball?

(1) 0 m/s   (3) 20.0 m/s
(2) 9.81 m/s   (4) 60.0 m/s

57 What is the approximate total time required for the ball to reach the ground? [Neglect air resistance.]

(1) 12.2 s   (3) 3.00 s
(2) 2.04 s   (4) 3.50 s

58 What is the horizontal velocity of the ball just before it reaches the ground? [Neglect air resistance.]

(1) 9.81 m/s   (3) 34.3 m/s
(2) 20.0 m/s   (4) 68.6 m/s

Base your answers to questions 59 and 60 on the information and diagram below.

A 60.-kilogram car travels clockwise in a horizontal circle of radius 10. meters at 5.0 meters per second.

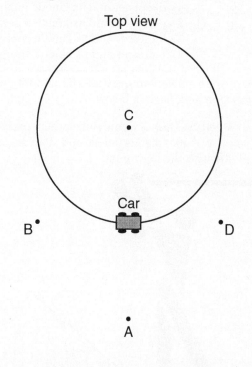

59 The centripetal acceleration of the car at the position shown is directed toward point

(1) A   (3) C
(2) B   (4) D

60 The magnitude of the centripetal force acting on the car is

(1) 590 N   (3) 30. N
(2) 150 N   (4) 2.5 N

61 The diagram below represents the path of Earth around the Sun.

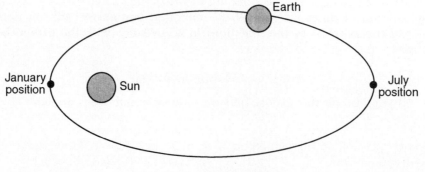

(not drawn to scale)

As Earth travels in its orbit from its January position to its July position, the potential energy of Earth

(1) decreases and its kinetic energy decreases
(2) decreases and its kinetic energy increases
(3) increases and its kinetic energy decreases
(4) increases and its kinetic energy increases

Base your answers to questions 62 and 63 on the information and diagram below

A golf ball leaves a golf club with an initial velocity of 40.0 meters per second at an angle of 40.° with the horizontal.

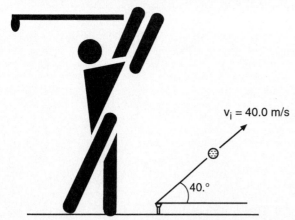

v_i = 40.0 m/s

40.°

62 What is the vertical component of the golf ball's initial velocity?

(1) 25.7 m/s   (3) 40.0 m/s
(2) 30.6 m/s   (4) 61.3 m/s

63 What is the total horizontal distance traveled by the golf ball during the first 2.50 seconds of its flight?

(1) 100. m   (3) 64.3 m
(2) 76.6 m   (4) 40.0 m

64 What is the period of orbit of a communications satellite in geosynchronous orbit about Earth?

(1) 1 year   (3) 12 hours
(2) 24 hours   (4) 60 minutes

65 The table below gives information about the Moon and a satellite orbiting Earth.

R_m = mean radius of orbit of the Moon around Earth
R_s = mean radius of orbit of satellite around Earth
T_m = period of orbit of the Moon around Earth
T_s = period of orbit of satellite around Earth

Which equation correctly relates these quantities?

(1) $R_m T_m = R_s T_s$ (3) $\dfrac{R_m{}^2}{T_m} = \dfrac{R_s{}^2}{T_s}$

(2) $R_m T_s = R_s T_m$ (4) $\dfrac{R_m{}^3}{T_m{}^2} = \dfrac{R_s{}^3}{T_s{}^2}$

Group 2 — Internal Energy

If you choose this group, be sure to answer questions 66–75.

66 The diagram below represents an experiment in which a student placed a 0.030-kilogram lead cube in a beaker of water at 20.°C and then heated the beaker until the water began to boil.

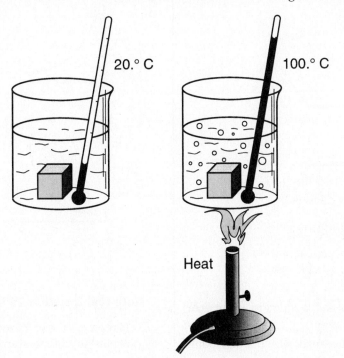

20.° C   100.° C

Heat

The maximum amount of heat absorbed by the lead cube during the experiment was approximately

(1) 0.31 kJ   (3) 60. kJ

(2) 10. kJ   (4) 790 kJ

---

67 Absolute zero is best described as the temperature at which

(1) water freezes at standard pressure
(2) water is at its triple point
(3) the molecules of a substance have maximum kinetic energy
(4) the molecules of a substance have minimum kinetic energy

68 A temperature change of 20. Celsius degrees is equal to a temperature change of

(1) 20. Kelvins   (3) 253 Kelvins
(2) 120. Kelvins   (4) 293 Kelvins

69 Heat will always flow from object A to object B if object B has a lower

(1) mass   (3) temperature
(2) total energy   (4) specific heat

70 Equal amounts of heat energy are given off by 1.0-kilogram samples of aluminum, iron, platinum, and zinc, all initially at 100.°C. Which sample has the greatest decrease in temperature?

(1) aluminum   (3) platinum
(2) iron   (4) zinc

71 The graph below shows the temperature of 3.0 kilograms of a pure substance initially in the solid phase as heat is added to it at a constant rate.

Temperature vs. Heat Added

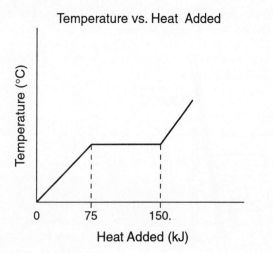

The substance is most likely

(1) alcohol   (3) copper
(2) silver   (4) lead

72 As a large quantity of salt is added to a container of boiling water, the water

(1) stops boiling because the boiling point decreases
(2) stops boiling because the boiling point increases
(3) boils faster because the boiling point decreases
(4) boils faster because the boiling point increases

73 The total effect of all the processes that occur in the universe is an increase in

(1) entropy   (3) order
(2) temperature   (4) energy

74 Which graph best represents the relationship between volume V and absolute temperature T for a fixed mass of an ideal gas at constant pressure?

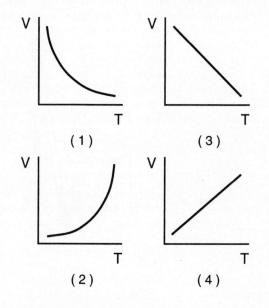

Note that question 75 has only three choices.

75 As the pressure of a fixed mass of gas is increased at constant temperature, the density of that gas

(1) decreases
(2) increases
(3) remains the same

Group 3 — Electromagnetic Applications

If you choose this group, be sure to answer questions 76–85.

76 If the current in an ammeter's coil is doubled, the resulting torque on the coil will be

(1) unchanged   (3) halved
(2) doubled   (4) quadrupled

77 An operating electric motor induces an EMF in the armature that opposes the applied potential difference. This phenomenon is an example of conservation of

(1) inertia   (3) momentum
(2) electric charge   (4) energy

78 The rate of thermionic emission from a surface increases as the surface's

(1) temperature decreases
(2) thickness decreases
(3) temperature increases
(4) thickness increases

79 An electron moves at 2.0×10^6 meters per second perpendicular to a magnetic field having a flux density of 2.0 teslas. What is the magnitude of the magnetic force on the electron?

(1) 1.0×10^{-6} N   (3) 3.6×10^{-24} N
(2) 6.4×10^{-13} N   (4) 4.0×10^6 N

80 The Millikan oil drop experiment determined the smallest unit of

(1) mass
(2) weight
(3) electric charge
(4) electric field strength

81 Which device transforms mechanical energy into electrical energy?

(1) generator
(2) motor
(3) transformer
(4) mass spectrometer

82 Power would most effectively be supplied to the primary coil of a step-up transformer by

(1) an ac generator   (3) a battery
(2) a dc generator   (4) an ac motor

83 The 200.-turn primary coil of a transformer is connected to a 120-volt line. How many turns must the secondary coil of the transformer have if it is to provide 240 volts? [Assume 100% efficiency.]

(1) 100   (3) 1,200
(2) 400   (4) 2,400

84 Which device is used in the ignition system of a car to induce a time-varying potential difference from the car's battery?

(1) electric motor   (3) transistor
(2) electromagnet   (4) induction coil

85 A helium-neon laser emits energy in the visible red region in the form of

(1) alpha particles   (3) electrons
(2) gamma rays   (4) photons

Group 4 — Geometric Optics

If you choose this group, be sure to answer questions 86–95.

86 The diagram below shows the letter P in front of a plane mirror.

Mirror

Which diagram best represents the image of P produced by the plane mirror?

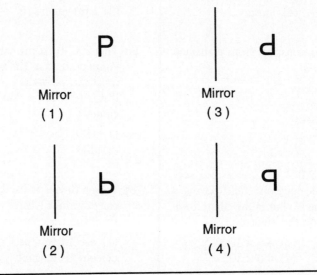

87 A student stands 2.0 meters in front of a vertical plane mirror. As the student walks toward the mirror, the image

(1) decreases in size and remains virtual
(2) decreases in size and remains real
(3) remains the same size and remains virtual
(4) remains the same size and remains real

88 An incident light ray travels parallel to the principal axis of a concave spherical mirror. After reflecting from the mirror, the light ray will travel

(1) through the mirror's principal focus
(2) through the mirror's center of curvature
(3) parallel to the mirror's principal axis
(4) normal to the mirror's principal axis

89 The focal length of a concave spherical mirror is 0.060 meter. What is the radius of curvature of the mirror?

(1) 0.060 m   (3) 8.3 m
(2) 0.12 m   (4) 17 m

90 An image that is 1.0×10^{-2} meter tall is formed on a screen behind a converging lens when an object 2.0 meters tall is placed 8.0 meters in front of the lens. What is the distance from the lens to the screen?

(1) 2.5×10^{-3} m   (3) 2.5×10^{-1} m
(2) 4.0×10^{-2} m   (4) 4.0×10^{-1} m

91 The diagram below shows an object placed between 1 and 2 focal lengths from a converging lens.

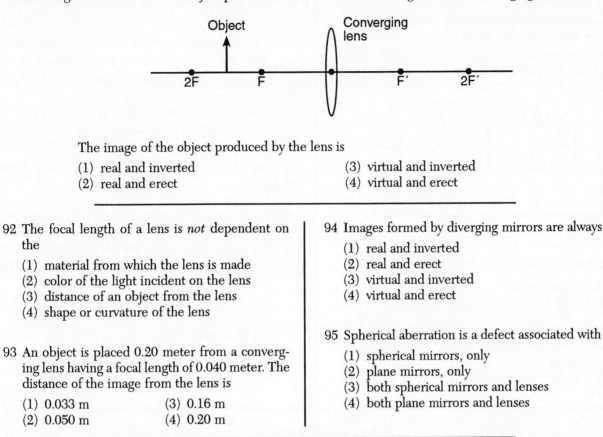

The image of the object produced by the lens is

(1) real and inverted
(2) real and erect
(3) virtual and inverted
(4) virtual and erect

92 The focal length of a lens is *not* dependent on the

(1) material from which the lens is made
(2) color of the light incident on the lens
(3) distance of an object from the lens
(4) shape or curvature of the lens

93 An object is placed 0.20 meter from a converging lens having a focal length of 0.040 meter. The distance of the image from the lens is

(1) 0.033 m   (3) 0.16 m
(2) 0.050 m   (4) 0.20 m

94 Images formed by diverging mirrors are always

(1) real and inverted
(2) real and erect
(3) virtual and inverted
(4) virtual and erect

95 Spherical aberration is a defect associated with

(1) spherical mirrors, only
(2) plane mirrors, only
(3) both spherical mirrors and lenses
(4) both plane mirrors and lenses

Group 5 — Solid State

If you choose this group, be sure to answer questions 96–105.

96 The conductivity of a material is equivalent to

(1) its resistivity
(2) the square of its resistivity
(3) the reciprocal of its resistivity
(4) the square of the reciprocal of its resistivity

97 Which model most successfully explains conduction in solids?

(1) electron-cloud model
(2) electron-sea model
(3) band model
(4) doping model

98 As a donor material, arsenic provides a semiconducting material with extra

(1) electrons   (3) protons
(2) holes   (4) neutrons

99 The diagram below shows a circuit with a battery applying a potential difference across an *N*-type semiconductor.

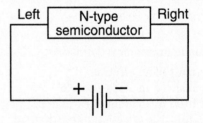

The majority charge carriers in the semiconductor are

(1) negative electrons moving to the right
(2) negative electrons moving to the left
(3) positive holes moving to the right
(4) positive holes moving to the left

100 Pulsating direct current results when a *P-N* junction is connected to

    (1) a battery
    (2) an oscilloscope
    (3) a source of direct current voltage
    (4) a source of alternating current

Base your answers to questions 101 and 102 on the diagram below, which represents a silicon semiconductor.

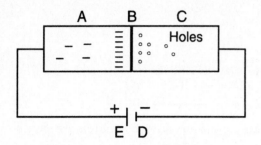

101 In the diagram, *C* represents the

    (1) *N*-type silicon   (3) anode
    (2) *P*-type silicon   (4) diode

102 The *P-N* junction in the diagram is biased

    (1) reverse   (3) *A* to *E*
    (2) forward   (4) *C* to *D*

103 The primary source of holes in a *P-N-P* transistor is the

    (1) *N*-type base   (3) *N*-type emitter
    (2) *P*-type base   (4) *P*-type emitter

104 In a working transistor circuit, as the emitter-base current is increased, the collector current

    (1) decreases a small amount
    (2) decreases a large amount
    (3) increases a small amount
    (4) increases a large amount

Note that question 105 has only three choices.

105 An *N*-type semiconductor and a *P*-type semiconductor are joined to form a diode. Compared to the total number of electrons in the semiconductors before joining, the number of electrons in the diode is

    (1) fewer
    (2) greater
    (3) the same

Group 6 — Nuclear Energy

If you choose this group, be sure to answer questions 106–115.

106 If nitrogen nuclei are bombarded with alpha particles they can be changed into oxygen nuclei. This phenomenon is known as

    (1) nuclear fission
    (2) nuclear fusion
    (3) artificial transmutation
    (4) particle scattering

107 One atomic mass unit is defined as

    (1) the mass of an electron
    (2) the mass of an alpha particle
    (3) the mass of an atom of carbon-12
    (4) $\frac{1}{12}$ the mass of an atom of carbon-12

108 According to the Uranium Disintegration Series, which nuclide is an isotope of lead (Pb)?

    (1) $^{206}_{82}\text{Pb}$ (3) $^{214}_{84}\text{Pb}$
    (2) $^{214}_{83}\text{Pb}$ (4) $^{222}_{86}\text{Pb}$

109 The nuclei of all the atoms in a single nuclide have

    (1) the same number of neutrons and the same number of protons
    (2) the same number of neutrons, but different numbers of protons
    (3) different numbers of neutrons, but the same number of protons
    (4) different numbers of neutrons and different numbers of protons

110 What occurs when an atom emits gamma radiation?

(1) The excited nucleus changes to a more stable state by absorbing a photon.
(2) The excited nucleus changes to a more stable state by emitting a photon.
(3) The stable nucleus changes to an excited state by emitting a photon.
(4) The stable nucleus changes to an excited state by absorbing a photon.

111 What particle is represented by X in the nuclear reaction $^{9}_{4}\text{Be} + ^{4}_{2}\text{He} \rightarrow ^{12}_{6}\text{C} + X$?

(1) $^{0}_{-1}\text{e}$ (3) $^{1}_{0}\text{n}$

(2) $^{1}_{1}\text{H}$ (4) $^{2}_{1}\text{H}$

112 The half-life of a particular radioactive material is 6.0 hours. What fraction of a sample of the material would remain after 1 day?

(1) $\frac{1}{4}$ (3) $\frac{3}{8}$

(2) $\frac{2}{3}$ (4) $\frac{1}{16}$

113 Which device can be used to detect subatomic particles that exit nuclei?

(1) Van de Graaff generator
(2) Geiger counter
(3) linear accelerator
(4) cyclotron

114 In a nuclear reactor, which substance can be used as both the moderator and the coolant?

(1) cadmium   (3) water
(2) boron   (4) uranium

115 If the nucleus of an atom emits a positron, the atomic number of the atom will

(1) decrease by one
(2) increase by one
(3) remain unchanged
(4) decrease by two

Part III

You must answer *all* questions in this part. Record your answers in the spaces provided on the separate answer paper. Pen or pencil may be used. [15]

Base your answers to questions 116 through 119 on the information, diagram, and data table below.

The diagram shows a light string attached to mass m forming a pendulum of length ℓ. One complete vibration of the pendulum consists of mass m moving from position A to position B and back to position A. The data table shows the results of an experiment measuring the time for 10 complete vibrations of the pendulum for various pendulum lengths.

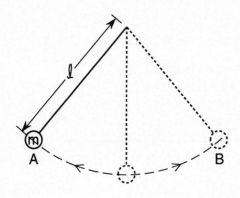

Pendulum Length (meters)	Time for 10 Vibrations (seconds)
0	0
0.2	9
0.5	14
1.0	20.
1.5	25
2.0	28
2.5	32

Using the information in the data table, construct a graph on the grid provided *on your answer paper*, following the directions below. The grid below is provided for practice purposes only. Be sure your final answer appears *on your answer paper*.

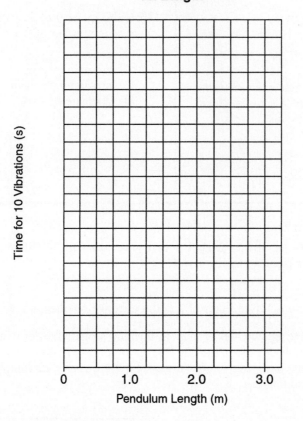

116 Mark an appropriate scale on the axis labeled "Time for 10 Vibrations."   [1]

117 Plot the data points for time for 10 vibrations versus length.   [1]

118 Draw the best-fit curve.   [1]

119 Determine the period of the 1.0-meter pendulum.   [1]

Base your answers to questions 120 through 122 on the information and diagram below. The diagram below is provided for practice purposes only. Be sure your final answer appears *on your answer paper*.

A 10.0-kilogram block slides at constant speed down a plane inclined at 20.° to the horizontal, as shown.

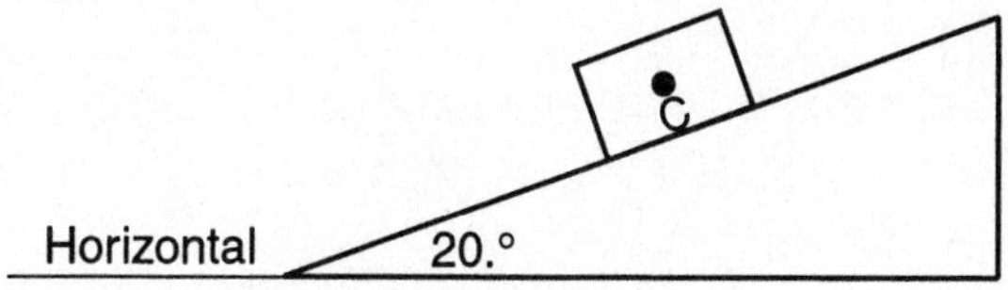

120 On the diagram *on your answer paper,* draw an arrow to represent and identify the direction of each of the *three* forces (weight, friction, normal force) acting on the block. Begin *each* arrow at point C and label *each* arrow with the force that it represents.   [3]

121 Determine the weight of the block. [Show all calculations, including the equation and substitution with units.]   [2]

122 In one or more complete sentences, describe the change in the motion of the block as the angle of inclination is increased to 30.°.   [1]

Base your answers to questions 123 through 126 on the information and diagram below. The diagram below is provided for practice purposes only. Be sure your final answer appears *on your answer paper.*

A ray of monochromatic light of frequency 5.00×10^{14} hertz is incident on a mirror and reflected, as shown.

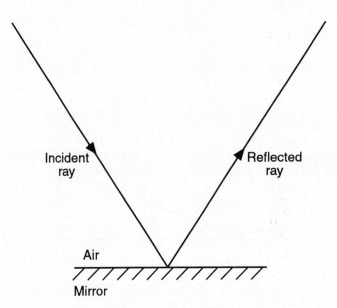

Incident ray

Reflected ray

Air

Mirror

123 Using a protractor and ruler, construct and label the normal to the mirror at the point of incidence on the diagram *on your answer paper.* [1]

124 Using a protractor, measure the angle of incidence to the nearest degree and record the value *on your answer paper.* [1]

125 Determine the wavelength of the ray of light. [Show all calculations, including the equation and substitution with units.] [2]

126 What is the color of the ray of light? [1]

The University of the State of New York

REGENTS HIGH SCHOOL EXAMINATION

PHYSICS

Tuesday, January 22, 2002 — 9:15 a.m. to 12:15 p.m., only

ANSWER PAPER

Student . . . .   Sex: ☐ Female
☐ Male

Teacher . . . .

School . . . .

Record all of your answers on this answer paper in accordance with the instructions on the front page of the test booklet.

Part I (65 credits)

1	1 2 3 4	21	1 2 3 4	41	1 2 3 4
2	1 2 3 4	22	1 2 3 4	42	1 2 3 4
3	1 2 3 4	23	1 2 3 4	43	1 2 3 4
4	1 2 3 4	24	1 2 3 4	44	1 2 3 4
5	1 2 3 4	25	1 2 3 4	45	1 2 3 4
6	1 2 3 4	26	1 2 3 4	46	1 2 3 4
7	1 2 3 4	27	1 2 3 4	47	1 2 3 4
8	1 2 3 4	28	1 2 3 4	48	1 2 3 4
9	1 2 3 4	29	1 2 3 4	49	1 2 3 4
10	1 2 3 4	30	1 2 3 4	50	1 2 3 4
11	1 2 3 4	31	1 2 3 4	51	1 2 3 4
12	1 2 3 4	32	1 2 3 4	52	1 2 3 4
13	1 2 3 4	33	1 2 3 4	53	1 2 3
14	1 2 3 4	34	1 2 3 4	54	1 2 3
15	1 2 3 4	35	1 2 3 4	55	1 2 3
16	1 2 3 4	36	1 2 3 4		
17	1 2 3 4	37	1 2 3 4		
18	1 2 3 4	38	1 2 3 4		
19	1 2 3 4	39	1 2 3 4		
20	1 2 3 4	40	1 2 3 4		

Part II (20 credits)

Answer the questions in only two of the six groups in this part. Be sure to mark the answers to the groups of questions you choose in accordance with the instructions on the front page of the test booklet. Leave blank the four groups of questions you do not choose to answer.

	Group 1 Motion in a Plane					Group 3 Electromagnetic Applications					Group 5 Solid State			
56	1	2	3	4	76	1	2	3	4	96	1	2	3	4
57	1	2	3	4	77	1	2	3	4	97	1	2	3	4
58	1	2	3	4	78	1	2	3	4	98	1	2	3	4
59	1	2	3	4	79	1	2	3	4	99	1	2	3	4
60	1	2	3	4	80	1	2	3	4	100	1	2	3	4
61	1	2	3	4	81	1	2	3	4	101	1	2	3	4
62	1	2	3	4	82	1	2	3	4	102	1	2	3	4
63	1	2	3	4	83	1	2	3	4	103	1	2	3	4
64	1	2	3	4	84	1	2	3	4	104	1	2	3	4
65	1	2	3	4	85	1	2	3	4	105	1	2	3	

	Group 2 Internal Energy					Group 4 Geometric Optics					Group 6 Nuclear Energy			
66	1	2	3	4	86	1	2	3	4	106	1	2	3	4
67	1	2	3	4	87	1	2	3	4	107	1	2	3	4
68	1	2	3	4	88	1	2	3	4	108	1	2	3	4
69	1	2	3	4	89	1	2	3	4	109	1	2	3	4
70	1	2	3	4	90	1	2	3	4	110	1	2	3	4
71	1	2	3	4	91	1	2	3	4	111	1	2	3	4
72	1	2	3	4	92	1	2	3	4	112	1	2	3	4
73	1	2	3	4	93	1	2	3	4	113	1	2	3	4
74	1	2	3	4	94	1	2	3	4	114	1	2	3	4
75	1	2	3		95	1	2	3	4	115	1	2	3	4

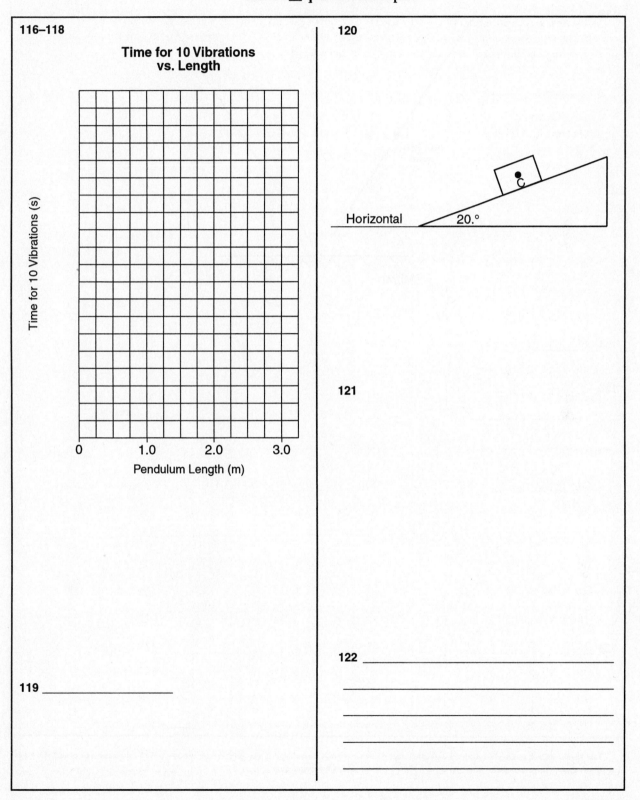

116–118

Time for 10 Vibrations vs. Length

Time for 10 Vibrations (s)

Pendulum Length (m)

120

Horizontal   20.°

C

121

122 _____

_____

_____

_____

_____

119 _____

123

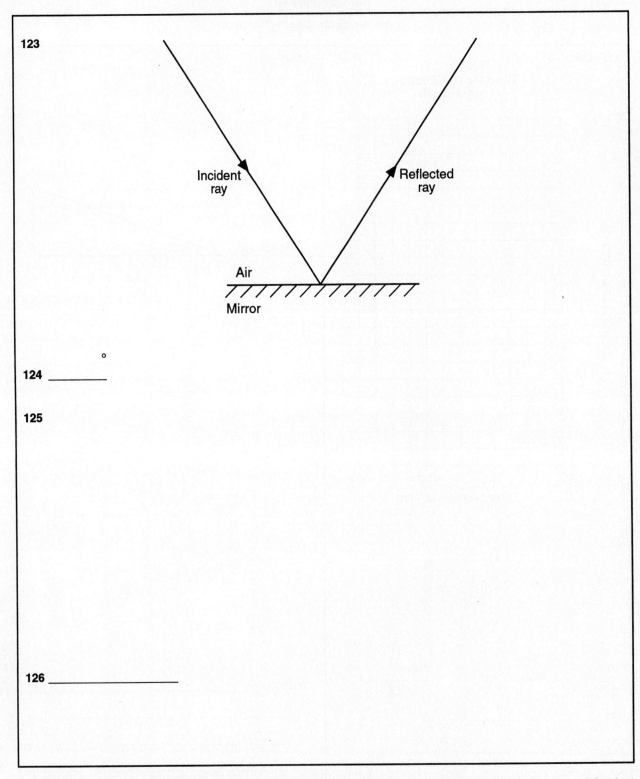

Incident
ray

Reflected
ray

Air

Mirror

124 _____ °

125

126 _____

Additional Reference Information

VALUES OF TRIGONOMETRIC FUNCTIONS

Angle	Sine	Cosine	Angle	Sine	Cosine
5°	.0872	.9962	50°	.7660	.6428
10°	.1736	.9848	55°	.8192	.5736
15°	.2588	.9659	60°	.8660	.5000
20°	.3420	.9397	65°	.9063	.4226
25°	.4226	.9063	70°	.9397	.3420
30°	.5000	.8660	75°	.9659	.2588
35°	.5736	.8192	80°	.9848	.1736
40°	.6428	.7660	85°	.9962	.0872
45°	.7071	.7071	90°	1.0000	.0000

MOTION IN A PLANE

$$v_{iy} = v_i \sin \theta$$

$$v_{ix} = v_i \cos \theta$$

$$a_c = \frac{v^2}{r}$$

$$F_c = \frac{mv^2}{r}$$

a_c = centripetal acceleration
F_c = centripetal force
m = mass
r = radius
v = velocity
θ = angle

INTERNAL ENERGY

$$Q = mc\Delta T_C$$

$$Q_f = mH_f$$

$$Q_v = mH_v$$

c = specific heat
H_f = heat of fusion
H_v = heat of vaporization
m = mass
Q = amount of heat
T_C = Celsius temperature

HEAT CONSTANTS

	Specific Heat (average) (kJ/kg•C°)	Melting Point (°C)	Boiling Point (°C)	Heat of Fusion (kJ/kg)	Heat of Vaporization (kJ/kg)
Alcohol (ethyl)	2.43 (liq.)	−117	79	109	855
Aluminum	0.90 (sol.)	660	2467	396	10500
Ammonia	4.71 (liq.)	−78	−33	332	1370
Copper	0.39 (sol.)	1083	2567	205	4790
Iron	0.45 (sol.)	1535	2750	267	6290
Lead	0.13 (sol.)	328	1740	25	866
Mercury	0.14 (liq.)	−39	357	11	295
Platinum	0.13 (sol.)	1772	3827	101	229
Silver	0.24 (sol.)	962	2212	105	2370
Tungsten	0.13 (sol.)	3410	5660	192	4350
Water { ice	2.05 (sol.)	0	—	334	—
water	4.19 (liq.)	—	100	—	2260
steam	2.01 (gas)	—	—	—	—
Zinc	0.39 (sol.)	420	907	113	1770

Tear Here

Tear Here

ELECTROMAGNETIC APPLICATIONS

$F = qvB$

$\dfrac{N_p}{N_s} = \dfrac{V_p}{V_s}$

$V_p I_p = V_s I_s$
  (ideal)

B = flux density

F = force

I_p = current in primary coil

I_s = current in secondary coil

N_p = number of turns of primary coil

N_s = number of turns of secondary coil

q = charge

v = velocity

V_p = voltage of primary coil

V_s = voltage of secondary coil

GEOMETRIC OPTICS

$\dfrac{1}{d_o} + \dfrac{1}{d_i} = \dfrac{1}{f}$

$\dfrac{S_o}{S_i} = \dfrac{d_o}{d_i}$

d_i = image distance

d_o = object distance

f = focal length

S_i = image size

S_o = object size

NUCLEAR ENERGY

$E = mc^2$

$m_f = \dfrac{m_i}{2^n}$

c = speed of light in a vacuum

E = energy

m = mass

n = number of half-lives

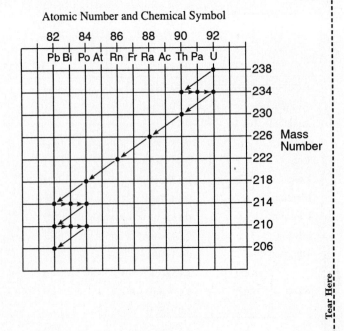

URANIUM DISINTEGRATION SERIES

Atomic Number and Chemical Symbol

Tear Here

Tear Here

Part I

Answer all 55 questions in this part. [65]

Directions (1–55): For *each* statement or question, select the word or expression that, of those given, best completes the statement or answers the question. Record your answer on the separate answer paper in accordance with the directions on the front page of this booklet.

1 Which terms both represent scalar quantities?

(1) displacement and velocity
(2) distance and speed
(3) displacement and speed
(4) distance and velocity

2 A mass of one kilogram of nickels has a monetary value in United States dollars of approximately

(1) $1.00   (3) $10.00
(2) $0.10   (4) $1000.00

3 Which graph best represents the motion of an object whose speed is increasing?

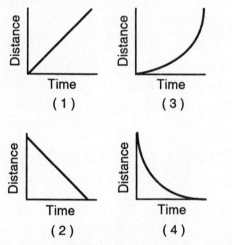

4 An astronaut weighs 500 newtons on Earth and 25 newtons on asteroid X. The acceleration due to gravity on asteroid X is approximately

(1) 1 m/s^2 (3) 0.2 m/s^2
(2) 2 m/s^2 (4) 0.5 m/s^2

5 A car having an initial velocity of 12 meters per second east slows uniformly to 2 meters per second east in 4.0 seconds. The acceleration of the car during this 4.0-second interval is

(1) 2.5 m/s^2 west   (3) 6.0 m/s^2 west
(2) 2.5 m/s^2 east   (4) 6.0 m/s^2 east

6 Two students push on a sled. One pushes with a force of 30. newtons east and the other exerts a force of 40. newtons south, as shown in the top-view diagram below.

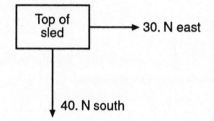

Which vector best represents the resultant of these two forces?

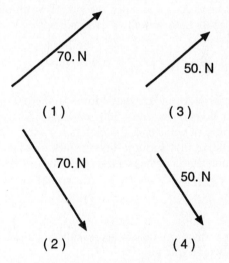

7 In an automobile collision, a 44-kilogram passenger moving at 15 meters per second is brought to rest by an air bag during a 0.10-second time interval. What is the magnitude of the average force exerted on the passenger during this time?

(1) 440 N   (3) 4400 N
(2) 660 N   (4) 6600 N

8 A series of unbalanced forces was applied to each of two blocks, *A* and *B*. The graphs below show the relationship between unbalanced force and acceleration for each block.

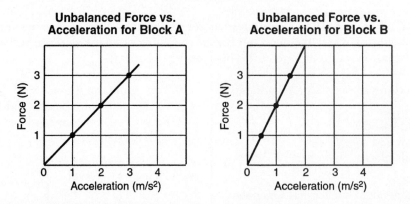

Compared to the mass of block *A*, the mass of block *B* is

(1) the same
(2) twice as great

(3) half as great
(4) four times as great

9 Two cars, *A* and *B*, are 400. meters apart. Car *A* travels due east at 30. meters per second on a collision course with car *B*, which travels due west at 20. meters per second. How much time elapses before the two cars collide?

(1) 8.0 s
(2) 13 s

(3) 20. s
(4) 40. s

10 A 50.-newton horizontal force is needed to keep an object weighing 500. newtons moving at a constant velocity of 2.0 meters per second across a horizontal surface. The magnitude of the frictional force acting on the object is

(1) 500. N
(2) 450. N

(3) 50. N
(4) 0 N

11 The diagram below represents a block sliding down an incline.

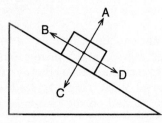

Which vector best represents the frictional force acting on the block?

(1) *A*
(2) *B*

(3) *C*
(4) *D*

12 A different force is applied to each of four 1-kilogram blocks to slide them across a uniform steel surface at constant speed as shown below. In which diagram is the coefficient of friction between the block and steel *smallest*?

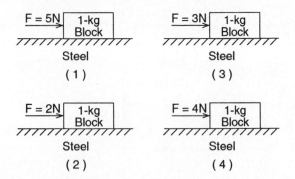

13 The magnitude of the momentum of an object is 64.0 kilogram•meter per second. If the velocity of the object is doubled, the magnitude of the momentum of the object will be

(1) 32.0 kg•m/s
(2) 64.0 kg•m/s

(3) 128 kg•m/s
(4) 256 kg•m/s

14 An airplane originally at rest on a runway accelerates uniformly at 6.0 meters per second^2 for 12 seconds. During this 12-second interval, the airplane travels a distance of approximately

(1) 72 m
(2) 220 m

(3) 430 m
(4) 860 m

15 Satellite A has a mass of 1.5×10^3 kilograms and is traveling east at 8.0×10^3 meters per second. Satellite B is traveling west at 6.0×10^3 meters per second. The satellites collide head-on and come to rest. What is the mass of satellite B?

(1) 2.7×10^3 kg (3) 1.5×10^3 kg
(2) 2.0×10^3 kg (4) 1.1×10^3 kg

16 Which combination of units can be used to express work?

(1) $\dfrac{\text{newton} \cdot \text{second}}{\text{meter}}$ (3) newton/meter

(2) $\dfrac{\text{newton} \cdot \text{meter}}{\text{second}}$ (4) newton•meter

17 A 2000-watt motor working at full capacity can vertically lift a 400-newton weight at a constant speed of

(1) 2×10^3 m/s (3) 5 m/s
(2) 50 m/s (4) 0.2 m/s

18 Which graph best represents the relationship between gravitational potential energy (PE) and height (h) above the ground for an object near the surface of Earth?

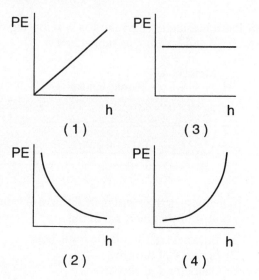

20 A 3.0-kilogram mass is attached to a spring having a spring constant of 30. newtons per meter. The mass is pulled 0.20 meter from the spring's equilibrium position and released. What is the maximum kinetic energy achieved by the mass-spring system?

(1) 2.4 J (3) 1.2 J
(2) 1.5 J (4) 0.60 J

21 The diagram below shows block A, having mass $2m$ and speed v, and block B having mass m and speed $2v$.

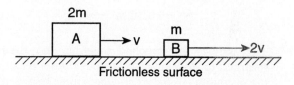

Frictionless surface

Compared to the kinetic energy of block A, the kinetic energy of block B is

(1) the same (3) one-half as great
(2) twice as great (4) four times as great

22 Two similar metal spheres possessing $+1.0$ coulomb of charge and -1.0 coulomb of charge, respectively, are brought toward each other. Which graph best represents the relationship between the magnitude of the electric force between the spheres and the distance between them?

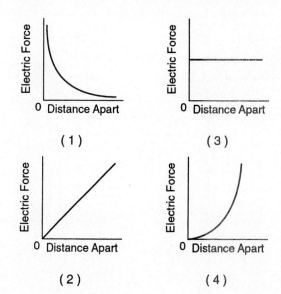

19 An alpha particle consists of two protons and two neutrons. The alpha particle's charge of $+2$ elementary charges is equivalent to

(1) 8.0×10^{-20} C (3) 1.2×10^{19} C
(2) 3.2×10^{-19} C (4) 3.2×10^{19} C

23 The diagram below shows two metal spheres charged to $+1.0 \times 10^{-6}$ coulomb and $+3.0 \times 10^{-6}$ coulomb, respectively, on insulating stands separated by a distance of 0.10 meter.

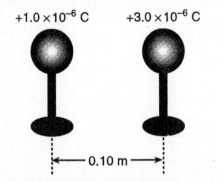

$+1.0 \times 10^{-6}$ C $+3.0 \times 10^{-6}$ C

0.10 m

The spheres are touched together and then returned to their original positions. As a result, the magnitude of the electrostatic force between the spheres changes from 2.7 N to

(1) 1.4 N   (3) 3.6 N
(2) 1.8 N   (4) 14 N

24 An electrostatic force of 20. newtons is exerted on a charge of 8.0×10^{-2} coulomb at point P in an electric field. The magnitude of the electric field intensity at P is

(1) 4.0×10^{-3} N/C   (3) 20. N/C
(2) 1.6 N/C   (4) 2.5×10^2 N/C

25 Which diagram best represents the electric field around a negatively charged conducting sphere?

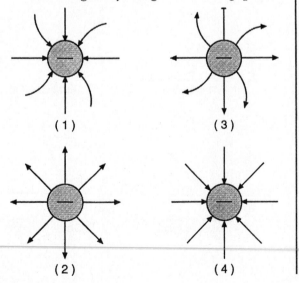

(1)   (3)

(2)   (4)

26 A 12-volt automobile battery has 8.4×10^3 coulombs of electric charge. The amount of electrical energy stored in the battery is approximately

(1) 1.0×10^5 J   (3) 7.0×10^2 J
(2) 8.4×10^3 J   (4) 1.4×10^{-3} J

27 Which graph best represents the relationship between potential difference across a metallic conductor and the resulting current through the conductor at a constant temperature?

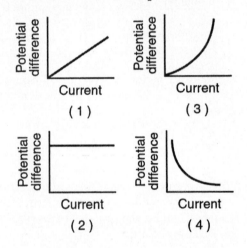

(1)   (3)

(2)   (4)

28 Plastic insulation surrounds a wire having diameter d and length ℓ as shown below.

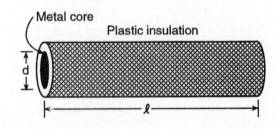

Metal core   Plastic insulation

d

ℓ

A decrease in the resistance of the wire would be produced by an increase in the

(1) thickness of the plastic insulation
(2) length ℓ of the wire
(3) diameter d of the wire
(4) temperature of the wire

29 Which diagram below correctly shows currents traveling near junction P in an electric circuit?

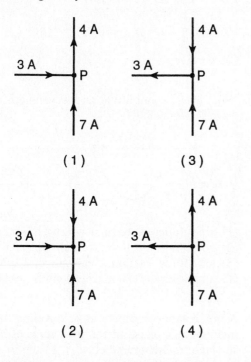

(1)

(3)

(2)

(4)

30 The diagram below shows three resistors, R_1, R_2, and R_3, connected to a 12-volt battery.

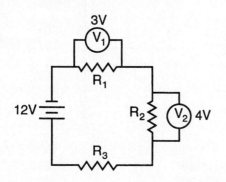

If voltmeter V_1 reads 3 volts and voltmeter V_2 reads 4 volts, what is the potential drop across resistor R_3?

(1) 12 V   (3) 0 V
(2) 5 V   (4) 4 V

31 A current of 3.0 amperes is flowing in a circuit. How much charge passes a given point in the circuit in 30. seconds?

(1) 0.10 C   (3) 33 C
(2) 10. C   (4) 90. C

Base your answers to questions 32 and 33 on the diagram below, which shows two resistors connected in parallel across a 6.0-volt source.

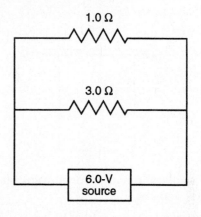

32 The equivalent resistance of the two resistors is

(1) 0.75   (3) 1.3
(2) 2.0   (4) 4.0

Note that question 33 has only three choices.

33 Compared to the power dissipated in the 1.0-ohm resistor, the power dissipated in the 3.0-ohm resistor is

(1) less
(2) greater
(3) the same

34 The diagram below represents the magnetic lines of force around a bar magnet.

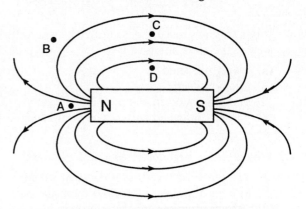

At which point is the magnitude of the magnetic field strength of the bar magnet the greatest?

(1) A (3) C
(2) B (4) D

35 The diagram below shows an electromagnet made from a nail, a coil of insulated wire, and a battery.

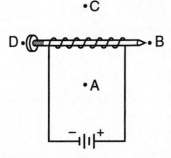

The south pole of the electromagnet is located closest to point

(1) A   (3) C
(2) B   (4) D

36 The diagram below shows light rays in air about to strike a glass window.

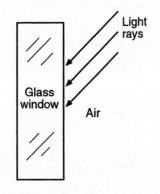

When the rays reach the boundary between the air and the glass, the light is

(1) totally refracted
(2) totally reflected
(3) partially reflected and partially diffracted
(4) partially reflected and partially refracted

37 Which phrase best describes a periodic wave?

(1) a single pulse traveling at constant speed
(2) a series of pulses at irregular intervals
(3) a series of pulses at regular intervals
(4) a single pulse traveling at different speeds in the same medium

38 Which equation correctly relates the speed v, wavelength λ, and period T of a periodic wave?

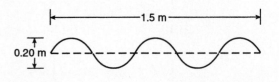

(1) $v = \dfrac{T}{\lambda}$ (3) $v = \dfrac{\lambda}{T}$

(2) $v = T\lambda$ (4) $v = \dfrac{\lambda^2}{T}$

39 What are the amplitude and wavelength of the wave shown below?

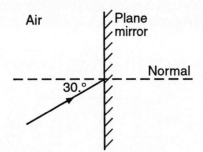

(1) amplitude = 0.10 m, wavelength = 0.30 m
(2) amplitude = 0.10 m, wavelength = 0.60 m
(3) amplitude = 0.20 m, wavelength = 0.30 m
(4) amplitude = 0.20 m, wavelength = 0.60 m

40 A ray of monochromatic light traveling in air is incident on a plane mirror at an angle of 30.°, as shown in the diagram below.

The angle of reflection for the light ray is

(1) 15°   (3) 60.°
(2) 30.°   (4) 90.°

41 What type of wave is sound traveling in water?

(1) torsional   (3) elliptical
(2) transverse   (4) longitudinal

42 The diagram below shows two waves, A and B.

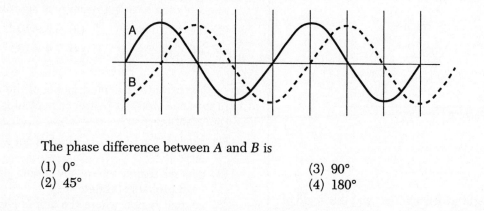

The phase difference between A and B is

(1) 0°

(2) 45°

(3) 90°

(4) 180°

43 The diagram below represents monochromatic light incident on a pair of slits, S_1 and S_2, that are separated by a distance of 2.0×10^{-6} meter. A, B, and C are adjacent antinodal areas that appear on a screen 1.0 meter from the slits. The distance from A to B is 0.34 meter.

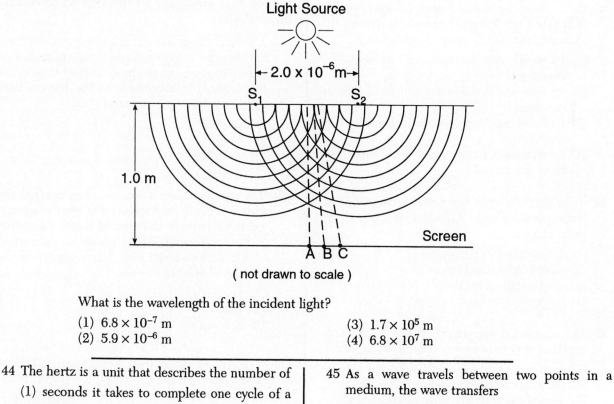

What is the wavelength of the incident light?

(1) 6.8×10^{-7} m

(2) 5.9×10^{-6} m

(3) 1.7×10^5 m

(4) 6.8×10^7 m

44 The hertz is a unit that describes the number of

(1) seconds it takes to complete one cycle of a wave

(2) cycles of a wave completed in one second

(3) points that are in phase along one meter of a wave

(4) points that are out of phase along one meter of a wave

45 As a wave travels between two points in a medium, the wave transfers

(1) energy, only

(2) mass, only

(3) both energy and mass

(4) neither energy nor mass

46 The diagram below shows a ray of light ($\lambda = 5.9 \times 10^{-7}$ meter) traveling from air into medium X.

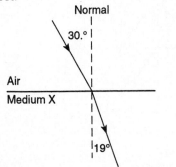

If the angle of incidence is 30.° and the angle of refraction is 19°, medium X could be

(1) air
(2) alcohol
(3) Canada balsam
(4) glycerol

47 As a monochromatic beam of light passes obliquely from flint glass into water, how do the characteristics of the beam of light change?

(1) Its wavelength decreases and its frequency decreases.
(2) Its wavelength decreases and its frequency increases.
(3) Its wavelength increases and it bends toward the normal.
(4) Its wavelength increases and it bends away from the normal.

48 Alpha particles were directed at a thin metal foil. Some particles were deflected into hyperbolic paths due to

(1) gravitational attraction
(2) electrostatic repulsion
(3) electrostatic attraction
(4) magnetic repulsion

49 The threshold frequency in a photoelectric experiment is most closely related to the

(1) brightness of the incident light
(2) thickness of the photoemissive metal
(3) area of the photoemissive metal
(4) work function of the photoemissive metal

50 The momentum of a photon is inversely proportional to the photon's

(1) frequency
(2) mass
(3) weight
(4) wavelength

51 The electron in a hydrogen atom drops from energy level $n = 2$ to energy level $n = 1$ by emitting a photon having an energy of approximately

(1) 5.4×10^{-19} J
(2) 1.6×10^{-18} J
(3) 2.2×10^{-18} J
(4) 7.4×10^{-18} J

52 In the currently accepted model of the atom, a fuzzy cloud around a hydrogen nucleus is used to represent the

(1) electron's actual path, which is not a circular orbit
(2) general region where the atom's proton is most probably located
(3) general region where the atom's electron is most probably located
(4) presence of water vapor in the atom

Note that questions 53 through 55 have only three choices.

53 A softball player leaves the batter's box, overruns first base by 3.0 meters, and then returns to first base. Compared to the total distance traveled by the player, the magnitude of the player's total displacement from the batter's box is

(1) smaller
(2) larger
(3) the same

54 The radius of Mars is approximately one-half the radius of Earth, and the mass of Mars is approximately one-tenth the mass of Earth. Compared to the acceleration due to gravity on the surface of Earth, the acceleration due to gravity on the surface of Mars is

(1) smaller
(2) larger
(3) the same

55 A mosquito flying over a highway strikes the windshield of a moving truck. Compared to the magnitude of the force of the truck on the mosquito during the collision, the magnitude of the force of the mosquito on the truck is

(1) smaller
(2) larger
(3) the same

Part II

This part consists of six groups, each containing ten questions. Each group tests an optional area of the course. Choose two of these six groups. Be sure that you answer all ten questions in each group chosen. Record the answers to the questions in accordance with the directions on the front page of this booklet.   [20]

Group 1 — Motion in a Plane

If you choose this group, be sure to answer questions 56–65.

56 A football player kicks a ball with an initial velocity of 25 meters per second at an angle of 53° above the horizontal. The vertical component of the initial velocity of the ball is

  (1) 25 m/s   (3) 15 m/s
  (2) 20. m/s   (4) 10. m/s

57 A student throws a stone upward at an angle of 45°. Which statement best describes the stone at the highest point that it reaches?

  (1) Its acceleration is zero.
  (2) Its acceleration is at a maximum.
  (3) Its potential energy is at a minimum.
  (4) Its kinetic energy is at a minimum.

58 A red ball and a green ball are simultaneously thrown horizontally from the same height. The red ball has an initial speed of 40. meters per second and the green ball has an initial speed of 20. meters per second. Compared to the time it takes the red ball to reach the ground, the time it takes the green ball to reach the ground will be

  (1) the same   (3) half as much
  (2) twice as much   (4) four times as much

59 A baseball player throws a ball horizontally. Which statement best describes the ball's motion after it is thrown? [Neglect the effect of friction.]

  (1) Its vertical speed remains the same, and its horizontal speed increases.
  (2) Its vertical speed remains the same, and its horizontal speed remains the same.
  (3) Its vertical speed increases, and its horizontal speed increases.
  (4) Its vertical speed increases, and its horizontal speed remains the same.

Base your answers to questions 60 and 61 on the information and diagram below.

A 1200-kilogram car traveling at a constant speed of 9.0 meters per second turns at an intersection. The car follows a horizontal circular path with a radius of 25 meters to point P.

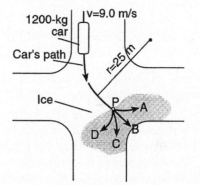

60 The magnitude of the centripetal force acting on the car as it travels around the circular path is approximately

  (1) 1.1×10^4 N   (3) 3.9×10^3 N
  (2) 1.2×10^4 N   (4) 4.3×10^2 N

61 At point P, the car hits an area of ice and loses all frictional force on its tires. Which path does the car follow on the ice?

  (1) A (3) C
  (2) B (4) D

62 An amusement park ride moves a rider at a constant speed of 14 meters per second in a horizontal circular path of radius 10. meters. What is the rider's centripetal acceleration in terms of g, the acceleration due to gravity?

(1) 1g   (3) 3g
(2) 2g   (4) 0g

63 The diagram below shows the elliptical orbit of a comet around the Sun. The comet's closest approach to the Sun is at point A.

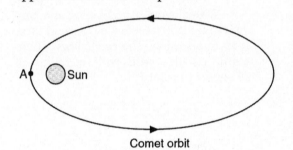

Comet orbit

Which statement best describes the comet's energy as it passes through point A?

(1) Its kinetic energy is at a minimum and its potential energy is at a minimum.
(2) Its kinetic energy is at a minimum and its potential energy is at a maximum.
(3) Its kinetic energy is at a maximum and its potential energy is at a minimum.
(4) Its kinetic energy is at a maximum and its potential energy is at a maximum.

64 The chart below gives the mass and orbital period of each of four satellites, A, B, C, and D, orbiting Earth in circular paths.

Satellite	Mass (kilograms)	Orbital Period (hours)
A	500	4
B	500	2
C	100	6
D	100	3

Which satellite is closest to Earth?

(1) A (3) C
(2) B (4) D

65 The Moon's orbit is *not* classified as geosynchronous because

(1) the Moon's position over Earth's surface varies with time
(2) the Moon's mass is very large compared to the mass of all other Earth satellites
(3) the Moon is a natural satellite, rather than an artificial one
(4) the Moon always has the same half of its surface facing Earth

Group 2 — Internal Energy

If you choose this group, be sure to answer questions 66–75.

Base your answers to questions 66 and 67 on the graph and information below.

The graph below represents a cooling curve for 10. kilograms of a substance as it cools from a vapor at 160.°C to a solid at 20.°C. Energy is removed from the sample at a constant rate.

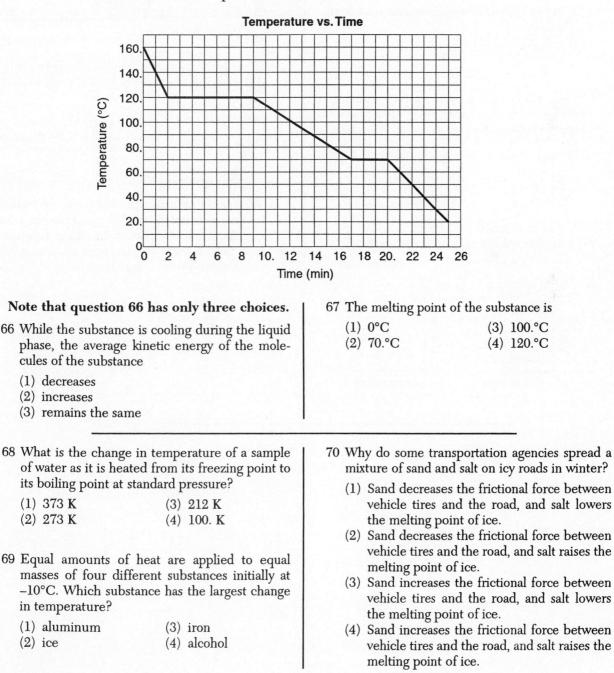

Temperature vs. Time

Note that question 66 has only three choices.

66 While the substance is cooling during the liquid phase, the average kinetic energy of the molecules of the substance

(1) decreases
(2) increases
(3) remains the same

67 The melting point of the substance is

(1) 0°C   (3) 100.°C
(2) 70.°C   (4) 120.°C

68 What is the change in temperature of a sample of water as it is heated from its freezing point to its boiling point at standard pressure?

(1) 373 K   (3) 212 K
(2) 273 K   (4) 100. K

69 Equal amounts of heat are applied to equal masses of four different substances initially at –10°C. Which substance has the largest change in temperature?

(1) aluminum   (3) iron
(2) ice   (4) alcohol

70 Why do some transportation agencies spread a mixture of sand and salt on icy roads in winter?

(1) Sand decreases the frictional force between vehicle tires and the road, and salt lowers the melting point of ice.
(2) Sand decreases the frictional force between vehicle tires and the road, and salt raises the melting point of ice.
(3) Sand increases the frictional force between vehicle tires and the road, and salt lowers the melting point of ice.
(4) Sand increases the frictional force between vehicle tires and the road, and salt raises the melting point of ice.

71 The air pressure inside an automobile tire is lower during cold weather than during warm weather. The lower air pressure is most likely due to

(1) an increase in molecular potential energy of the air molecules in the tire
(2) a decrease in the speed of the air molecules in the tire
(3) salt on the roads producing a decrease in tire volume
(4) cold air in the tire producing an increase in tire volume

72 Which graph best represents the relationship between volume and absolute temperature for a fixed mass of an ideal gas at constant pressure?

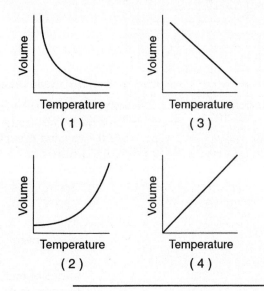

73 Heat will flow from a region of low temperature to a region of higher temperature if

(1) the specific heat of the cooler region is greater than the specific heat of the warmer region
(2) the temperature of the cooler region is near absolute zero
(3) work is done to produce the flow
(4) the cooler region is liquid and the warmer region is solid

74 What is the minimum heat required to change 5.0 kilograms of copper at 1083°C from a solid to a liquid?

(1) 0.20 kJ   (3) 41 kJ
(2) 0.39 kJ   (4) 1.0×10^3 kJ

Note that question 75 has only three choices.

75 When a box of beakers was dropped, the beakers broke into many pieces. Dropping the box a second time could *not* cause the pieces to reform into the original beakers because this would require entropy to

(1) decrease
(2) increase
(3) remain the same

Group 3 — Electromagnetic Applications

If you choose this group, be sure to answer questions 76–85.

Base your answers to questions 76 and 77 on the information and diagram below.

An electromagnet with an air core is located within the magnetic field between two permanent magnets.

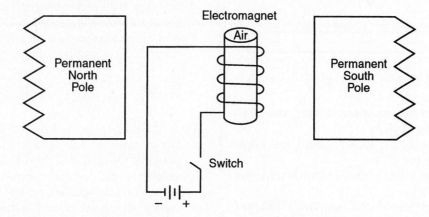

76 At the instant the switch is closed and a current begins to flow through the coil of the electromagnet, the coil will experience

(1) no electromagnetic force
(2) a force directed out of the page
(3) a counterclockwise torque
(4) a clockwise torque

Note that question 77 has only three choices.

77 The air core of the electromagnet is replaced with an iron core. Compared to the strength of the magnetic field in the air core, the strength of the magnetic field in the iron core is

(1) less
(2) greater
(3) the same

78 The two ends of a wire are connected to a galvanometer, forming a complete electric circuit. The wire is then moved through a magnetic field, as shown in the diagram below.

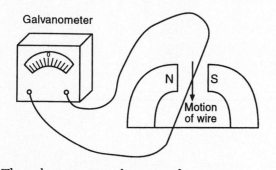

The galvanometer is being used to measure

(1) current
(2) potential difference
(3) temperature change
(4) resistance

79 Which device converts electrical energy into mechanical energy?

(1) motor   (3) source of emf
(2) generator   (4) thermocouple

80 The diagram below shows a point, *P*, located midway between two oppositely charged parallel plates.

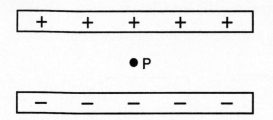

If an electron is introduced at point *P*, the electron will

(1) travel at constant speed toward the positively charged plate
(2) travel at constant speed toward the negatively charged plate
(3) accelerate toward the positively charged plate
(4) accelerate toward the negatively charged plate

81 The diagram below shows a proton moving with velocity *v* about to enter a uniform magnetic field directed into the page. As the proton moves in the magnetic field, the magnitude of the magnetic force on the proton is *F*.

```
        X   X   X   X
        X   X   X   X   Magnetic Field
(+) v→                   Directed into
        X   X   X   X      the Page
        X   X   X   X
```

If the proton were replaced by an alpha particle under the same conditions, the magnitude of the magnetic force on the alpha particle would be

(1) *F*
(2) 2*F*
(3) $\frac{F}{2}$
(4) 4*F*

82 The isotopes of an element can be separated using a

(1) cathode ray tube
(2) diffraction grating
(3) Geiger counter
(4) mass spectrometer

83 A potential difference of 12 volts is induced across a 0.20-meter-long straight wire as it is moved at a constant speed of 3.0 meters per second perpendicular to a uniform magnetic field. What is the strength of the magnetic field?

(1) 180 T
(2) 20. T
(3) 13 T
(4) 7.2 T

84 A step-down transformer used to run a toy train has an input of 120 volts to its primary coil. A potential difference of 12 volts is induced in the secondary coil, which carries a current of 12 amperes. If the transformer operates at 75% efficiency, what is the current in the primary coil?

(1) 0.90 A
(2) 1.6 A
(3) 90. A
(4) 160 A

85 What is the origin of the light emitted by a laser?

(1) thermionic emission from an incandescent filament
(2) emission of mechanical waves from vibrating matter
(3) emission of photoelectrons from a photosensitive surface
(4) emission of photons from excited atoms

Group 4 — Geometric Optics

If you choose this group, be sure to answer questions 86–95.

86 Which diagram best represents image *I*, which is formed by placing object *O* in front of a plane mirror?

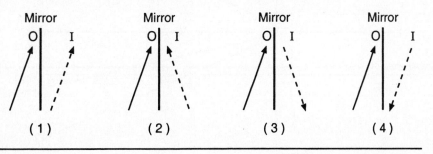

(1)   (2)   (3)   (4)

87 The diagram below shows an arrow placed in front of a converging lens.

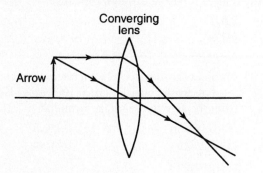

The lens forms an image of the arrow that is

(1) real and inverted
(2) real and erect
(3) virtual and inverted
(4) virtual and erect

88 Light rays from a candle flame are incident on a convex mirror. After reflecting from the mirror, these light rays

(1) converge and form a virtual image
(2) converge and form a real image
(3) diverge and form a virtual image
(4) diverge and form a real image

89 The diagram below shows an object located at point *P*, 0.25 meter from a concave spherical mirror with principal focus *F*. The focal length of the mirror is 0.10 meter.

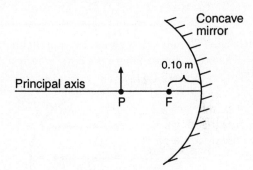

How does the image change as the object is moved from point *P* toward point *F*?

(1) Its distance from the mirror decreases and the size of the image decreases.
(2) Its distance from the mirror decreases and the size of the image increases.
(3) Its distance from the mirror increases and the size of the image decreases.
(4) Its distance from the mirror increases and the size of the image increases.

90 The diagram below shows light ray R incident on a glass lens in air.

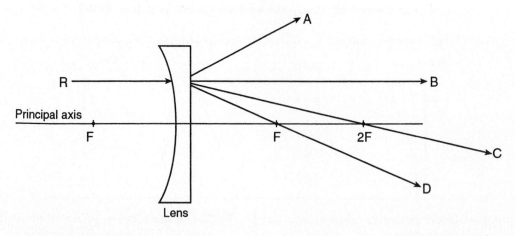

Lens

Which ray best represents the path of light ray R after it passes through the lens?

(1) A (3) C
(2) B (4) D

91 The diagram below shows two parallel light rays, X and Y, approaching a concave spherical mirror.

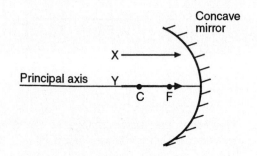

Which light will reflect through the mirror's center of curvature, C?

(1) ray X, only
(2) ray Y, only
(3) both ray X and ray Y
(4) neither ray X nor ray Y

92 Which optical devices in air can both form real images?

(1) concave mirror and convex lens
(2) concave mirror and concave lens
(3) plane mirror and convex lens
(4) plane mirror and concave lens

93 An object is located 0.15 meter from a converging lens with focal length 0.10 meter. How far from the lens is the image formed?

(1) 0.060 m   (3) 0.15 m
(2) 0.10 m   (4) 0.30 m

94 When a student 1.5 meters tall stands 5.0 meters in front of a lens, his image forms on a screen located 0.50 meter behind the lens. What is the height of the student's image?

(1) 0.015 m   (3) 1.5 m
(2) 0.15 m   (4) 15 m

95 Which phenomena cause chromatic aberration to occur when polychromatic light passes through a lens?

(1) diffraction and refraction
(2) diffraction and reflection
(3) dispersion and refraction
(4) dispersion and reflection

Group 5 — Solid State

If you choose this group, be sure to answer questions 96–105.

96 A material having extremely low conductivity would be classified as

(1) a conductor   (3) an insulator
(2) a semiconductor   (4) a metalloid

97 The diagram below represents the band model of a substance.

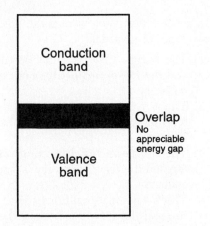

The substance is best classified as

(1) an insulator   (3) a conductor
(2) a semiconductor   (4) a nonmetal

98 Magnetic-card door locks utilize many electronic components on one small piece of semiconductor material. This combination of components on a single chip is called

(1) a transistor
(2) an integrated circuit
(3) a printed circuit board
(4) a diode

99 The Band Model has replaced the Electron-sea Model of conduction because the Electron-sea Model

(1) only works for gases
(2) only works for liquids
(3) does not account for the conduction properties of metals
(4) does not account for the conduction properties of semiconductors

100 The diagram below shows a portion of the Periodic Table of the Elements.

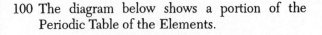

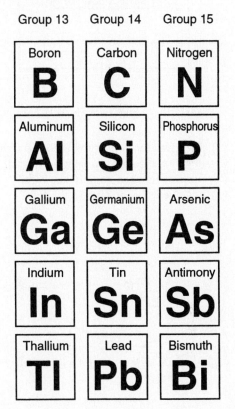

Based on the information in this diagram, which three elements could all be used as doping agents to produce the holes of a P-type semiconductor?

(1) boron, aluminum, and gallium
(2) boron, carbon, and nitrogen
(3) thallium, germanium, and phosphorus
(4) nitrogen, phosphorus, and arsenic

101 The diagram below shows a circuit with a battery applying a potential difference across a *P*-type semiconductor.

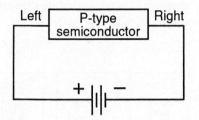

The majority charge carriers in the semiconductor are

(1) negative electrons moving to the right
(2) negative electrons moving to the left
(3) positive holes moving to the right
(4) positive holes moving to the left

102 Which diagram best represents a diode?

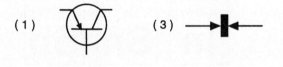

103 In the *P-N* junction region of an operating diode, an electric field barrier is produced by free electrons in the

(1) *N*-type material crossing into the *P*-type material
(2) *N*-type material going away from the *P*-type material
(3) *P*-type material crossing into the *N*-type material
(4) *P*-type material going away from the *N*-type material

104 In a *P-N-P* transistor, what is the function of the two types of material?

(1) The *N*-type material functions as the base, and the *P*-type material is both emitter and collector.
(2) The *N*-type material functions as both base and emitter, and the *P*-type material is the collector.
(3) The *N*-type material functions as the emitter, and the *P*-type material is both base and collector.
(4) The *N*-type material functions as the collector, and the *P*-type material is both emitter and base.

Note that question 105 has only three choices.

105 As the temperature of a semiconductor increases, the number of holes in the valence band will

(1) decrease
(2) increase
(3) remain the same

Group 6 — Nuclear Energy

If you choose this group, be sure to answer questions 106–115.

106 Which nuclide has a mass number of 8?

(1) $^{6}_{2}\text{He}$ (3) $^{15}_{7}\text{N}$

(2) $^{8}_{4}\text{Be}$ (4) $^{16}_{8}\text{O}$

107 The binding energy of a uranium-235 nucleus is the energy equivalent of its

(1) total mass   (3) critical mass
(2) mass number   (4) mass defect

108 Which device is used to detect nuclear radiation?

(1) cyclotron
(2) Geiger counter
(3) linear accelerator
(4) Van de Graaff generator

109 When an atom of $^{238}_{92}\text{U}$ decays to an atom of $^{206}_{82}\text{Pb}$, the total number of alpha particles emitted is

(1) 5   (3) 8
(2) 6   (4) 14

110 A medical lab has a 16-gram sample of a radioactive isotope. After 6.0 hours, it is found that 12 grams of the sample have decayed. What is the half-life of the isotope?

(1) 6.0 hr   (3) 3.0 hr
(2) 2.0 hr   (4) 12.0 hr

111 The nuclear equation $^{30}_{15}\text{P} \rightarrow {}^{30}_{14}\text{Si} + {}^{0}_{+1}\text{e}$ represents

(1) alpha bombardment
(2) electron capture
(3) neutron emission
(4) positron emission

112 In a nuclear reactor, one of the primary functions of the coolant is to

(1) promote overheating in the reactor core
(2) transfer thermal energy to a heat exchanger
(3) adjust the number of neutrons
(4) protect the reactor operators from radiation

113 Protons and neutrons are composed of smaller particles called

(1) quarks   (3) alpha particles
(2) baryons   (4) bosons

114 The equation below represents a fission reaction in a nuclear reactor.

$$^{1}_{0}\text{n} + {}^{235}_{92}\text{U} \rightarrow {}^{141}_{56}\text{Ba} + {}^{92}_{36}\text{Kr} + 3{}^{1}_{0}\text{n} + \text{energy}$$

Which product of this reaction must be absorbed by other $^{235}_{92}\text{U}$ nuclei to sustain a chain reaction?

(1) $^{141}_{56}\text{Ba}$ (3) $^{1}_{0}\text{n}$

(2) $^{92}_{36}\text{Kr}$ (4) energy

115 Which equation represents the process by which the Sun produces energy?

(1) $^{3}_{1}\text{H} + {}^{1}_{1}\text{H} \rightarrow {}^{4}_{2}\text{He} + \text{Q}$

(2) $^{235}_{92}\text{U} + {}^{1}_{0}\text{n} \rightarrow {}^{138}_{56}\text{Ba} + {}^{95}_{36}\text{Kr} + 3{}^{1}_{0}\text{n} + \text{Q}$

(3) $^{14}_{6}\text{C} \rightarrow {}^{14}_{7}\text{N} + {}^{0}_{-1}\text{e} + \text{Q}$

(4) $^{40}_{19}\text{K} + {}^{0}_{-1}\text{e} \rightarrow {}^{40}_{18}\text{Ar} + \text{Q}$

Part III

You must answer *all* questions in this part. Record your answers in the spaces provided on the separate answer paper. Pen or pencil may be used. [15]

Base your answers to questions 116 through 119 on the information and diagram below, which is drawn to a scale of 1.0 centimeter = 30. meters.

A student on building X is located 240. meters from the launch site B of a rocket on building Y. The rocket reaches its maximum altitude at point A. The student's eyes are level with the launch site on building Y.

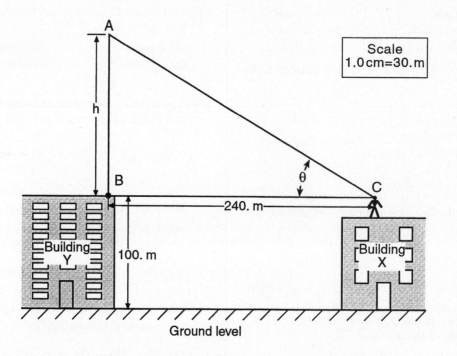

116 Using the scale diagram and a protractor, measure the angle of elevation, θ, of the rocket and record it to the *nearest degree*. [1]

117 Determine the height, *h*, of the rocket above the student's eye level. [1]

118 What is the total distance the rocket must fall from its maximum altitude to reach the ground? [1]

119 Determine how much time is required for the rocket to fall freely from point A back to ground level. [Show all calculations, including the equation and substitution with units.] [2]

120 A 0.65-meter-long pendulum consists of a 1.0-kilogram mass at the end of a string. The pendulum is released from rest at position A, 0.25 meter above its lowest point. The pendulum is timed at five positions, A through E.

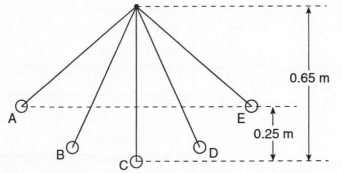

Data Table	
Position	Elapsed Time
A	0.00 s
B	0.20 s
C	0.40 s
D	0.60 s
E	0.80 s

Based on the information in the diagram and the data table, determine the period of the pendulum. [1]

Base your answers to questions 121 through 123 on the information below.

A 680-newton student runs up a flight of stairs 3.5 meters high in 11.4 seconds. The student takes 8.5 seconds to run up the same flight of stairs during a second trial.

121 Determine the work done by the 680-newton student in climbing the stairs. [Show all calculations, including the equation and substitution with units.] [2]

122 Determine the power developed by the student during the 11.4-second climb. [Show all calculations, including the equation and substitution with units.] [2]

123 Using one or more complete sentences, compare the power developed by the student climbing the stairs in 11.4 seconds to the power developed during the 8.5-second trial. [1]

Base your answers to questions 124 through 126 on the information below.

A 0.12-meter-long electromagnetic (radar) wave is emitted by a weather station and reflected from a nearby thunderstorm.

124 Determine the frequency of the radar wave. [Show all calculations, including the equation and substitution with units.] [2]

125 Using one or more complete sentences, define the Doppler effect. [1]

126 The thunderstorm is moving toward the weather station. Using one or more complete sentences, explain how the Doppler effect could have been used to determine the direction in which the storm is moving. [1]

The University of the State of New York

REGENTS HIGH SCHOOL EXAMINATION

PHYSICS

Wednesday, June 20, 2001 — 1:15 to 4:15 p.m., only

ANSWER PAPER

Student . . . . Sex: ☐ Male ☐ Female

Teacher . . . .

School . . . .

Record all of your answers on this answer paper in accordance with the instructions on the front page of the test booklet.

Part I (65 credits)

1	1	2	3	4	**21**	1	2	3	4	**41**	1	2	3	4
2	1	2	3	4	**22**	1	2	3	4	**42**	1	2	3	4
3	1	2	3	4	**23**	1	2	3	4	**43**	1	2	3	4
4	1	2	3	4	**24**	1	2	3	4	**44**	1	2	3	4
5	1	2	3	4	**25**	1	2	3	4	**45**	1	2	3	4
6	1	2	3	4	**26**	1	2	3	4	**46**	1	2	3	4
7	1	2	3	4	**27**	1	2	3	4	**47**	1	2	3	4
8	1	2	3	4	**28**	1	2	3	4	**48**	1	2	3	4
9	1	2	3	4	**29**	1	2	3	4	**49**	1	2	3	4
10	1	2	3	4	**30**	1	2	3	4	**50**	1	2	3	4
11	1	2	3	4	**31**	1	2	3	4	**51**	1	2	3	4
12	1	2	3	4	**32**	1	2	3	4	**52**	1	2	3	4
13	1	2	3	4	**33**	1	2	3		**53**	1	2	3	
14	1	2	3	4	**34**	1	2	3	4	**54**	1	2	3	
15	1	2	3	4	**35**	1	2	3	4	**55**	1	2	3	
16	1	2	3	4	**36**	1	2	3	4					
17	1	2	3	4	**37**	1	2	3	4					
18	1	2	3	4	**38**	1	2	3	4					
19	1	2	3	4	**39**	1	2	3	4					
20	1	2	3	4	**40**	1	2	3	4					

FOR TEACHER USE ONLY

Part I Score . . . . . .
(Use table below)

Part II Score . . . . . .

Part III Score . . . . . .

Total Score . . . . . .

Rater's Initials: . . . .

PART I CREDITS

Directions to Teacher:

In the table below, draw a circle around the number of right answers and the adjacent number of credits. Then write the number of credits (not the number right) in the space provided above.

No. Right	Credits	No. Right	Credits
55	65	27	45
54	64	26	44
53	64	25	43
52	63	24	43
51	62	23	42
50	61	22	41
49	61	21	41
48	60	20	40
47	59	19	39
46	59	18	38
45	58	17	38
44	57	16	37
43	56	15	36
42	56	14	36
41	55	13	35
40	54	12	32
39	54	11	30
38	53	10	27
37	52	9	24
36	51	8	22
35	51	7	19
34	50	6	16
33	49	5	13
32	48	4	11
31	48	3	8
30	47	2	5
29	46	1	3
28	46	0	0

No. right . . . .

Part II (20 credits)

Answer the questions in only two of the six groups in this part. Be sure to mark the answers to the groups of questions you choose in accordance with the instructions on the front page of the test booklet. Leave blank the four groups of questions you do not choose to answer.

Group 1
Motion in a Plane

56   1   2   3   4

57   1   2   3   4

58   1   2   3   4

59   1   2   3   4

60   1   2   3   4

61   1   2   3   4

62   1   2   3   4

63   1   2   3   4

64   1   2   3   4

65   1   2   3   4

Group 2
Internal Energy

66   1   2   3

67   1   2   3   4

68   1   2   3   4

69   1   2   3   4

70   1   2   3   4

71   1   2   3   4

72   1   2   3   4

73   1   2   3   4

74   1   2   3   4

75   1   2   3

Group 3
Electromagnetic Applications

76   1   2   3   4

77   1   2   3

78   1   2   3   4

79   1   2   3   4

80   1   2   3   4

81   1   2   3   4

82   1   2   3   4

83   1   2   3   4

84   1   2   3   4

85   1   2   3   4

Group 4
Geometric Optics

86   1   2   3   4

87   1   2   3   4

88   1   2   3   4

89   1   2   3   4

90   1   2   3   4

91   1   2   3   4

92   1   2   3   4

93   1   2   3   4

94   1   2   3   4

95   1   2   3   4

Group 5
Solid State

96   1   2   3   4

97   1   2   3   4

98   1   2   3   4

99   1   2   3   4

100   1   2   3   4

101   1   2   3   4

102   1   2   3   4

103   1   2   3   4

104   1   2   3   4

105   1   2   3

Group 6
Nuclear Energy

106   1   2   3   4

107   1   2   3   4

108   1   2   3   4

109   1   2   3   4

110   1   2   3   4

111   1   2   3   4

112   1   2   3   4

113   1   2   3   4

114   1   2   3   4

115   1   2   3   4

Glossary

absolute error the difference between an experimental value and the accepted value of a measured quantity

absolute index of refraction a property of a material medium equal to the ratio of the speed of light in a vacuum to the speed of light in the material medium

absorption spectrum a series of dark lines resulting from the selective absorption of particular frequencies of the continuous spectrum produced by white light

acceleration the time rate of change of velocity; a vector quantity

accepted value the most probable value for a measured quantity, which is usually published in reference books

accurate describes a measurement that is the same or very close to the accepted value

ammeter a device for measuring electrical current when connected in series in an electrical circuit

ampere (A) the fundamental SI unit of electric current; equal to one coulomb per second

amplitude the magnitude of the maximum displacement of a particle of the medium from its rest or equilibrium position

angle of incidence the angle between an incident ray and the normal to the surface at the point where the ray strikes the surface

angle of reflection the angle between a reflected ray and the normal to the surface at the point where the ray is reflected

angle of refraction the angle between a ray emerging from the interface of two media and the normal to that interface at the point where the ray emerges

antimatter material consisting of atoms which are composed of antiprotons, antineutrons, and positrons

antinode the point of maximum displacement of a medium when two waves are interacting

antiparticle a particle having mass, lifetime, and spin identical to the associated particle, but with charge of opposite sign (if charged) and magnetic moment reversed in sign

antiquark the antiparticle of a quark, having electric charge, baryon number, and strangeness opposite in sign to those of the corresponding quark

atom the smallest particle of an element

atomic spectrum a specific series of frequencies of electromagnetic radiation produced when electrons in excited atoms of an element in the gaseous state return to lower energy states

baryon an elementary particle which can be transformed into a proton or neutron and some number of mesons and lighter particles

battery a combination of two or more electrochemical cells; also, a direct-current voltage source which converts chemical, thermal, nuclear, or solar energy into electrical energy

bright-line spectrum an emission spectrum or a series of bright lines against a dark background that results from the emission of radiation of specific frequencies by a heated gas

cell a device that converts chemical energy to electrical energy

centripetal acceleration the acceleration that results in the uniform motion of an object in a circular path; a vector quantity directed toward the center of curvature

centripetal force the force needed to keep an object moving in a circular path; a vector quantity directed toward the center of curvature

closed system a group of objects, not acted upon by any external force

coefficient of friction the ratio of the frictional force to the normal force

compression a decrease in spring length from its equilibrium position or length

condensation a region of maximum compression in a longitudinal wave

conductivity a property of a material that describes the availability of charges that are free to move under the influence of an electric field

conductor a material, usually a metal, in which electric charge moves easily

conservative force name given to a force when work done against it is independent of the path taken

constant proportion the relationship that exists between two quantities when an increase in one causes no change in the other

constructive interference the effect produced when two in-phase waves pass simultaneously through a medium causing an increase in amplitude

coulomb (C) the derived SI unit of electric charge equal to one ampere per second passing through a given area

Coulomb's law states that the magnitude of force between two point charges is directly proportional to the product of the charges and inversely proportional to the square of the distance between them

crest in a transverse wave, the position of maximum displacement of a particle of the medium in the positive direction (for example, upward)

current in an electrical circuit, the rate at which charge passes a given point

dependent variable the quantity that changes in an experiment as a result of changes made by the experimenter

derived unit a combination of two or more fundamental units used to simplify notation

destructive interference the effect produced when two waves of equal frequency and amplitude, whose phase difference is 180° or $\frac{1}{2}\lambda$ pass simultaneously through a medium

diffraction the spreading of wave fronts into the region behind a barrier in the wave's path

direct squared proportion the relationship that exists between two quantities in which an increase in one causes a squared increase in the other

directly proportional applies to the relationship between two quantities in which an increase in one quantity causes an increase in the other or a decrease in one quantity causes a decrease in the other

displacement the change in position of an object described by the vector that begins at the initial position of the object and ends at its final position

distance the total length of the path that an object travels; a scalar quantity

Doppler effect a change in observed frequency and wavelength due to the relative motion of a wave source and observer

dynamics the branch of mechanics dealing with how forces affect an object's motion

elastic potential energy the energy stored in a spring when work is done in compressing or stretching it; a scalar quantity

electric circuit a closed path along which charged particles move

electric field the region around a charged particle through which a force is exerted on another charged particle

electric field line the imaginary line along which a positive test charge would move in an electric field

electric field strength the force per unit charge on a stationary positive test charge in an electric field; a vector quantity

electrical energy the total amount of energy in an electric circuit; equal to the product of power consumed and the time of the charge flow; a scalar quantity

electrical power the rate at which electrical energy is converted into other forms; a scalar quantity

electromagnetic energy the energy associated with electric or magnetic fields

electromagnetic induction the process of generating a potential difference in a conductor due to the relative motion between the conductor and a magnetic field

electromagnetic spectrum the complete range of frequencies and wavelengths of electromagnetic waves

electromagnetic wave periodically changing electric and magnetic fields that move through a vacuum at speed $c = 3.00 \times 10^8$ m/s

electron the fundamental negatively charged (−) subatomic particle of matter; particle charge is equal in magnitude to that of a proton; mass is negligible compared to a proton

electronvolt (eV) a unit of energy equal to the work done in moving an elementary charge through a potential difference of one volt

electrostatic force the force that acts on two points charges; magnitude of force is directly proportional to the product of the charges and inversely proportional to the square of the distance between them; a vector quantity

elementary charge denoted by e, the charge equal in magnitude to the charge of an electron ($-e$) or the charge of a proton ($+e$)

elongation an increase in spring length from its equilibrium length or position

emission spectrum a series of bright lines against a dark background, resulting from the emission of radiation of specific frequencies

energy level a stationary state of the electrons in an atom which represents a specific amount of energy

energy the ability to do work; a scalar quantity

energy-level diagram diagram in which the energy levels of a quantized system are indicated by distances of horizontal lines from a zero energy level

equilibrium state of an object when the net force acting on it is zero

equivalent resistance the single resistance that could replace several resistors in a circuit

excitation any process that raises the energy level of electrons in an atom

excited state the condition of an electron in an atom which is in any level above the ground state because of the absorption of a quantum of energy

experimental value measurement made during laboratory work which may stand alone or be incorporated into one or more formulas to yield a value for a physical quantity

extrapolation the extension of a graphed line beyond the region in which data was taken

force a push or pull on a mass; a vector quantity

free fall the ideal falling motion of an object acted upon only by the force of gravity

free-body diagram a sketch, or scale drawing, that shows all the forces acting concurrently on an object

frequency the number of cycles per unit time of an oscillating particle; a scalar quantity

friction the force that opposes the relative motion of two objects in contact; a vector quantity

fundamental unit one of a set of units in which all quantities measured by physicists can be expressed

generator device that converts mechanical energy into electrical energy by rotating a large coil of wire in a magnetic field

gravitational field a region in space where a test particle would experience a gravitational force

gravitational field strength the force per unit mass at a given point in a gravitational field; a vector quantity

gravitational force the attractive force between two objects due to their masses; a vector quantity

gravitational potential energy the work done or the energy change of an object resulting from lifting the object to a height above Earth's surface; a scalar quantity

gravity the force between the mass of Earth and the mass of any object in the vicinity of Earth; a vector quantity

ground state the lowest energy level of an electron in an atom when it is not absorbing or radiating energy

hadron a particle that interacts through the strong nuclear force, as well as electromagnetic, weak, and gravitational forces

hertz (Hz) derived SI unit of frequency equivalent to 1 cycle per second; in fundamental units, 1 Hz equals $1/s$

horizontal component (of velocity) a component velocity vector whose direction is parallel to the horizon

ideal mechanical system a closed system in which no friction or other nonconservative force is acting

impulse the product of the average force applied to an object and the time during which the force acts; a vector quantity

incident ray a ray that originates in a medium and is incident on a boundary or an interface with another medium

independent variable the quantity that the experimenter changes in an experiment

indirect squared proportion the relationship that exists between two quantities in which an increase in one causes a squared decrease in the other

induced potential difference the difference in potential created in a conductor due to its relative motion in a magnetic field

inertia the resistance of an object to a change in its motion; directly proportional to object's mass

instantaneous velocity the velocity of an object at any particular instant in time; a vector quantity

insulator a substance, usually a compound or a nonmetallic element, in which electric charge flows poorly

interference the superposition of one wave on another

internal energy the total potential and kinetic energy possessed by the particles that make up an object, but excluding the potential and kinetic energy of the system as a whole

inversely proportional applies to the relationship between two quantities in which an increase in one quantity causes a decrease in the other or a decrease in one quantity causes an increase in the other

ionization potential the energy required to remove an electron from an atom to form an ion

joule (J) a derived SI unit equal to the work done when a force of one newton produces a displacement of one meter; the unit for electrical energy

kilogram (kg) the fundamental SI unit of mass

kinetic energy the energy of an object due to its motion; a scalar quantity

kinetic friction the friction of motion between objects in contact; a vector quantity

law of conservation of charge states that in a closed, isolated system, the total charge of the system remains constant

law of conservation of energy states that energy can be neither created nor destroyed

law of conservation of momentum states that the total momentum of the objects in a closed system is constant

law of reflection states that the angle of incidence is equal to the angle of reflection

lepton a particle that interacts through the electromagnetic, weak, and gravitational forces, but not the strong nuclear force

line of best fit a straight or curved line on a graph which approximates the relationship among a set of data points

linear motion an object's change of position along a straight line

longitudinal wave a wave in which the motion of the vibratory disturbance is parallel to the direction of propagation or travel of the wave through the medium

magnet a material in which the spinning electrons of its atoms are aligned with one another

magnetic field the region where magnetic force exists around a magnet or any moving charged object

magnetic field (flux) line the imaginary lines that map out the magnetic field around a magnet

magnetic field strength the number of magnetic flux lines per unit area passing through a plane perpendicular to the direction of the lines; a vector quantity

magnetic force the force produced by the motion of charges relative to each other; a vector quantity

magnetism the force of attraction or repulsion between magnetic poles

mass the amount of matter contained in an object

mean the average, $\bar{x}$, of a set of n measurements, where x_i is the individual measurement and f_i is the frequency of measurement,

$$\bar{x} = \frac{\sum\limits_{i=1}^{n} x_i f_i}{\sum f_i}$$

mechanical energy the sum of the kinetic and potential energies in a system; a scalar quantity

mechanics the branch of physics that deals with forces and their effects in producing and changing motion

medium a body of matter through which waves propagate

meson a particle of intermediate mass

meter (m) the fundamental SI unit of length

momentum the product of an object's mass and velocity; a vector quantity

motor device that converts electrical energy into mechanical energy as a result of forces on a current-carrying conductor in a magnetic field

natural frequency a particular frequency at which every elastic body will vibrate if disturbed

net force the vector sum of the concurrent forces acting on an object

neutrino a neutral particle that possesses both energy and momentum but has little, if any, mass

neutron subatomic particle with no charge and a mass approximately equal to that of a proton

newton (N) the force that imparts an acceleration of one meter per second^2 to a one-kilogram mass

node zero displacement of the medium produced by maximum destructive interference of waves

nonconservative force name given to a force when work done against it is dependent on the path taken

non-ideal mechanical system a system in which a nonconservative force such as friction is acting

normal a line drawn perpendicular to a surface

normal force the force pressing two contacting surfaces together; on a horizontal surface, the normal force is equal in magnitude but opposite in direction to the weight of an object resting on the surface; a vector quantity

north magnetic pole the magnetic pole from which the magnetic flux of a magnet is considered to emerge

nuclear energy the energy released by nuclear fission, the division of a heavy atomic nucleus into parts of comparable mass, or by nuclear fusion, the combining of two light nuclei to form a heavier nucleus; a scalar quantity

nuclear force an attractive force between protons and neutrons in an atomic nucleus which is responsible for the stability of the nucleus; a vector quantity

nucleon name given to protons and neutrons that make up the nucleus of an atom

nucleus the core of an atom which is made up of one or more protons and (except for one of the isotopes of hydrogen) one or more neutrons

ohm (Ω) the derived SI unit of electrical resistance equivalent to one volt per ampere

ohm · meter (Ω · m) the SI unit for resistivity

Ohm's law states that at constant temperature the resistance of a conductor is equal to the ratio of the potential difference applied across it to the current that flows through it

parallel circuit an electrical circuit in which the circuit elements are connected between two points, with one end of each component connected to each point

pendulum a mass (bob) attached to one end of a string or wire that is attached at the other end to a pivot point

percent error a measure of the reliability of an experimental result calculated by dividing the absolute error by the accepted value and multiplying the quotient by 100

period (of a pendulum) the time required for a displaced pendulum to complete one cycle of motion; a scalar quantity

period (of a wave) the time required for one complete vibration to pass a given point in the medium; a scalar quantity

periodic wave a series of regularly repeated disturbances of a field or medium

phase the position of a point on a wave relative to another point on the same wave; two points on a wave are in phase when they are displaced from their rest position by the same amount in the same direction and are moving in the same direction

photocell a device that converts light, a form of electromagnetic radiation, into electrical energy

photon the quantum, or basic unit, of electromagnetic energy

Planck's constant (h) the proportionality constant in the mathematical relationship between the energy of a quantum and its frequency

positron a particle having mass equal to the mass of the electron, and positive electric charge equal in magnitude to the negative charge of the electron

potential difference the difference in potential energy per unit charge between two points in an electric field; a scalar quantity

potential energy the energy possessed by an object due to its position or condition; a scalar quantity

power the rate at which work is done or energy is consumed; a scalar quantity

precise describes several measurements taken of the same event that are nearly identical

principle of superposition states that the resultant displacement at any point on two or more superimposed waves is the algebraic sum of the displacements of the individual waves

proton the fundamental positively charged (+) subatomic particle of matter; particle charge is equal in magnitude to that of an electron; particle has a mass of approximately one universal mass unit

pulse a single short disturbance that moves from one position to another in a field or medium

quantized condition that restricts a system to the absorption or radiation of energy only in fixed amounts, or quanta

quantum a discrete packet of electromagnetic energy emitted or absorbed

quantum theory the theory that assumes that electromagnetic energy is emitted from and absorbed by matter in discrete amounts or packets of energy

quark one of the basic particles, having charges of $\pm \frac{1}{3}e$ or $\pm \frac{2}{3}e$, from which many of the elementary particles may be built up

range (in data analysis) the difference between the highest and lowest values in a data set

range the horizontal distance traveled by a projectile

rarefaction a region of maximum expansion in a longitudinal wave

ray a straight line that is drawn at right angles to a wave front and points in the direction of wave travel

reflected ray a ray that rebounded from a boundary or interface

reflection the rebounding of a pulse or wave as it strikes a barrier

refracted ray a ray that results from an incident ray entering a second medium of different density obliquely

refraction the change in direction of a wave due to a change in speed at the boundary between two media of different density

resistance a measure of the opposition that a device or conductor offers to the flow of electric current

resistivity a quantity-dependent property of a material, independent of the material's physical shape, that is closely related to resistance

resistor a device designed to have a definite amount of resistance

resolution of forces the process of determining the magnitude and direction of the components of a force

resonance the vibration of a body at its natural frequency due to the action of a vibrating source of the same frequency

resultant the single vector that is equivalent to the combined effect of two or more vectors

scalar a quantity that has magnitude only, with no direction specified

scientific notation a way of expressing quantities which consists of a number equal to or greater than one and less than ten followed by a multiplication sign and the base ten raised to some integral power

second (s) the fundamental SI unit of time

series circuit an electrical circuit in which all parts are connected end to end to provide a single path for current

SI prefix a prefix combined with an SI base unit to form a new unit that is larger or smaller than the base unit by a multiple or submultiple of 10

SI system (Système International) provides standardized units for scientific measurements

significant figures the digits in a measured quantity that are known with certainty plus the one digit whose value has been estimated

slope the inclination of a graphed line, determined as the ratio $\frac{\Delta y}{\Delta x}$ for any two points on the line

Snell's law the mathematical relationship that governs the refraction of light as it passes obliquely from one medium to another of different optical density; $n_1 \sin \theta_1 = n_2 \sin \theta_2$

spectral line a particular frequency of absorbed or emitted energy characteristic of an atom

speed the distance that an object moves in a unit of time; a scalar quantity

speed (of a wave) equal to the product of its wavelength and frequency; a scalar quantity

spring constant the constant of proportionality between the applied force and the compression or elongation of a spring

standard deviation the square root of the variance of a set of data

Standard Model of Particle Physics a theory used to explain the existence of all the particles that have been observed and the forces that hold atoms together or lead to their decay

standing wave a pattern of wave crests and troughs that remains stationary in a medium when two waves of equal frequency and amplitude pass through the medium in opposite directions

static friction the force that opposes the start of motion; a vector quantity

statics the branch of mechanics that treats forces that act on objects at rest

static equilibrium state of an object at rest

stationary state any particular orbit that can be occupied by an electron in an atom

superposition occurs when two or more waves travel through the same medium simultaneously

switch a device for making, breaking, or changing the connections in an electric circuit

tangent a line on a graph which passes through a point and has a slope equal to the slope of the curve at that point

tesla (T) the derived SI unit of magnetic flux density or magnetic field strength; equal to one weber per square meter

thermal energy also called heat; is the total kinetic energy possessed by the individual particles that comprise an object

transverse wave a wave in which the motion of the vibratory disturbance is perpendicular to the direction of travel of the wave

trough in a transverse wave, the position of maximum displacement in the negative direction (downward)

unbalanced force a nonzero net force acting on an object; a vector quantity

uniform circular motion the motion of an object traveling in a circular path at constant speed

uniform motion the motion of an object moving at constant speed

unit a standard quantity with which other similar quantities can be compared

universal mass unit or atomic mass unit; one-twelfth the mass of a carbon-12 atom

vacuum a region of empty space

variable resistor a coil of resistance wire whose effective resistance can be varied by sliding a contact point

variance the sum of the squares of the differences of the measurements in a set of data from the mean of the set, divided by the number of measurements

vector a quantity that has both magnitude and direction, often shown graphically as an arrow with definite length and direction

vector components (of a force) the two or more concurrent forces whose vector sum is the acting force

velocity the time rate of change of an object's displacement; a vector quantity

vertical component (of velocity) a component velocity vector whose direction is at right angles to the horizon

volt (V) the derived SI unit of electric potential difference; equal to one joule per coulomb

voltmeter a device for measuring potential difference across an element when connected in parallel with it in an electric circuit

virtual image a point behind a mirror from which light rays appear to diverge without actually doing so

watt (W) the derived SI unit of power equal to one joule per second

wave a vibratory disturbance that propagates through a medium or field

wave front all points on a wave that are in phase with each other

wavelength the distance between any two successive points in phase with one another in a periodic wave

weber (Wb) the derived SI unit for measuring magnetic flux

weight the gravitational force with which a planet attracts a mass; a vector quantity

work the transfer of energy to an object when the object moves due to the application of a force that is entirely in the direction of motion or has a component in the direction of the object's motion

Index

weight 46–47
    and friction 48
    and gravitational potential energy 79
work 75–78
    and electric fields 107–108
    and energy 75, 84, 85–91
    and kinetic energy 84

    and springs 82
    units of measurement 2
X rays 155
    and the photoelectric effect 172
zeroes
    in measurement 9